"Tamara Laing has introduced major ground-breaking insights into the whole field of energy medicine. ***Healing Arts*** *is an extremely well-referenced treatise and draws from a great number of separate sources to create a fluid, enlightening, and fascinating read. I love it. I challenge you to expand your perspective, open your heart and mind, and enjoy the inspiration in these pages. This is a treasure trove of healing."*

- Stan Gardner, M.D., CNS in Riverton, UT

"I ordered the book & could not put it down. WOW! You have really done quite a bit of research. This must have taken you A TON of time to put together. It is totally inspired. I have used some of the things from the book and seen instant results. Thank you so much. I'm grateful for your inspired obedience in compiling and writing this book. I will never be the same. "

-Tammy in Fielding, UT

"Your mission may be to save the energy workers from the challenges of the uninformed. I am very grateful for your diligence."

- Anonymous

"Even though I felt drawn to use "new" therapies for my growth and healing, I was always a little unsure of their origin and 'acceptability' within the LDS Church. After years of many unanswered questions, I have found solid answers in Tamara Laing's book . This is groundbreaking! . . . . A marriage between LDS theology of the "Light of Christ" and the scientifically recognized "Energy Fields" that surround, give life to, and control the human body. . . . The information will help overcome prejudice, ignorance, and fear about healing therapies. . . . Tamara is a pioneer for laying the foundation for a new era of healing among all who have faith to be healed. This is a must read for anyone looking for further light and knowledge in the area of healing illness: emotional or physical. 'By the mouth of two or three witnesses shall every word be established.' Here are two witnesses on healing (prophets and science); you can be the third."

- Shauna in Taylorsville, UT

"Your book has a TON of information in it!"

- Dr. Kenneth West in South Africa

"Tamara put years of research into this book (as the eight pages of references attest.) I was deeply inspired and uplifted at the first reading. I'm looking forward to re-reading it, and will keep it handy! ... It will enlighten minds & open hearts."

- Holli , Kaysville, UT

"Healing Arts - A Gift From God is the best collection known to me of quotations supporting energy healing from both a scientific and LDS viewpoint. Tamara's painstaking research is both broad and deep, covering a surprisingly wide spectrum of sources. This book is easy reading and truly enlightening."

- John Pratt

Healing Arts - A Gift from God

by Tamara Laing, MRET

Healing Arts a Gift From God: LDS Insight on the Light of Christ & Energy Medicine

ISBN 978-0-9884354-1-4
Library of Congress Registration Number: TX 7-615-586

Hope for a Better World
3813 W. 5800 S. ~ Roy, UT 84067
lightreader@xmission.com
www.tamarasbook.blogspot.com

Quantity discounts available on purchases by trade bookstores, wholesalers, and health professionals. For details, contact the above publisher.

First Printing, 2012
Printed in the United States of America

IMAGE CREDITS:

Most images are from Microsoft Office. A loyalty free license was purchased for "Woman silhouette with aura, chakras, energy" © by Deosum from Dreamstime.com. I gratefully acknowledge: Sharlene Young for permission to reprint the © 12 Chakras illustration and Dr. Ranae Johnson for the simplified RET Body Chart; Joseph Bennette for permission to use his EFT Treatment Points image; Guy Laing for his photographs; Masaru Emoto and The Emoto Project for making *The Message From Water - Children's Version* available online; and The Future Science Foundation for Platinum crystal under field ion microscope by Erwin W. Mueller taken at Pennsylvania State University. I appreciate NASA, National Human Genome Research Institute, National Institutes of Health, the Air Force, the Brooklyn Museum and Wikimedia for making public domain images available.

PUBLIC DOMAIN 🄍 IMAGE ATTRIBUTIONS:

"The healing hands of Penny the Wonder Nurse" by Greg Younger, courtesy flicker.com cc-by-sa-2.0.; "Spiral Galaxy M100" by NASA PD-NASA courtesy Wikipedia; "Woman at the Well," "Jesus Tempted," "The Raising of Lazarus," "Jesus Heals the Blind Man," "Sermon on the Mount," "Christ Healing by the Well of Bethesda," and "Consolator" by Carl Bloch PD-old courtesy Wikimedia; "NGC 0584SST" by NASA, PD-NASA courtesy Wikipedia; Healing the centurion's servant by Paolo Veronese PD-old, courtesy The Yorck Project and Wikimedia Commons; "The Blind and Mute Man Possessed by Devils" by James Tissot, courtesy Brooklyn Museum and Wikimedia Commons cc-pd-mark; "Outline-body-aura.png" unidentified artist, PD-self courtesy Wikipedia; Bioeletrografia by Plinio Ganzer Moreira, PD-self courtesy Wikimedia; "Czakry" by Plínio Ganzer Moreira, PD-self courtesy Wikimedia; "7-main-Chakras" illustrated-by-Gil-Dekel courtesy Wikipedia cc-by-sa 3.0; Joseph Smith First Vision Stained Glass by unknown artist PD-art-old, photograph from PBS website courtesy Wikimedia; "Leonardo Da Vinci's Vitruvian Couple with Chakra overlay" by William Vroman, PD-self courtesy Wikipedia; Christ healing the paralytic at Capernaum by Bernhard Rode PD- old courtesy Wikipedia; "DNA in Pipette," by Maggie Bartlett, PD-NIH, courtesy National Human Genome Research Institute; Christ healing the mother of Simon Peter" by John Bridges PD-old, courtesy Wikipedia; Aura image by Aurastar 2000 Bio-imaging system taken by Colleen Jensen; Brigham Young by Charles William Carter PD-old courtesy Wikipedia; Joseph Smith by unknown painter PD-anonymous courtesy Wikipedia; The Salt Lake temple spires by Ricardo630 courtesy wikipedia CC attribution share alike generic; Photons emitted in a coherent beam from a laser by US Air Force courtesy Wikimedia Commons PD-USGov-Military-Air Force; "Cornstarch Cymatics" photo by Collin Cunningham courtesy Wikimedia cc-by-sa 3.0; Moses and serpent photo by Mike Young PD-self, taken at St Marks Church, Gillingham, courtesy Wikipedia; Vial of medicine with DNA double helix ,Human chromosomes, Prescription Form with DNA double helix, and Stethoscope in shape of double helix by Jane Ades courtesy National Human Genome Research Institute PD-NIH; "Jesus camina sobre el agua" by Javier Oswaldo Rios Caicedo cc-by-sa-3.0; CTF MEG system a whole-head SQUID magnetometer by NIH, courtesy National Institutes of Health and Wikimedia Commons, PD-US-NIH; "SLC Replica of the Christus" by Barbaricino, PD-self courtesy Wikipedia

This compilation does not represent doctrinal beliefs of "The Church of Jesus Christ of Latter-day Saints." Opinions expressed are the author's. The author has taken the liberty of adding emphasis to quotations. Secular quotations are included for consideration only and do not imply an endorsement of entire philosophies or published works.

ABBREVIATIONS USED:

HC: History of the Church
JD: *Journal of Discourses*
TPJS: Teachings of the Prophet Joseph Smith
STPJS: Scriptural Teachings of the Prophet Joseph Smith
Hymns: Hymns of The Church of Jesus Christ of Latter-day Saints

Dedicated to my family,
and people whose gifts the eye may not see -
those labeled with mental illness, ADD, ADHD,
autism spectrum disorder . . .

Disclaimer

Integrative methods such as the healing arts in the field of Energy Medicine are intended to complement rather than substitute for medical care. They are not intended to diagnose, treat, cure or prevent any illness or disease. If you are suffering from a medical or psychological condition of any kind seek the advice of a qualified professional. The author does not assume responsibility for how the reader chooses to apply methods herein and recommends use with a certified facilitator.

TABLE OF CONTENTS

~ FOREWORD ~

by Stan Gardner, M.D., CNS, APCT

With her new book, *Healing Arts*, Tamara Laing has introduced major groundbreaking insights into the whole field of energy medicine.

As you read and ponder the messages and stories taught in *Healing Arts*, the web of interconnectedness becomes more apparent. It is wise to open our eyes, our minds, and our hearts to the elements of healing that cannot be answered through scientific reports, but rather rely on the teachings of thousands of years in religious history. Additionally, we should allow for individual guidance and inspiration through our spiritual interconnection. What was once thought as "weird" and "inexplicable" now is recognized as the realm of true reality. I believe energy medicine is the medicine of the future, available to us right now in ever-expanding regions.

In order to understand the interconnectedness of healing arts, first we need to recognize the volume of energy medicine that is already being utilized in conventional medicine. These are proven modalities, but we still do not understand fully their mechanisms of action. Do any of us fully understand electricity? By the same token, do we fully realize the impact of emotions, of movement, of communication upon our health and healing?

Time and time again, these concepts of healing have been introduced and too readily dismissed as quackery. It is my conviction that all these elements are, in fact, core to the healing process. *Healing Arts* pulls together vast resources to show how all of these relate to one another.

When Einstein first introduced quantum physics in the 1920's, many discounted his theories. Now these theories are increasingly embraced as the most plausible explanations for what we observe in the world of healing. While conventional medicine has not yet accepted as dogma the philosophies of quantum physics, it utilizes tools based upon quantum physics principles:

- electrocardiograms,
- electroencephalograms,
- ultrasound (both for diagnosis and treatment),
- hot and cold therapy,
- light therapy,
- music therapy,
- x-rays,
- MRI's (magnetic resonance imaging),
- acupuncture, and
- many other modalities in recognized conventional treatment.

Energy Medicine illustrates a powerful link between all elements of life. It explains unanswered questions in science, such as "what dictates the organization of the fetus into different tissue, even though all of the cells have the same DNA?"and "How could a few milligrams or micrograms of a substance cause such profound effects upon the body, when that small amount certainly should not be able to affect the more than 75 trillion cells of the body, unless it does so on an energetic level?" It is obvious that the body has communication systems of which we are not fully aware, all constantly "talking" with each other.

Tamara Laing has been able to bring together the philosophies of religion and the philosophies of science, recognizing that the reality is often simply a difference in terminology and not concept. In this book she is able to bring together disparate pieces and place them into a magnificent picture of the whole.

Healing Arts is an extremely well-referenced treatise. Tamara Laing draws from a great number of separate sources to create a fluid, enlightening, and fascinating read. I love it. I challenge you to expand your perspective, open your heart and mind, and enjoy the inspiration in these pages. This is a treasure trove of healing.

To YOUR dynamic health and energy!

Stan Gardner, M.D., CNS

June 2012

~ PREFACE ~

I am an LDS mother, a member of *The Church of Jesus Christ of Latter-day Saints*, who was repeatedly prompted to find answers in the healing arts to help my youngest daughter who was experiencing Schizo-Affective disorder bipolar type. She made remarkable turnarounds at sessions of Rapid Eye Technology, Graf Stress Management and other integrative methods in the healing arts.

I consider Healing Arts a subcategory of the broader field of Energy Medicine. These integrative health options are based on the existence of a life-giving, intelligent, universal energy. Decades of experiments by physicists have discovered an invisible yet universal, unifying field of energy. This energy is often called life force energy, an intelligence that regulates all physical life processes. This essence will not be completely foreign to Latter-day Saints familiar with the universal light spoken of in *The Doctrine and Covenants.* The healing art's foundational concept of a universal energy is harmonious with LDS beliefs about a divine, intelligent, life-giving light that fills the universe.

It is my desire that this compilation will aid Latter-day Saints who may not understand the premises of Energy Medicine and the Healing Arts. Because they have been a tremendous blessing to my family, I desire to help relieve emotional and physical suffering in the world by introducing Healing Arts principles in the language that Latter-Day Saints speak. I have been collecting quotes that may help discern what is appropriately taught in this field. I found answers to my concerns in the scriptures and from the words of modern day prophets and apostle and other LDS authors.

I desire that this collection aid the reader in judging for themselves whether principles of healing arts are plausible, Christian based, and in line with modern revelation. This collection of quotes is the information I wish I would have had easy access to on the first day I heard that energy healing existed. I have not found another book written to this narrow of a topic, although many books are supportive.

Energy healing techniques helped my family with physical and emotional challenges so much that I certified in several of them. I am a Master Rapid Eye Technician and Reiki Master also certified in Quantum Touch, Theta Healing, and trained in Emotional Freedom Technique, Vibrational Medicine, etc. I have assisted hundreds of clients in the Healing Arts since 2004.

I never intended for the healing arts to become a passion in my life. I simply followed inspiration even when it meant taking a few steps into the edge of the light where I could not see my way. I did not know when I began my search if prophets and apostles had said anything at all about the premises of Healing Arts. The same scenario played out again when I was prompted by the Holy Spirit to read a very unsettling library book. Following that prompting brought about a paradigm shift regarding illness that God evidently *wanted* me to learn. As before, finding validation from prophets for initially surprising findings came later on.

As I found and categorized validating quotes about healing, I was astonished that they taught principles that Quantum Physics teaches today. I enthusiastically compiled a comparison chart from discoveries in Quantum Physics about the characteristics and nature of universal energy and LDS teachings on the Light of Christ that I titled, "Comparison of Subtle Energy in Science and Religion."

Researching bits of science behind healing arts and making additions to this chart brought me unexplained joy. It also taught me that I had to give up many preconceived notions about the nature of the world around me and human bodies and health. What a learning curve it has been! I was guided to noteworthy, yet obscure quotes from prophets on subtle energy, mind/body medicine, and *what else* is involved in depression and illness. Words of prophets on all of these subjects give credibility to principles used in the Healing Arts today. I was prompted repeatedly to write down the things I learned.

I wondered why God wanted *me* to make note of these things instead of someone more qualified. I was inspired by the words of author Marianne Williamson:

> 'Our deepest fear is not that we are inadequate. Our deepest fear is that we are powerful beyond measure. It is our light, not our darkness that most frightens us.' We ask ourselves, Who am I to be brilliant, gorgeous, talented, fabulous? Actually, who are you *not* to be? You are a child of God. Your playing small does not serve the world. There's nothing enlightened about shrinking so that other people won't feel insecure around you. We are all meant to shine, as children do. We were born to make manifest the glory of God that is within us. It's not just in some of us; it's in everyone. And as we let our own light shine, we unconsciously give other people permission to do the same. As we're liberated from our own fear, our presence automatically liberates others. . . . The cosmic spotlight isn't pointed *at* you; it radiates from *within* you. . . . Our power lies in our clarity about why we're on the earth. We'll be important players if we think that way. And the important players of the coming years will be the people who see themselves as here to contribute to the healing of the world.[1]

I began to be asked to present my daughter's story of finding integrative help to community health groups in the Ogden, Utah area and then surrounding areas. I share my family's experiences with their permission. I was most enthusiastic about addressing a specific topic requested from community health groups. They wanted to hear what support I had found in the scriptures and from prophets for the subtle-energy related therapies that had helped my daughter so much.

In 2010 I was prompted to create a power point presentation. I didn't understand why or what it would be used for, but I knew it was a spiritual prompting I heard, so I proceeded. I put quotes from my comparison chart onto beautiful power point images. The presentation was only about 30 slides long (basically chapter 1) when I happened to share it with a few friends. They were thrilled with the validation it gave Healing Arts and told me I *had* to make it available to the public.

I added power point slides to become a "crash course" on energy healing with LDS language and made it available as a DVD. I was asked to present it at holistic health conferences and meetings

---

[1] Marianne Williamson, *A Return to Love*, 191, 209

in three states. Everywhere I went people asked for a hard copy. I've expanded and printed it here in book form.

A few "snapshot" personal stories on basic principles are included in Section One at the request of others. A few chapters in Section One may be more understandable for those new to this book's material, after reading the corresponding full color power point slides which follow in Section Two (which were actually created first). Section Two contains comparative quotes of LDS and world views on aspects of the Light of Christ which cover several major premises of Healing Arts. I fondly think of the scriptures after Dr. David Hawkins' "Map of Consciousness" in Chapter 5's slides as "God's Map on Emotion." I want to make it clear that material in Chapter 6's slides, "Chase Darkness with Light," was not taught outright in any of the modalities I certified in.

Another powerful inspiration for this project has been the ad copy of a commercial that can leave me teary:

> Here's to the crazy ones. The misfits. The rebels. The troublemakers. The round pegs in the square holes. The ones who see things differently. They're not fond of rules. And they have no respect for the status quo. You can quote them, disagree with them, glorify or vilify them. About the only thing you can't do is ignore them. Because they change things. They push the human race forward. While some may see them as the crazy ones, we see genius. Because the people who are crazy enough to think they can change the world, are the ones who do. [2]

God Bless You!

Tamara Laing, MRET

June 2012

[2] "Crazy Ones," Apple Inc, 1997, Advertisement, TBWA/Chiat/Day, Los Angeles

ACKNOWLEDGEMENTS

Many thanks to my husband, Guy Laing, for giving me room to explore mind-bending ideas, and for proofreading the manuscript and supporting me in this project. I express appreciation to my children for their patience with years of research and for teaching me so many concepts. I have enthusiastic gratitude for Sylvia and Joan's professional examples and for following where the Holy Spirit guides. An abundance of appreciation goes to my neighbor and friend, Shon, for believing in Healing Arts and for her understanding and clarity. I express love and gratitude to Crystal and Amber for their empathy.

I appreciate Cliff and Judy Dunston for permission to use "Process for Staying in the Light" and Jan Graf for permission to use "Forgiveness Steps." I am deeply grateful to Fred for writing his personal story of healing through forgiveness and for following promptings to share copies of it. The impact that had on my family was monumental. I thank Rebecca for telling her story publically which gave me courage to do the same. I am grateful to Karin for first extending the invitation to address these topics publically and for teaching with me. I am very appreciative of Mark and Tonya for courageous examples of living what they believe.

Many thanks to NanC, Jan, Karyn, Christine, Chloe, Holli, Kurt, Ruth, Becky, Cliff, David, Vickie, Misty, Lynelle, Sharlene and Courtney for sharing their spiritual gifts. I express my appreciation to Jill, Cristy, Rhonda, Marj, Natalie, Karma, Katherine, and Michelle for believing in me and cheering me on. I thank Lynette for pointing a few important quotations from prophets out to me. I thank Mark M. for believing that everything happens for a reason.

Thank you to Juleen, Judy, and Teresa for reading the early manuscript and to Michael, Cristi, Marnae and Canah for reviewing the early power point. I appreciate Cindy B. for sharing John Pratt's article, Kim for sharing Julie Beck's talk at BYU Women's Conference, and Cindy S. for sharing two of Rex Wadham's papers. I appreciate Marcie for asking "why?" I express gratitude to Tim for sharing teachings from the scriptures. I appreciate many wonderful clients who taught me so much by their powerful examples of forgiveness in the most difficult of circumstances.

I am grateful to facilitators of healing arts who have been misunderstood. Your pioneering experiences contributed to the making of this book. I pay tribute to great people throughout history: the brave souls who were courageous and relentless truth seekers. The men and women who were willing to set aside the status quo and investigate what the evidence in front of them revealed, the people who were willing to think "outside the box." I pay tribute to these pioneers who often stood alone for truth and were willing to search in the depths to find it.

I thank Dr. Ranae Johnson; Stan Gardner, M.D., CNS; Judith Moore, D.O. and many relatives, friends, and others who encouraged this project. Foremost, I express deep love and gratitude to my Father in Heaven and His Son.

~ INTRODUCTION ~

I have come across some mind-bending ideas over the last several years. The reader may want to "buckle up" for the ride! Studying the healing arts brought about huge paradigm shifts for me. I learned that the world is not operating the way I thought it was and had been taught in science class. Recent science is changing to an energetic view of *all* creation. While it's an ancient concept, it can be quite a foreign one to people in western society.

Quantum physicists have demonstrated under laboratory conditions that an invisible, unified field of energy does exist. Some scientists call it the Zero Point Energy field. It fills the universe and appears to be intelligent. That should excite Latter-day Saints because modern day scriptures teach about a universal field of energy.

A First Presidency statement says, "There is a universally diffused essence which is the light and the life of the world, 'which lighteth every man that cometh into the world,' which proceedeth forth from the presence of God throughout the immensity of space, the light and power of which God bestows in different degrees to 'them that ask him,' according to their faith and obedience."[3]

I believe the healing art's foundational concept of a *universal, vital, life-force energy* is harmonious with LDS beliefs about the Light of Christ—*a governing, life-giving, universal light*. Prophets teach that this governing light has *intelligence* and is a "mental light" of *information*.

Stanford Professor Emeritus, William Tiller, PhD, declares scientists have discovered energy that is a *communicator* and describe it using the words *light*, *information* and *energy*.

So . . . when will we start connecting the dots in the above paragraphs? Science appears to be uncovering spiritual principles! Modern science may have recently discovered the *energy* of the Light of Christ.

Cutting-edge science is helping new concepts to be accepted. Leading scientists have found that people have unseen energy fields of "biophoton" light around their physical bodies, thought to coordinate bodily processes. "Research converging from many fields of investigation indicates that the body is a complex energy system, rather than the mere clockwork machine of biological gears and parts that is often espoused in conventional medicine."[4]

Healing Arts clear, balance, and re-pattern a person's complex energy system, which in turn benefits health. Techniques based on a life-giving, universal energy are commonly referred to as "energy healing." Learning and applying principles related to life-giving energy assists with a wide variety of challenges in life.

---

[3] First Presidency, "'Receiving the Holy Ghost," *Improvement Era*, Mar. 1916, 460

[4] "Report of the experimental results of the educational Sessions of the International Academy for Scientific Mental Healing (Drossinakis IAWG) under the direction of Prof. Dr. Konstantin Korotkov," Appendix 16

Healing Arts take into account the whole person's being: physical body as well as mind and spirit. This includes the unseen light energy that envelops people, known to leading physicists as the "biofield." The healing arts use techniques that affect the biofield and complex energy system.

Author B. Grant Bishop, M.D. states, "The mysteries of God are the mysteries of light."[5] The mysteries of humans are also related to little-known, hidden light. God is "the Father of lights" (James 1:17) and tells us, "Ye are all the children of light" (1 Thes. 5:5). The reader will learn that our bodies have an intimate connection with light, although it mostly goes unseen.

The light of Christ is the life-giving light that actually keeps us alive. Bruce R. McConkie stated, "Without this light of life, the planets would not stay in their orbits, vegetation would not grow, men and animals would be devoid of the breath of life" (Gen. 2:7), and life would cease to exist. (D&C 88:50)."[6]

Mainstream western society doesn't realize yet that:

1. We live in an 'ocean' of universal subtle light.
2. We emanate nearly invisible light.
3. Our minds are quickened by a divine light.

Learning that Healing Arts can purposefully shift one's energy fields and vital life force energy (often called *Chi*) to benefit well-being is at times a difficult concept for some Christians to swallow. This book contains brief stories on my journey and the quotes I collected from scripture and religious leaders in my world that allowed me to alleviate fears and unite personal religious views with principles of holistic help found in Healing Arts.

It is wonderful to think that we can learn about characteristics of universal energy and vital life force energy in scripture. It wasn't until I learned the premises under this field of medicine, that I began to find examples of Healing Arts' seemingly unusual processes in those texts. I found that help in the Healing Arts is Christ-centered *when credit is given where credit is due.*

Science played a part in allowing these diverse disciplines to blend harmoniously for me. There is great significance in what cutting-edge science is telling us. Scientific discoveries have caused me to alter my concept of how a human body functions. One scientist turned healer writes of the unseen, yet complex energy field:

> Since the physical body arises out of the energy field, an imbalance or distortion in this field will eventually cause a disease in the physical body that it governs. Therefore, healing distortions in the field will bring about healing in the physical body. Healing is a matter of learning how to heal the field by restructuring, balancing and charging it. . . .That means that

---

[5] *The LDS Gospel of Light*, 159
[6] *Mormon Doctrine*, 447

any illness will show in the field before it shows in the physical body and can therefore be healed in the field before it is precipitated into the physical body.[7]

Healing Arts' techniques focus on the underlying energetic structure instead of physical anatomy. Improving health in the healing arts, therefore, looks a lot different than conventional care. In order for a medical model to be of the utmost benefit, it must address this phenomenon. One might think of these energy fields as software. We are not only becoming more advanced in computer and electronic technology . . ., but also in "human technology."

There is a simple way to distinguish two different kinds of energy fields, which the National Institutes of Health website explains:

> Some CAM [Complementary Alternative Medicine] practices involve manipulation of various energy fields to affect health... [either] veritable (measurable) or putative (yet to be measured). Practices based on veritable forms of energy include those involving electro-magnetic fields (e.g., magnet therapy & light therapy). Practices based on putative energy fields (also called biofields) generally reflect the concept that human beings are infused with subtle forms of energy; qi gong, Reiki, and Healing Touch are examples.[8]

Healing arts generally focus on putative energy fields, according to my definition. My family has also benefitted by advanced technology machines in the broader field of Energy Medicine. These machines use veritable, measurable energy fields to benefit health.

Science is still learning about the unseen subtle energy involved in healing arts. The word "subtle" hints that this energy is not yet measurable by conventional equipment, although it *has* been detected and is beginning to be measured by leading technology. "It is unclear at this time whether the biofield is electromagnetic or is some other presently unmeasured but potentially quantifiable, medium. It is popularly hypothesized that the biofield is a form of bioelectricity, biomagnetism or bioelectromagnetism. This may well be the case but has yet to be established." [9]

A significant point about yet-to-be-measured energy is stated here, "It is not possible to measure this type of energy with regular scientific equipment. Scientific equipment can only measure electromagnetic fields and waves. What if *Chi* is not electromagnetic in nature? . . . Subtle energy, called *Chi* by traditional Chinese medicine, is the energy type belonging to the world of subatomic particles or the subatomic world." [10]

William Tiller, Ph.D. and Professor Emeritus of Stanford University reportedly stated that scientists do have the beginning technology to measure, "these higher dimensional levels of reality . . . . in which we can have a readout. That's very important, so that we can begin to monitor the

---

[7] Barbara Brennan, *Light Emerging,* 19
[8] "BIOFIELD THERAPEUTICS The Sub-Section from Alternative Medicine: Expanding Medical Horizons"
[9] "BIOFIELD THERAPEUTICS The Sub-Section from Alternative Medicine: Expanding Medical Horizons," 10
[10] Boyd Martin, "What Subtle Energy Is and Its Value to Health"

space in which healers work and describe the level of effectiveness of what they're doing on an energy level, in terms of a quantitative measurement of that particular space."

I intend to share premises of Healing Arts, or energy healing, and comparable quotes from LDS sources. Please note that opinions are mine and that this compilation does not represent beliefs of *The Church of Jesus Christ of Latter-day Saints*. I do not necessarily recommend all material in the secular books referenced. Most of these authors lack the eternal perspective that the restored gospel of Jesus Christ provides. I learned from scriptures and prophets:

1. The light of Christ fills the immensity of space and is in all things, including people.
2. This light in us has life-giving properties and may be shared with others, even distantly.
3. "The spirit of the living creature [is] in the wheels." (Ezek. 1:20)
4. Thoughts are *things.* The light of Christ is intelligent and manifests as consciousness.
5. The book of life is stored in heaven as well as in one's body. Water, blood and spirit record thoughts, words and emotions. . . which affect health.
6. The light of Christ is a shield from the darkness of the adversary.
7. We are transformed by the intelligent light of Christ quickening and renewing our mind/body.

I hope the public will understand new truths about health and healing so that *whole person health* in our medical model may follow. Quantum physics changed our scientific model over 80 years ago. Surprisingly, this new viewpoint has yet to be developed in our model of human biology. Progressive doctors and hospitals are embracing this energetic view. Shouldn't you? I did and it has made *all* the difference.

"For so many people, the breakthroughs in the world of quantum physics are little
more than interesting facts – things to talk about at conferences or workshops. . . .
Yet, as deep as the implications go and as high as the philosophy carries us,
the discoveries seem to have minimal relevance in our everyday lives.
What good does it do, for example, to know that a particle of matter
can be in two places at once or that electrons can travel faster than Einstein
said they could if this knowledge doesn't add to our lives in some way?
It's only when we can connect these mind-boggling discoveries
to the healing of our bodies or to what we experience in the malls, living rooms,
airports, and classrooms of our lives that they become important to us."

Gregg Braden[11]

[11] Gregg Braden, *The Divine Matrix*, xx

~1~ My Story Begins

I found the healing arts as many others do – in the midst of a crisis. My youngest daughter suffered from depression, mood swings and excessive anxiety. She was diagnosed with a bipolar type of illness. She was cutting, repeatedly suicidal and had to be hospitalized three times.

We endured years of living nightmares- in daylight as well as darkness. The illness was affecting my entire family. We lived on a roller coaster of emotions from day to day as we dealt with explosive mood swings while trying to shelter our younger children from the worst emergencies. Our oldest daughter didn't dare live in the same house with her sister for several months.

Our ill daughter said she felt like someone else was controlling her and that she was tired of "pretending to be herself." I didn't understand her at all back then. Adding to the stress was a set of parents who didn't always agree on how to discipline a chronically ill child experiencing such upsets. Simply put, there was more trauma than one could understand--unless you've lived this close to this kind of illness yourself. It didn't seem like the chaos would ever end. Back then it felt like my daughter was a victim of seemingly random poor genetics.

The answers the medical field had to offer were drugs and counseling. I took my daughter for those conventional methods for four years, trying one prescription drug 'cocktail' of three or four medications at a time, one after another. There was no lasting improvement; the medications still left her ill and even suicidal. Additionally, the side-effects of the drugs were horrendous. Suddenly gaining forty pounds in a couple of months is *never* a good thing for an already depressed teenage girl; however, this therapy from the conventional medical establishment was all we had ever heard of. We erroneously thought it was our only option.

In this heartrending situation I experienced depression for a year myself. That year I often felt like I was holding on to the end of my rope. Yet, I never ceased to pray fervently and fast often for help, sometimes weekly during the worst months. Spiritual convictions, prayer and temple attendance got me through very difficult years. I knew God in heaven heard my pleas. I believed helpful answers would come.

We took opportunities to ask for priesthood blessings and I asked our young, brand new bishop for advice. He gave my daughter a blessing of comfort, telling her to pray and read her scriptures because "answers were to be found there." To be honest, I was disappointed at first with such advice. She had such *enormous* trials that initially I felt this was a very "generic" blessing. However, I repented of that thought and took the Lord's counsel to heart. We had been promised *answers* in the scriptures -- not help, but **answers!** I continued the habit I learned in seminary to read scriptures daily, although over time I began to study more by topic.

Our bishop was right, answers were found in the scriptures. In time, I came across many educational and helpful answers to health problems in the scriptures. Even my alternative health questions were answered!

~2~ What Else Is There?

"And I will bring the blind by a way that they knew not;
I will lead them in paths that they have not known:
I will make darkness light before them, and crooked things straight.
These things will I do unto them, and not forsake them." (Isaiah 42:16)

The most obvious reason I believe there is truth to be found in the healing arts is that it was the *insistence* of the Holy Spirit that initiated my learning of its existence. A quiet voice in my mind prompted me repeatedly to call the wife of a past bishop of ours. I hadn't kept in touch with her and didn't understand how a stay-at-home mother of seven children could possibly be of much help for trials as major as a daughter with suicidal tendencies. I didn't understand why I was supposed to call her, so I felt a little silly. I finally dialed her long-distance phone number.

She listened as I tearfully recounted some of the trials we'd been through. Then she said something that still stands out as being profoundly important.

She asked, "So, you've only looked for help in the medical field?" Startled, I answered "Yes, of course. What else is there?"

"Oh," she said, "there is a whole other field of medicine." "Really?" I asked incredulously. "Yes, it is called Energy Medicine," she replied in a matter-of-fact way.

She said it was an alternative but complementary treatment. We could continue to follow the doctors' orders while investigating its effectiveness. I believed her because she was a woman of complete trustworthiness. Besides that, my child was frighteningly ill, the medical field's answers weren't long lasting, and honestly – I was desperate.

The bishop's wife, who I will call Sue, told me she had certified as a Rapid Eye Technician, as well as in other energy healing techniques called modalities. She had been prompted over and over to take classes in Reiki and other healing arts. I had never heard of such things. I was willing to look into these techniques because I knew the woman who told me about them was absolutely trustworthy.

Sue told me there was light or some sort of electromagnetic field around living things. I didn't think I had heard of that before, although similar concepts are found in the scriptures. Sue told me she did Rapid Eye Technology and Reiki to clear and re-pattern the subtle energy that was in and around the body. She said the techniques she had learned, called energy healing, helped her family release negative emotions (such as fear, anger, and anxiety) and recover from illness, a car accident, and even abuse. I felt assured that she spoke the truth.

She told a little about what she did in her work and said she'd be glad to explain more and demonstrate a few techniques for me. We agreed to meet. I hung up the phone with new hope in my heart, although what she had just spoken of seemed more than unusual and actually quite strange.

All of this may be a brand new concept to the reader, as it was for me years ago. For some, their first impression upon hearing the phrase "Energy Medicine" is to visualize images of pills; however, Energy Medicine is not prescriptions! Rather, it is a field of medicine that takes into account that our bodies are complex systems of energies. It is a collection of therapies which have demonstrated the ability to impact the unseen subtle energy system of the body. It includes tools and techniques called "modalities," commonly referred to as "energy work" to clear and balance the subtle energy system, which in turn restores improved function to the body and its organs and systems.

These methods are complementary and in no way does it lessen my appreciation of Allopathic care and its marvels. I believe God has blessed the world with both. An enlightened medical doctor, Christiane Northrup, speaks of several benefits of these methods, and their place alongside traditional care:

> Hands-on energy medicine techniques are already starting to be used in conventional care settings. Some hospitals routinely give patients an opportunity to have their energy fields balanced prior to and following surgery, chemotherapy, radiation, or other invasive procedures. It diminished the shock to the body, hastens healing, and ameliorates many adverse effects, from pain to nausea to hair loss. In the medicine of the future, as I envision it, working with the patient's energy field will be the first intervention. Surgery will be a last resort. Drugs will be a last resort. They will still have their place but shifting the energy patterns that caused the disease will be the first line of treatment. And before that, teaching people how to keep their energies in healthy patterns will be as much a part of physical hygiene as flossing or exercise.[12]

[12] Christiane Northrup, MD, Foreword in Donna Eden, *Energy Medicine for Women*

~3~ A Crash Course in Energy Medicine

As I met with Sue, the new health principles she shared concerning a subtle energy were so foreign to me that they raised questions. She spoke of an electromagnetic-like field of energy around people's bodies that was mostly unseen. She said it could be discerned by some people all the time. She told me the story of Donna Eden seeing her fourth grade teacher's aura of light. I had never heard of such things before, but I innately believed that young girl's story.[13] Donna simply saw colors of light around her teacher that adults could not detect. Moses' face shone with light and Stephen's too. Mortal Abinadi's countenance had a luster. I simply trusted my instinct at first that light might truthfully exist around bodies.

Sue introduced me to Kirlian photography and the phantom leaf effect. She explained that a Russian electrician, Semyon Kirlian, also an amateur photographer, invented equipment that captured the invisible glowing light around living things. She told me that someone cut a leaf in half and destroyed one portion. Then a picture was taken of the remaining half leaf using Kirlian photography. The resulting photograph was quite surprising. It revealed the entire image of an intact leaf with a glowing ring of white light emanating from its edges. The picture was of a *complete* leaf! My curiosity about light surrounding living things was piqued. On the hour drive home, I determined to stop at the public library (this was before the web was a household term) to check out books that mentioned auras and Kirlian photography.

I wondered if I could reconcile what I was learning with the gospel of Jesus Christ. One of the first things I learned from the library books I checked out was that the unseen field *precedes* the physical body. Barbara Brennan wrote, "The energy field exists prior to the physical body. This is a fundamental difference from many scientific researchers. They assume that the field emanates from the body, rather than that the body is created by the field. . . [The] field is primary rather than the physical. . . . The energy field could not arise from the physical; rather the physical arises from the energetic."[14]

I felt this idea could fit comfortably with my beliefs if the human energy field had anything to do with the spirit body that existed beforehand. I would learn later that it does from Ezekiel's words on wheels of light. Energy healing, or what I more fondly call "Healing Arts" is founded upon a spiritual understanding of human bodies. The author continued:

> Since the physical body arises out of the energy field, an imbalance or distortion in this field will eventually cause a disease in the physical body that it governs. Therefore, healing distortions in the field will bring about healing in the physical body. Healing is a matter of learning how to heal the field by restructuring, balancing and charging it. . . . That means that any illness will show in the field before it shows in the physical body and can therefore be healed in the field before it is precipitated into the physical body. [15]

I had hope for my daughter, although I didn't understand how anyone could affect her field. Sue taught me, "Each of us has in the center of our palms an energy vortex from which energy flows. That's why it feels soothing for a little child when his mother puts her hand on his forehead. That's why holding hands

---

[13] see Donna Eden, *Energy Medicine*, 17
[14] *Light Emerging*, 18-19
[15] *Light Emerging*, 19

is so exciting - there is an exchange of energy taking place. Not only does that energy feel good to us, but it has healing properties. It is understood that we all have it, but we obviously don't all know we have it, so we don't capitalize on it. Those who practice energy healing techniques, DO capitalize on it."

The curious information Sue shared on chakras of spinning light in the body got me thinking. I remembered that decades before, when I was on a date with my future husband, I felt strong swirling sensations through and out in front of my torso. Guy experienced the same thing at the same time and turned to me in the movie theater and said with a look of surprise, "Do you feel that? *What is that*?" We never had any idea what that might have been until over twenty years later when I learned about energy centers in the body that are twirling vortices of light. Understanding that, it was even more interesting to read in Alma 32:28 - 35 about "swelling motions" that "enlarge [our] soul" and "enlighten our understanding. . . . O then, is not this real? Yea, because it is light and whatsoever is light is good, because it is discernible."

I came to agree with Richard Gordon who states, "No one can really heal anyone else. The person in need of healing is the healer. The practitioner simply holds a resonance to allow the body to heal itself."[16] A real learning moment for me came when I did Reiki on a friend who had lost a limb. He was shocked to discover he could feel the supposed "missing part" of his entire being – that limb's energetic presence. It was quite an assurance to me of the reality of the spirit body and of the spiritual work I had been led to.

Sometime after I was attuned to Reiki, I was watching the movie "Narnia" at the movie theater with my family. Aslan the lion was willingly walking to the stone table where he would voluntarily sacrifice his own life to save his friends' lives. I thought of the obvious parallel to Jesus Christ and how He was able to willingly and lovingly walk to the cross. I pondered and felt deep gratitude for His unending love.

As I was filled with loving gratitude, all of a sudden I noticed a warm flowing sensation streaming out the palm of my empty right hand. It felt like light was pouring out of my body from the center of my palm. Everyone has an energy vortex there. The life-promoting energy that I felt leaving my hand -- whether it is called "Reiki," "Quantum Touch" or another name – is obviously amplified by heartfelt, loving, grateful thoughts. I knew it was there *because* of the love I had inside of me at that moment. I learned that love truly is involved in facilitating healing energy!

---

[16] Quantum Touch, 26

~4~ What's a Nice Girl Like You...?

I desire to bring greater understanding to misunderstood topics in the healing arts. This alternative health field is gaining familiarity with the public. Sometimes, however, I have sensed in others an attitude of, "What's a nice girl like you *doing in a place like this?"* In all honesty, God seemed to open the front door to this 'place' for me and additionally invited a look around – for it was numerous promptings from the spirit that directed me to discover healing arts in the first place and then to study them.

I had never heard of *any* kind of subtle energy, the biofield, or healing with energy, so naturally I had concerns. My concerns fueled a thirst for answers. I spent a few years reading every book I could about energy healing methods. I wanted to be careful and use wisdom in deciphering whether each new principle I learned fit with my beliefs. In the beginning, I had absolutely no understanding of energy healing and was wary of using it. Its methods involved concepts I had never heard of before. Energy clearing techniques were so far removed from traditional care that they seemed strange *until I understood the principles behind them.* I am profoundly grateful that I remained open-minded about alternate methods; for, they proved to be indispensable to my family. I wouldn't want to deal with mental illness in a family without them! They are a spectacular addition to what the medical field does which is what integrative medicine is about.

Initially, I wondered if it was proper for Latter-day Saints and other Christians to be involved with unconventional healing techniques. I mistakenly thought I had never heard of anything like the methods that clearing energy involved. I was wrong for I had read and studied the Bible and the other standard works.

Being uninformed about the healing arts, I wondered if they would involve questionable practices or beliefs. There seems to be a lot of confusion on this subject and I believe it often stems from fear and misconceptions. Some of this confusion is language-based. Several terms used in this field come from foreign countries. If we asked a typical Latter-Day Saint in America if they believed in *Chi* life force energy, I'm guessing the answer would typically be "no." That is ironic because Latter-day Saints use several different terms that seem to equate in meaning to this word. However, it took some time to make that connection due to the unique language used in the respective disciplines I was studying.

For some Latter-day Saints, there seems to be a cloud of confusion regarding the appropriateness of involvement in energy modalities, whether as clients or practitioners. Exodus 15:26 teaches, "I am the Lord that healeth thee." All healing comes from the Savior, so people may wonder if Healing Arts' principles fit with Christian beliefs. Having little information to go on, some people are prone to immediate doubt and suspicion. The Bible offers sensible keys to follow: "Prove all things; hold fast that which is good." (1 Thes. 5:21)

A favorite Bible story of mine depicts a man with palsy lowered through a roof by four friends in order to reach the Savior in an overly crowded home. When Jesus saw such great faith, he told the palsied man that his sins were forgiven. Immediately, the afflicted man stood, picked up his bed and walked out, "insomuch that they were all amazed, and glorified God, saying, we never saw it on this fashion." (Mark

2:12) After reading about options available today in the healing arts, perhaps the reader will also glorify God saying, "I never heard it on this fashion!"

Just as the Savior used what appeared to be 'unconventional' methods to heal in New Testament times, there are valuable integrative healing methods accessible today that the reader may be unaware of. *The Holy Bible* contains accounts of Jesus Christ healing people using various novel approaches for that day, including forgiving and commanding evil spirits out of the afflicted.

Years ago, a neighbor shared with me her initial disinterest in an Energy Medicine machine her husband bought. She told me that one day it occurred to her that she might want to liken the scripture story about the Israelites and the serpent on the staff to her own life. She wondered if it was possible that the Lord *in her lifetime*, had "prepared a way that they might be healed; and the labor which they had to perform was to look; and because of the simpleness of the way, or the easiness of it, there were many who perished." (1 Nephi 17:41) She realized that like some of the suffering Israelites, she had been unwilling to even *look* at the device her husband brought home.

God is just. Since He prepared a way for the Israelites to be healed, we can be assured that the Lord has also prepared a way to help us today! The question is, do we have enough faith to believe that He will help us? My neighbor wondered if a possible healing option might be sitting right in her own home—while she remained unwilling *to even look at it!* She chose to have a new perception from that moment on and discovered that alternative methods and technologically advanced machines had helpful benefits for herself as well as her husband. God tells us all, "He that answereth a matter before he heareth it, it is folly and shame unto him." (Prov. 18:13).

Perhaps Energy Medicine just sounds too unconventional to others. I would ask, how many times in Sunday School have we heard the amazing story of Amanda Smith[17] who lost her husband and a son in the Haun's Mill Massacre? Amanda found another son severely wounded with his hip blown away. She knelt down and pled with the Lord for help asking Him to direct her with what to do. A voice gave her step-by-step directions so that the Lord could make her son a new hip. The answer wasn't anything "conventional." The procedures may have sounded strange. Yet, surely we believe this story is true and that a novel approach was indeed what was needed.

I don't think people back then went around whispering about how strange and untraditional the methods she used to treat her son were. I believe they rejoiced that the Lord through the Spirit gave her the wisdom to help heal her son in a manner previously unknown and certainly not understood. We have the same options today. We can choose to whisper, or we can rejoice that new options in healing are available today.

People aren't "strange" for believing in these therapies . . . they are simply ahead of their time! Let us rejoice in saying, "I never heard of healing on this fashion!"

[17] see *Our Heritage*, 47-48

~5~ Patterns

Initially, I wondered how unfamiliar techniques outside of western medicine's conventional practices could possibly be a part of healing truths. What a myopic view I had! Studying what prophets have taught about the topic of "Truth" itself helped alleviate the narrow-mindedness I had entertained about who could propose to have true healing principles. I found many quotes similar to this one from the prophet Joseph who stated, "We should gather all the good and true principles in the world and treasure them up, or we shall not come out true "Mormons."[18]

I voraciously read books about various kinds of energy healing techniques as fast as I could in an attempt to understand whether this field's atypical methods aligned with my beliefs. I was full of questions. I even took notes and prayed to know what was true. With all my heart I wanted to know if what I read about fit with Christian beliefs. I had a persistent desire to seek answers as to why the Holy Spirit had encouraged a look into what appeared to be a very unorthodox looking health arena. That took time to decipher. New ideas about healing were worded in a whole new set of vocabulary.

I began to find similarities in what I read. Several authors and founders of various modalities used principles of forgiveness in their processes and taught of its critical importance to health. I certainly didn't have a problem with that, although I wasn't convinced of significant health benefits from it. Another similarity I found was that *tapping* on acupressure points of the body was beneficial *as well as* using needles on those points. Something was interesting and puzzling and unseen.

My husband, however, working as a sales representative to health food stores was getting more and more confused about energy work. He was troubled because every health food store owner he confided in seemed to have a different technique to suggest for our daughter's benefit. One store owner told him our daughter needed polarity work, another said she needed Cranial Sacral Therapy, while another one recommended chakra balancing . . . and the list went on.

My husband's perception was that we were being sent in several unrelated directions. On the other hand, in all my reading I discovered a pattern. Almost every modality that I read about spoke of an unseen *vital life force* energy enveloping the body and flowing through it. They all agreed on that point! I came to understand that energy healing modalities are different methods of clearing the subtle energy disturbances that contribute to ill health. I also learned that there is more than one way to clear energy. My monumental question was, ***"What is that elusive energy?!"***

I learned that life force, often known as *Chi* which many cultures believe in, sustains life and departs at death. That sounded familiar! Studying "life force energy" was getting more interesting all the time. Healing methods included a focus on the subtle energy of light that surrounded and enveloped physical bodies. Conventional medicine largely ignored these energy fields while religions used varied and different language to describe them. Did Christians have a name for these as well as Eastern religions? Yes! I just didn't realize it yet.

---

[18] *STPJS*, 316. www.scriptures.byu.edu

I had wondered how anyone would be able to affect my daughter's energy field. I watched Sue do just that at my daughter's first appointment. Rapid Eye Technology was literally, and figuratively an eye-opening way to release stress: my daughter was to blink more rapidly than normal and to breathe deeply. "An eye-directing device moves rapidly in a neuro-linguistic pattern in front of the eyes; the peripheral vision picks this up and the brain thinks it is in REM sleep. . . . Much of the trapped energy comes out through the eyes."[19] "R.E.T. physiologically and psychologically opens up the neuropathways where the energetic memories of our personal and inherited traumatic experiences are trapped. We believe neurons in the brain stem switch on the same way they do in REM sleep, causing communication at the cellular level throughout the body. Energy confined at the cellular level by emotional or physical trauma is thus accessed allowing energy discharge . . . Clients release issues and emotions at a comfortable rate without reliving incidents."[20] The brain lets go of issues *the body knows* are out of balance and positive reframes follow.

My daughter calmly let go of trapped emotions and trauma in RET sessions. Her transformations during these appointments were graceful, easily letting go of unresolved issues. My daughter told me she "felt more like herself' after these sessions. I was greatly encouraged to see the improvement my daughter made during and after these appointments, sometimes combined with other modalities such as Reiki or Christ-centered Theta. Her attitude and behavior before and after sessions was quite a contrast. Her stress level shifted from "off the chart" to manageable at the appointment. I was very enthused about the results. I learned later that "most people with psychosis are [neurologically] nonintegrated," [21] which R.E.T. addresses in another eye-work process.

Neuroscientist Candace Pert explains, "When people do seek help, often what is offered through mainstream psychology . . . is what I call 'talk and dose' therapy: lots of talking and even more pills, which are supposed to make the unacceptable feelings go away. A treatment, yes, but one that really only Band-Aids the symptoms and consigns people to a drug dependency rather than directing them toward an opportunity for really healing feeling[s]."[22] Rapid Eye was quickly helping my daughter to release the energy of *feelings*. Lifting these trapped emotions, which are vibrations, from her energy field was liberating.

I also learned for myself that clearing this energy has powerful effects. As a stressed out mother of a child with a chronic illness, I felt physically and emotionally greatly improved after my own sessions of Rapid Eye Technology. These clearing sessions left me feeling as though a burden had actually been lifted from my body. I literally felt lighter afterward.

We believe the wind exists, although we only see its effects. We believe in electricity we do not see and a magnet's pull, although we do not view these unseen forces with our eyes. Likewise, I began to understand that some sort of unseen electromagnetic field existed around our bodies. Intelligent, communicative light seemed to be part of the very elusive energy I was searching for.

As I read books, some principles in Healing Arts were compatible with LDS beliefs. At other times, authors got off on interpretations that I knew were forbidden in the Bible and opposed to what modern prophets taught. I threw such ideas completely out of the circle of possible healing truths I was gathering. I

---

[19] Ranae Johnson, *Reclaim Your Light Through the Miracle of Rapid Eye Technology* 28, 44
[20] "What Makes RET Work?" www.rapideyetechnology.com
[21] Ranae Johnson, *Reclaim Your Light Through the Miracle of Rapid Eye Technology*, 76
[22] Candace Pert, *Molecules of Emotion*, 265

put other questionable ideas on a "mental shelf" waiting until I found a prophet's words on that subject to decipher whether I should embrace or reject such teachings. Many authors did not have the eternal perspective that the restored gospel of Jesus Christ afforded, yet they did have some truth to share. I prayed to be enlightened by the spirit so as to be able to distinguish truth from error as I read.

I *knew* the techniques we found were helping my daughter and yearned to understand why. I was like a sponge thirsting to understand the science behind these methods, and especially how they fit with Christian beliefs. Beginning to understand the science behind them was helpful. Laboratory experiments relating to universal energy that Dawson Church, PhD; Gregg Braden; and Larry Dossey, M.D. describe in ordinary English are fascinating. An elementary example of experiments unveiling universal energy was done by quantum biologist Vladimir Poponin, Peter Gariaev and colleagues. Their research in Russia was a real surprise in its day. An overly simplified description of "The DNA Phantom Effect" is summarized here.

A tube was emptied such that a vacuum was created. The only things left inside were photons, or discrete bundles of electromagnetic (or light) energy. Scientists measured the location of the photons and found they were completely random inside the container, as was to be expected. Next, samples of human DNA were placed inside the tube and the location of the photons was re-measured. To the researchers' amazement, the "particles *arranged themselves*"[23] in an ordered way. A further shock to the researchers came when the DNA was removed from the container and the photons stayed in order instead of scattering! The scientists asked themselves, what are the light particles connected to? According to Poponin, the researchers were "forced to accept the working hypothesis that some new field structure is being excited."[24]

I was excited to read about this experiment, about other distance experiments, and about experiments on emotion and intention on the HeartMath Institute website, and even foreign studies.

[23]Gregg Braden, *The Divine Matrix*, 44
[24] Vladimir Poponin as qtd. in Gregg Braden, *The Divine Matrix*, 45

~6~ The Rest of the Story

"We speak, not in the words which man's wisdom teacheth, but which the Holy Ghost teacheth." 1 Cor. 2:13

Almost as suddenly as I was introduced to energy healing, I was also drawn into the question of whether it was appropriate for members of *The Church of Jesus Christ of Latter-day Saints* to be involved with it. Soon after we got to experience a few sessions of Rapid Eye Technology, my friend Sue found herself in an awkward situation. She sadly explained that suddenly she was not able to do sessions of energy work with anyone. Her Stake President was investigating a complaint by the spouse of a client about her work. The Stake President asked Sue to refrain from seeing any clients until he came to a conclusion. Sue was honoring his request, feeling in her heart that she had been working with principles consistent with gospel teachings and had been involved in no wrong-doing, yet feeling tremendous stress about the whole situation.

So there I was, led by the spirit to a novel treatment that held incredible help for my daughter and myself, yet detained from using it by someone else's fears about it. I had several pressing questions. Could my friend possibly be deceived about energy work? Was I? The deep motivation I had to find answers for myself is partly due to the circumstances my friend found herself in at that time. I determined that I was not going to be deceived. I would investigate this field until I found the truth for myself.

In the end, my friend's Stake President called her back in and shared that he learned over and over, after interviewing numerous people in his stake, the immense good that she was doing for those members. They gave dozens of positive examples of how sessions with my friend had blessed them and members of their families. The Stake President concluded that Sue could resume her practice. My friend was exonerated and the censoring ceased. I was able to take my daughter, myself and other family members to her for help again.

In the meantime, we had been seeing a local Rapid Eye Technician that I found on the Rapid Eye Technology website. I resonated with what she had posted there. I spoke to her first and found that we had the same values and standards. This technician used a Light and Sound Machine (LSM) in addition to the Rapid Eye processes. Since my daughter and I came together to appointments, she would have one of us use the LSM while she did Rapid Eye Technology on the other and then have us switch places.

One day as she handed me the LSM's full spectrum light eyeglasses, she had me think firmly on an intention to change specific patterns of behavior I felt stuck in. The light program was beginning so I had to keep my eyes shut. However, within a few minutes I saw my deceased great-grandmother's face looking down at me. This tiny woman smiled at me and then vanished. I was left wondering what that was about. I felt that "Granny Brown" was telling me I had found something very good. I didn't realize at that time that healing had anything to do with clearing generational issues, the patterns passed down to us from our ancestors in the DNA, or that a person's *intention* to change is highly significant - as lab experiments show.

~ 7 ~ Hear No Evil, Speak No Evil

"When our souls hurt, our pain is transmitted into our bodies as the spiritual quality of the life force that we feed into each cell." [25]

Healing Arts clear energy blockages such as trapped emotions. They restore balance and function to the energy system which benefits health. Emotional release processes were very therapeutic for our daughter. Clearing trapped trauma, unresolved issues, emotional blocks, and generational patterns alleviated agony, saved our family untold suffering and relieved personal heartbreak. Louise Hay says:

> The mental thought patterns that cause the most dis-ease in the body are criticism, anger, resentment, and guilt. For instance, criticism indulged in long enough will often lead to dis-ease such as arthritis. Anger turns into things that boil, burn, and infect the body. Resentment long held festers and eats away at the self and ultimately can lead to tumors and cancer. Guilt always seeks punishment and leads to pain. It's so much easier to release these negative thinking patterns from our minds when we're healthy than to try to dig them out when we're in a state of pain and under the threat of the surgeon's knife. [26]

Scriptures lend support to what mind/body authors write. It was amazing to me to see the progress my daughter made in RET sessions. She seemed to be getting over issues that talk therapy hadn't resolved in years. Dr. Ranae Johnson, the founder of Rapid Eye, writes, "We believe Rapid Eye Technology is the safest, fastest, least painful and most natural way to clear negative energy from all levels of our being.... Many professionals have found that after only one session, RET will unlock blocks in a client that conventional methods were ineffective with over a period of months or even years!"[27] My daughter was clearing energy blocks that *contributed* to her physical and mental distress. My daughter and I noticed the increased quality of life-force energy in our bodies after RET's emotional release sessions.

Every time my daughter went to a new therapist or psychologist for traditional talk therapy she had to repeat all of the heart-wrenching history. We learned that revealing one's story is unnecessary in RET, for it is the trapped *emotional energy* that needs lifted. In Rapid Eye Technology past trauma does not have to be relived or discussed to be released. What a *huge* blessing that was for my daughter! (RET is wonderful for PTSD.) At home, it felt like the "camera" of our family life was again set to capture in full color after years of sepia and black and white use. Our family had hope again!

I credit Rapid Eye Technology and another eye work process called Deep Emotion Release with enabling me to leave depression behind. I found a much better, more natural solution. Even better yet, it went after the source of the problem. Altering energy flows may be precisely what is needed for improvement. Rapid Eye was so beneficial that later on I certified in it. I have witnessed what may appear to be seemingly benign processes in several healing arts make remarkable differences for my family's well-being as well as for hundreds of my clients.

---

[25] Gregg Braden, *Secrets of the Lost Mode of Prayer*, 75
[26] Louise Hay, *Heal Your Body* 7-8
[27] Dr. Ranae Johnson, *Reclaim Your Light Through the Miracle of Rapid Eye Technology*, 29, 193

Healing Arts release techniques may be accompanied by teachings on creating one's life in line with universal laws, such as in the Rapid Eye model that includes teaching positive living Life Skills. Combining an *education and practice of higher consciousness* with emotional and energetic release processes is wise preventive medicine so the same kind of energy blocks are not created all over again prompting the need for future release work. A person can find great help today for well being if they are willing to expand their perspective of what is possible. I learned from working with clients that when release processes in Healing Arts are coupled with learning and living universal creation laws, the results are more likely to last.

It was disheartening that sometimes my daughter refused to have an RET appointment until she was desperate. Sue encouraged us not to wait so long in between sessions. It was great advice I wish I had valued earlier. My teenage daughter's belief in her gifted Rapid Eye Technician's ability to help her, even in times of great distress, grew until she declared in a crisis, "Take me to the emergency room or straight to that 'R.E.T. lady!'" Witnesses to my daughter's quick recoveries after energy clearing sessions were members of her NAMI (National Alliance on Mental Illness) support group. They were astonished at times with her remarkable turnarounds and several of them also found help in this field.

As I continued to read dozens of books, I was astounded to find a wealth of options to help *not only* my daughter, but those with a whole array of other illnesses and troubles as well. This field of help wasn't just for emotional issues. There were a plethora of anecdotal accounts for many physical troubles as well.

As our trust of this field grew we sought and found the help of other forms of healing arts such as: Emotional Freedom Technique, Quantum Touch, Foot Zoning, Reflexology, Vibrational Medicine, Christ-Centered Theta Healing, Y.U.E.N. Method, Reconnective Healing and more. I was just as concerned with the integrity of the facilitator we sought help from as the specific methods used in a session. We also found by experience that pure essential oils were very helpful and grounding. My ill teenage daughter told me, "Mom, I feel more spiritual when you have me wear that oil." Clients have also reported great benefits from this wonderful help - what I like to call "God's Pharmacy."

One of my teenagers had problems with IBS. I took this child for Rapid Eye sessions in addition to following the doctor's orders and this teen told me, "Mom, I feel like Rapid Eye is helping me more than the doctors are." I felt that was quite a statement. When a son had a bout with mild depression I took him to a medical doctor trained in both eastern and western medicine who treated him with acupuncture instead of anti-depressants. We were learning there were viable "alternative" options opening up even in conventional care.

I learned how powerful a self help tool, Emotional Freedom Technique can be, by trying an experiment on myself. I was very scared and upset as I was driving one day. I thought, this is a perfect time to see if EFT really works. I began tapping a couple of rounds on the acupressure points EFT uses with only one hand while speaking release statements out loud, followed by positive statements. Within a few minutes I was *no* longer full of anxiety and tears - although I still faced the very same situation. The heavy emotional charge was gone! I was calmer and able to think with much more clarity. I just knew I could handle what was before me. The difference EFT made was obvious although it had been simple to learn.

Another example comes from my husband who lost his hearing overnight in one ear 15 years ago. He spent a whole week in the hospital where doctors could not find any *physical* reason for his hearing loss. The doctors did the best they could with their limited perspective. Unfortunately, the medical field largely ignores the complex energy system included in holistic health. Eight years later, after my husband visited just a few minutes with a gifted Cranio-Sacral Therapist, she sensed an energy block over my husband's ear. She found there were layers of *emotional issues* blocking his hearing. She asked, "*What didn't you want to hear* at the time you lost your hearing?" He thought about it and knew the answer was possibly losing his job. She had him forgive that situation and similar ones layered underneath it to clear trapped energy over his ear. During his one hour session he began to be able to *hear again* in that ear! What a great blessing!

While in Oregon at my first Rapid Eye Training, I experienced a profound release of trapped, negative emotions. I set a strong intention to release fears about speaking up. During my session, I actually saw a cloudy mist in front of my face clearing up and dissolving as an RET technician worked on me. I have witnessed this happening on myself two other times since then and once when I was working on a client.
I believe the visible release I had at training was letting go of many strong unresolved fears I had stored in my body. I felt a strong tingling sensation on my face and then more so on my nose. The feeling was so strong it was almost a buzzing sensation. The tingling moved to under my nose and then traveled to my top lip before leaving my body altogether.

Later on, I realized that at one of the lowest times in my life, when my daughter was labeled with a diagnosis I felt *I could not speak of*, I had sat on my bed bawling. I was paralyzed with fear, unable to even bring myself to phone my mother. I cried so hard and so long about my daughter and how it all would look to others that my face turned extremely red and *tingled strongly* in all of the places I just described above. I felt there was a connection between those two events: once when the strong emotions were stored, and again when they were released.

Oh, that someone might have shared the *other* side of the coin with me before then. Words of hope might have included, "Your daughter is not 'broken.' Your daughter has *gifts!* The world does not acknowledge or understand these gifts, yet. Such gifted souls are here to teach the rest of us."

~8~ Synchronicity

To use David O. McKay's term, I must have been "radiating" a request for healing information to be sent my way. Curiously timed events started happening one after another. One synchronicity happened while flying from Salt Lake City on Southwest Airlines. A quiet thought suddenly popped into my head as I boarded the plane, "first open window seat." So I found just that, and sat down -- although I wouldn't normally have chosen a row with a man already seated there. All I wanted to do was sleep with my head against the window. With five children at home to care for, I was exhausted from all the preparations I had made ahead of time to make my absence easier on my husband. I leaned against the window and hoped for a lengthy rest.

A few minutes later though, the man put a book down on the seat in between us. I was made abruptly alert by the surprise that he was reading a book related to subtle energy. I pulled out my copy of Dr. Masaru Emoto's book *The Hidden Messages in Water* and flashed it at my seat companion. He got a big grin on his face and said that he had five friends in the movie *"What the Bleep!?"* that showcased that scientist's work. As it turned out, that prompting had led me to a seat by a Materials Scientist who was on the board chairing the forthcoming Whole Person Health Summit in Baltimore, Maryland. When he found out I intended to write a book about the incredible help I had found for my daughter using alternative health modalities, he started suggesting websites and recommending authors and scientific research that could help me. He told of scientific studies about the *structure* of water and spoke of the Schuman resonance and intention experiments and on and on.

We talked all the way across the country to Baltimore, which was entirely out of the ordinary for my quiet nature. I got off the plane with fourteen pages of notes from a complete stranger who had become an esteemed acquaintance. He had offered valuable advice and we exchanged e-mail addresses. A few weeks later my new friend offered me another valuable avenue of learning: a complimentary entrance ticket to the Whole Person Health Summit worth a few hundred dollars. My husband and I prayed about it and knew I was supposed to attend the event.

The health summit drew people from as far away as Asia and India, although it was held just a few miles from my sister's home. I went eager to take notes. Enlightened doctors such as Larry Dossey, M.D. were keynote speakers. Addresses were on various new findings about health and healing and the scientific research being done which supported it. Rustom Roy emphasized that a new mindset was needed because human beings are more than just physical bodies. I felt at home. These people were speaking my "language," whereas, when I actually was home I felt like such an oddity in my neighborhood.

The summit's program directory I was handed said this on the inside cover, "Sit down before the facts as a little child, be prepared to give up every preconceived notion, follow humbly wherever and to whatever abyss Nature leads, or you shall learn nothing. I have only begun to learn content and peace of mind since I resolved at all risks to do this. (Thomas Huxley in a letter to Charles Kingley)." I felt that this was precisely the path I had been taking and would continue to follow. Promptings from the spirit had led me to have several epiphanies about the world I lived in, including an entire change to my paradigm about health and illness.

At the Summit I learned that top scientists such as William Tiller, PhD were studying the very same things I had been wondering about. Was long-distance healing really possible? Yes, research was continuing to show that it was. One speaker gave the example that mere *mortals* in the Bible did long-distance healing. That's when a proverbial light bulb went off in my head – with floodlight wattage! When questions arose over whether to accept a new idea, I could look directly to *examples* in the scriptures. In all my research, I only wanted to accept as truth the principles that fit within the gospel of Jesus Christ, but I had never thought of *this* idea before. If I could find a healing principle by *righteous example* in the scriptures then it was true. I felt I had been given another standard that would help me.

The conference taught me that there were a dozen major conferences on Alternative Medicine. The "Whole Person Healing" movement was sweeping the nation. This was cutting edge medicine- the medicine of the future. There had to be pioneers in every new field. Was I willing to risk being called "different" at church or wherever I went, if it would help someone else?

I had wondered if proxy healing was real. Scientists at the Summit said it was. Many of my puzzling questions were answered by the scientists and medical doctors who spoke. Could a person's DNA actually change? Yes, epigenetic markers on DNA were found to turn on or off depending on *outside* factors. I came home with another stack of notes from the Health Summit. Perhaps the most important thing I learned, though, was not written down in my notes. It was the realization that it was NOT A COINCIDENCE where I had sat on that airplane. It gave me a sure knowledge and confidence that God wanted me, a very conservative Mormon mom, to study a subject that seemed to others to be quite strange.

~ 9 ~ Light and Life of the World

I became fascinated by the science behind subtle energy therapies because they made a huge difference for my family. In the last few decades, science has discovered a mysterious energy connected to other things *even* when distanced and shielded from them. Lab experiments have confirmed that we are surrounded by a field of energy that connects us all. Einstein referred to the entanglement of such separated objects as "spooky action at a distance."

These experiments have caught the attention of other scientists as well as theologians. I noted Pastor Joel Osteen's comments on the ramifications of one experiment, among many, which are fascinating and mind boggling. These teach that the universal energy is intelligent.

> I read of an interesting study done in 1993 by the United States military. They were curious about what traits get passed down from one generation to the next. . . .The researchers extracted some white blood cells from a volunteer and they carefully placed them in a test tube. They then put a probe [like] a lie detector machine down in that test tube, to measure the person's emotional response. Next, they instructed this same volunteer to go a couple of doors down and watch some violent scenes from an old war movie on television. When this man watched the scenes, even though the blood that was being tested was in another room, when he got all uptight and tense, that lie detector test shot off the page. It was detecting his emotional response even though the blood was no longer in his body. The experimenters did this with person after person with the same results.
>
> They concluded that the blood cells seem to "remember" where they came from. Now, if sicknesses and addictions and wrong mind-sets can be passed down, how much more can God's blessings, favors and good habits be passed down through our blood? As important as it may be to understand the generational curse, it is vital that we understand the generational blessings we can obtain.[28]

This is just one example of mind-bending experiments! Today's science has caused me to alter my concept of what a human body is. I have learned over and over the wisdom of incorporating life-giving light and the biofield into my family's healthcare. Until this is added to conventional medicine's model, one is only addressing the physical level of a person instead of the *entire* person's being that also includes emotional, mental and spiritual levels. My children who were chronically ill improved remarkably when we added energy based technology and processes to what the medical field was doing.

Energy Medicine's technology was very beneficial for my youngest son when he experienced an ongoing illness that the medical field wasn't pinpointing. Understanding the importance of seeking medical help from those who practice from the entire paradigm of "Person = Body + Mind + Spirit" was critical to his improvement. We sought health practitioners who would address my son's entire being, not just a portion

---

[28] Joel Osteen, *Become A Better You*, 60-61

of himself - the physical level only.

Frequency based technology by ASYRA was most helpful in steering us toward a diagnosis of the mysterious symptoms my son had. Knowledge of such technology's existence was invaluable because it pinpointed the vibrational signature of frequencies found in his body which doctors then ordered lab tests for. Soon after that he was clinically diagnosed by three different doctors with Lyme disease (when his western blot blood test came back equivocal). And then when his doctor of osteopathy found through lab tests that he was also experiencing a heavy metal burden and environmental toxin overload, the energy frequencies of constitutional homeopathy worked remarkably for him.

Leading edge science reveals that we must change our old beliefs to a new paradigm of understanding about human bodies and the world we live in. D&C 88:67 says, "And if your eye," (notice that is singular), "be single to my glory, your whole bodies" (plural!), "shall be filled with light." It is taught in Healing Arts that we have light bodies beyond our physical level including an emotional body, mental body and spirit body.

Biophoton physics research may not be popular in mainstream science yet; but, I believe it deserves careful consideration. A German researcher, Fritz-Albert Popp, did studies that found weak **light** is continuously being discharged from living beings. His laboratory experiments show that DNA is an all important source of this light which is called biophoton emission. Another scientist writes,

> "As is generally known, a photon is a particle of light, but all the same is equivalent to an electromagnetic oscillation. According to Popp, 'biophotons' are weak emissions of light radiated from the cells of all living systems. All organisms constantly emit photons as part of their vital activities. . . . The light of the photon is too faint to be seen by the naked eye, its intensity comparable to that of a candle's light seen at a distance of 20km."[29]

Fritz-Albert Popp teaches that now we know human beings are essentially beings of light. It appears that scientists are telling us the very things that prophets have told us all along: we truly are **beings of light!** Latter-day Saints have long known about a light that fills the immensity of space and is life giving. I always wondered what the mysterious verses in Doctrine and Covenants sections 84, 88 and 93. . . were referring to. These are incredible scriptures!

[29] Dietrich Vastenburg, "Morphology of isolated Rat Cortical Neurons and Information Transferred via a Biophoton Device," 3

~ 10 ~ The Energy of Science Meets the Light of Christ

"God wants to dress us in layers of light." B. Grant Bishop [30]

After a couple years of frenzied reading, I had a distinct impression to stop studying so many of the world's books and concentrate on learning more from LDS sources. What a thrill it was to find many subtle energy healing principles in books by prophets and apostles. I was quite surprised to find so many available and on many topics I had covered in my early research.

In my reading, quantum physics and truths of the gospel often said the same thing *using completely different language*. I studied what prophets have said about life force, chakras (energy centers in the body) and other foundational principles in the healing arts, such as consciousness. I felt that the LDS authored quotes I was led to as well as quotes on quantum physics principles offered support for framework principles of Energy Medicine.

Imagine my surprise to learn from Pres. Joseph F. Smith and John A. Widtsoe. . . what the equivalent of the universal life-giving energy that other teachers called life force was! I was astounded that long ago a prophet and an apostle compared *intelligence in the light of Christ* to the universal energy of science!

I believe the light of Christ, or intelligence in it, manifests as consciousness which enables and sharpens our understanding of everything. The light of Christ may be the same as, or related to, Zero Point Energy that fills all of space. This divine light is IN all matter and GIVES LIFE to all creation, including human bodies. We live in this sea of light! This light is the very law by which all matter- visible and invisible- is governed.

Cutting-edge science suggests that the unheralded subtle energy system involves unseen light thought to orchestrate the processes that keep us alive! Marco Bischoff explains:

> "According to the biophoton theory . . . biophoton light is stored in the cells of the organism - more precisely, in the DNA molecules of their nuclei - and a dynamic web of light constantly released and absorbed by the DNA may connect cell organelles, cells, tissues, and organs within the body and serve as the organism's main *communication network* and as the *principal regulating instance for all life processes.* The processes of morphogenesis, growth, differentiation and regeneration are also explained by the *structuring and regulating activity* of the coherent biophoton field. The holographic biophoton field of the brain and the nervous system, and maybe even that of the whole organism, may also be basis of memory and other phenomena of *consciousness,* as postulated by neurophysiologist Karl Pribram and others."[31]

---

[30] B. Grant Bishop, *The LDS Gospel of Light*, 5-6

[31] Marco Bischoff , "Biophotons- The Light in Our Cells," (emphasis added)

All that regulating and communicating by unseen light reminded me of characteristics of divine light that GOVERNS ALL things! Phenomenally, the vital life force energy in Healing Arts behaved similarly to characteristics of the governing, universal light in scripture! Startling conclusions drawn from experiments were already spoken of in scripture. Had science and religion *and the Healing Arts* been describing the same subtle energy all along? Scientists were possibly describing aspects of the light of Christ!

Characteristics of the governing, universal light in scripture seemed very similar to 'behavior' of the universal subtle energy that physicists were studying. I wondered if scripture's universal energy was involved, knowingly or unknowingly, in healing arts. When I first surmised that the energy in healing arts might be related to the Light of Christ, I didn't dare speak such words aloud. I pondered them in my heart until I noticed that a few LDS authors were wondering the same thing.

It is exciting that scientists are now studying how light is involved in healing! Marco Bischof writes, "The discovery of biophoton emission also lends scientific support to some unconventional methods of healing."[32] William A. Tiller, Ph.D. reportedly explained that there is a light which is a *communicator* used in energy medicine:

> "There are many energies involved in light. There is, of course, electromagnetic light, which everyone knows about. The coarsest level of the human body is all about electromagnetic energy. So you can use light in the way it's used in energy medicine, especially on acupuncture points, to systemically provide healing in the body. Or you can go to a higher level... magnetoelectric energy. That has an aspect of light as well. And at all of these higher dimensional levels there is a light which is the **communicator** between the aspects of substance at that level of being."[33]

That is interesting because Parley P. Pratt taught that a divine light has "**communicative** properties." And God tells us, "The light which is in all things, which giveth life to all things, . . . is the law by which all things are **governed**"(D&C 88: 13). John A. Widtsoe wrote about a controlling energy in the language of his day which used the term "ether." "The pores of wood, soil, lead, gold, and the human body are filled with the ether. It is quite impossible by any known process to obtain a portion of space free from it. . . . Joseph Smith taught space is filled with a substance comparable to the ether of science. . . .The prophet goes farther than some modern scientists, when he says that this universal substance bears a **controlling** relation to all things.[34]

The light of Christ, or something in connection with it, is likely the answer that world renowned scientists are searching for. I believe the intelligent, universal, life-force energy of the Healing Arts may be related to the universal energy of science as well as the divine, life-giving, universal light of Christ. These various fields of study appear to be teaching about the same controlling or governing essence using entirely

---

[32] Bischoff, Marco. "Biophotons- The Light in Our Cells."
[33] William Tiller, PhD as quoted on sjlreconnectivehealingar.com/science.php
[34] John A. Widtsoe, *Joseph Smith as Scientist*, 21,24, 25

different terminology! Universal energy is known in religion as the light of Christ, to science as Zero Point Energy, and to Healing Arts as life-force energy. Johan Boswinkel's opinion is similar:

"Biophotons are considered main stream science by universities. They have been proven to exist and it is very likely that they control all biochemical reactions. Approximately 60 Universities do research into the biophotons. . . The biophotons are so incredibly weak that a very strong photomultiplier was needed to be able to detect them. . . . I have come to the belief that the biophotons are actually the light of the soul."[35] Author Brian Luke Seaward shares two more related opinions:

> In his book, *The Tao of Physics*, Fritjof Capra outlined many similarities and parallels between the disciplines of physics and the Eastern mystical philosophies... suggesting that there is an incredible linkage between them and that whether it is called "energy," "the Tao," or "the Holy Spirit" its essence appears to be very similar. . . . The collective unconscious and subtle energy in which all things connect may, in fact, be the same component of human spirituality. As science continues to explore the realm of human consciousness and energy, the fields of physics and theology may not only connect, but someday become one and the same.[36]

Latter-day Saints share conclusions about science and religion being compatible. John A. Widtsoe wrote, "There is no real difference between science and religion. The great, fundamental laws of the Universe are foundation stones in religion as well as in science."[37]

I discovered that Latter-day Saints use many different terms for the subtle, universal essence and that I certainly could believe in universal *life force* energy. In the LDS culture we appear to have our own unique terminology for it! I am thrilled to know that I can learn about characteristics of universal light energy in scripture.

I firmly believe that science and religion can work together in teaching truth for that describes the last few years of my research. The science I have come across has strengthened my testimony of the gospel of Jesus Christ. That's not so surprising since all truth comes from God and He makes no distinction between scientific truth and religious truth. It is all His truth! Scientific truth and religious truth fit together because God's truth encompasses them all. God is the author of all truth!

---

[35] Johan Boswinkel, "The Science of Biophotons Healing with Light"
[36] Brian Luke Seaward, *Managing Stress*, 176-177
[37] John A. Widtsoe, *Rational Theology*, 1

~11~ Consciousness

Consciousness, thoughts and emotions play a great deal into health whether *we* realize it or not. Remember that experiments show that the intelligent universal energy responds to human emotion. It is curious to learn that "Feelings are carried in the auric field"[38] and that "Feeling is the language that 'speaks' to the Divine Matrix."[39]

Barbara Brennan, a scientist turned healer, speaks about one's energy field/ vibrational signature/ aura, "From the viewpoint of a healer, all disease is psychosomatic. A balanced functioning of our auric field is necessary to maintain our health. Yet, the auric field is not the source of the event. It is the vehicle through which the creative consciousness from the core reaches the physical."[40]

Dr. Masaru Emoto's scientific experiments exposing water samples to different words or music or prayers, and then photographing the resulting differences in the water's crystals when frozen are stunning examples of consciousness affecting matter. These and other experiments are evidence that the consciousness of thoughts and words and emotions *affect matter.*

I learned that it is just as imperative to address *consciousness* in attempting to improve health as it is to clear our energy fields. Keeping our energies in healthy patterns also involves the mind. Raising our consciousness is preventive medicine! The news that one's own thought patterns and emotions affect health may initially be hard to accept, particularly if one is currently suffering. When I offer the mind/body view to friends or family who are complaining of ills, they are often quick to point out that their troubles are caused by chemical imbalances, physical misalignment, a past accident, or other more currently "socially acceptable" evidence.

All of us would be wise to consider that there are more precursors to pain and illness than what we have been led to believe. There are probable emotional roots adding to the "dis-ease" equation, no matter how vehemently people feel their problems are strictly physically based. Understanding illness from this perspective offers great hope to people because the person can actually *do something themselves* about the stressful mental patterns and other factors that play into developing pain or illness.

I want to make it very clear that illness is NOT about judgment! Richard G. Scott taught, "We lived in the presence of God our Holy Father and His Beloved Son, Jesus Christ, in a premortal existence. There we gained an understanding of the Father's plan of salvation and the promise of help when we would be born as mortals on earth. ... So that the period of mortal testing and growth would yield its greatest benefit, *you were taught and prepared for the circumstances you would personally encounter in mortality."*[41] We do not know the reasons why God or our soul may have chosen or agreed to experience certain diseases or

---

[38] Barbara Brennan, *Light Emerging*, 18
[39] Gregg Braden, *The Divine Matrix*, 85
[40] Barbara Brennan, *Light Emerging,* 19
[41] Elder Richard G. Scott, *Ensign,* Nov 2005, emphasis added

events in our life. We *can* learn, however, that every one of them is a blessing. Doing so raises our level of consciousness which is taught to improve well being, as well.

Elder Dallin H. Oaks' talk "Give Thanks in All Things" affected me greatly. This apostle taught, "The revelations, for which we are grateful, show that we should even give thanks for our afflictions because they turn our hearts to God and give us opportunities to prepare for what God would have us become."[42] I wanted to apply this counsel in my life. I really appreciated one author's story of the freeing power of gratitude in ALL things. His book taught by example how to express gratitude, even when one's world seems to have come crashing down.[43] I chose to begin expressing gratitude out loud for the worst things that ever happened in my life. It was initially, as the author said, like chewing on concrete. I kept at it and discovered there *were* hidden blessings disguised -- even in life's most difficult trials. As I expressed gratitude for the worst that had happened, a peace came and a broken heart began to heal: mine. My level of consciousness was raising.

When Sue introduced me to Dr. David Hawkins' chart in *Power vs. Force*, titled "Map of Consciousness," I felt right away that it had truth in it. Dr. Hawkins said emotions vibrating below 200 create degeneration in the body, while those above 200 regenerate us. "Shame" was listed as the very lowest level on the map, being the most destructive. I had already observed up close how debilitating shame could be to a physical body.

My daughter began slipping into her first psychotic break while at "Especially For Youth." According to my daughter, teen counselors "played bishop" at this summer camp, asking her to confess everything she had ever done wrong. By the time we picked her up in southern Utah and drove home, our daughter was losing the ability to walk or even answer simple yes/no questions. We took her to the emergency room and were later told that something very traumatic must have just occurred to her. I had personally witnessed how very debilitating shame could be to a body! My daughter was hospitalized for days. This was just the beginning of what I would learn about emotion affecting health. Our emotions determine the quality of the life force energy that passes through us.

I wondered how a person could ever feel "bliss" or "ineffable" which Dr. Hawkins had listed near the top of his map. I had to look up the second word. According to the Encarta Dictionary "ineffable" means "unable to be expressed in words." I learned over the years that in order to feel bliss, I could express out loud heartfelt forgiveness, gratitude and praise *in all things* - although there were storms all around me. The spirit whispered, "Can you love, even when you're not being loved?"

---

[42] Elder Dallin H. Oaks, "Give Thanks in All Things," *Ensign*, May 2003

[43] See Doug Mendenhall, *My Peace I Give Unto You*

~12~ Forgiveness Heals

"To extend forgiveness, that soothing balm, to those who have offended you is to heal."[44]

Several little miracles got my daughter down to St. George, Utah for an appointment with Jan Graf whose Stress Management practice centers on forgiveness. Marion G. Romney teaches, "From what Jesus said at the time he healed the man 'sick with the palsy' (Luke 5:18), it would seem that remittance of sins is the therapy which heals and that the two terms are synonymous. Concerning that incident, Luke says, '...the power of the Lord was present to heal.' (Luke 5:17) . . . . In this instance there was a physical healing. Sometimes there is also a healing of the nervous system, or of the mind. But always the remittance of sins which attends divine forgiveness heals the spirit. This accounts for the fact that in the scriptures conversion and healing are repeatedly associated. . . . For example, 'and after their temptations, and much tribulation, behold, I the Lord, will feel after them, and if they harden not their hearts, and stiffen not their necks against me, they shall be converted and I will heal them' (D&C 112:12-13)."[45]

I believe that my daughter was prepared for what could possibly occur in St. George. She read Jan Graf's booklet and was prepared to forgive everyone. She had certified in Quantum Touch, a healing modality, that very month which also prepared her with a weekly balancing of her energy by Sue and another gifted individual. My daughter had just taken all of the RET Life Skills classes. So she began expressing gratitude for her healing weeks before it happened. She went *believing* it was possible and *grateful* for the healing she created first spiritually. Where faith is, doubt *cannot* be! She went after much prayer and fasting. She 'acted as if' she had already received healing. She knew Christ's atonement was also for healing emotionally.

My daughter said Jan Graf balanced her energy field and then helped her forgive many people in that two hour appointment, including forgiving *herself* more than anyone else. He also had my daughter use another principle that will be discussed later on. My daughter felt totally different! She said she felt like she did before junior high school when she very first got depressed. Her mind was clear, she could think easily and her face truly beamed happiness. After the appointment, Jan came out with our teenager and said, "I think you have your daughter back!"

Jan Graf said my daughter went in to her appointment vibrating at 15 (meaning 10 to the 15th power according to David Hawkins Map of Consciousness) near the level of shame, and came out at 650 (or 10 to the power of 650)! That one visit was a remarkable turnaround. We learned firsthand that harboring feelings and thereby not forgiving others, or yourself, can actually make you PHYSICALLY ILL! The benefits of this session lasted for years. The greater task may be in the "homework" Jan Graf gives clients: to forgive again at every remembering. This experience exemplifies Dr. Hawkins' Map to me. It teaches the *power of love* versus the love of power.

---

[44] Boyd K. Packer, *Ensign* , Nov 1987, 16

[45] Marion G. Romney, "Conversion", Conf Report 1963, 25

I had my own experience which reinforced how important forgiveness is to health when my gallbladder was removed. This was supposed to be out-patient surgery, but I was in the hospital five days with doctor influenced pancreatitis. A good friend, the man who had encouraged us to take our daughter to see Jan Graf, stopped by to see how I was doing after a week or so back home from the hospital. He thought I looked kind of down. My friend asked me if I had forgiven the doctors for causing pancreatitis. I replied that I never had held any animosity towards them. He asked again *if I had forgiven them out loud* (because that is an important principle that Jan Graf emphasizes in his work). I had to confess that I had not.

My friend set the intention of filling me with positive energy while one of his fingers touched the middle of my forehead and suggested I spend some time voicing every negative thought I had ever allowed in my head about the doctors' involvement. I forgave the general surgeon for suggesting we do a scope procedure just prior to surgery that irritated my pancreas. I forgave the other doctor who did the scope. I forgave them for putting a micro-tear in my bile duct. I forgave myself for ever even thinking pancreatitis was their fault. I forgave myself for thinking recovery had to be long. I forgave my body for believing it had to continue to hurt . . . for having needed a drain left in . . . and on and on I forgave.

Amazingly, I began feeling physically different as I finished speaking those words of forgiveness! I felt an almost warm subtle light energy coming into the crown of my head, flowing down my neck and into my shoulders and down into my whole body- filling me up with light and renewing me physically and emotionally. It was an incredibly wonderful sensation, similar to reports I had read of in church history.

I felt *much* better, more energetic and full of hope. I sprang off the couch and began cleaning the kitchen. My husband and the branch president both commented that I looked different. I am *so* grateful this friend stopped by to remind me of the healing power of forgiveness. I knew it was powerful, but forgot amidst pain to apply it and hadn't even admitted I needed to.

~ 13 In Praise of Trial ~

"Be not overcome of evil, but overcome evil with good." Romans 12:21

Members of my family have applied principles of higher consciousness. We have experienced the frequencies of forgiveness, gratitude and praise in all things overcoming emotional, situational and even physical issues. I have put the Praise principle to the test again and again over the last two years. This helped me to feel peace amidst chaos. As a simple example, a loved one was falsely accused. At home we expressed gratitude for the opportunity and forgave the accusers out loud. We praised God for the opportunity to learn. We didn't allow the indulgence of lower vibration emotions, such as speaking ill of the accusers . . . and the accusation was dropped.

We forgave out loud and aimed to stay in a state of gratitude when hospital regulations refused to allow my son to take his homeopathic remedies during a hospital stay. While under great stress, several Lyme symptoms suddenly started returning and my son *really* wanted to take his remedies! I remind the reader that it took over half of a year to win the battle with Lyme the first time around. We all politely asked hospital staff again and again for an exception to the rule but were repeatedly denied day after day for about two weeks. The hospital's regulations didn't budge (yet). We continue to praise anytime that situation comes back to mind – praising that the current medical model refuses to look at whole person health. My son tested to needing a stronger homeopathic remedy once he was out of the hospital and we express gratitude that the symptoms that reappeared are gone again.

Praise *in all things* has helped me to overcome crisis situations over the last two years with grace and dignity that formerly would have been devastating. If I slip down into fear, I catch myself doing it much earlier. I'm getting better at recognizing that unpleasant vibration and choosing back into faith. I *aspire* to live at that high level of consciousness. It puts attention on peace. This is another benefit of the Healing Arts. They teach practical steps and processes that allow one to live calmly "in the eye of the storm" while torrential winds may blow all around.

I am a much better person for all that my family has been through. Lessons aren't always easy, but learning is priceless. I am grateful now for all the growing that chaotic and terrifying experiences gave me. My involvement in the healing arts has helped me to be a much better person, empathetic and far less likely to judge. I have emerged a much stronger person. I grew from feeling I was a victim of despairing circumstances to feeling empowered *because* of them. I am grateful that trials enabled me to have firsthand knowledge that faith is a principle of *power*.

Nature teaches a remarkable lesson on chaos in our lives. Cymatics video footage mesmerizes me. Seeing sands, powders and pastes "come to life" formed only by sound vibrations is spellbinding. Some animated forms resemble moving skeletal bones and other recognizable shapes. Jeff Volk's words on Cymatics struck a chord with my soul:

> Unfortunately, most of us have a strong aversion to [disorder in our lives], fearing a loss of self-control. Yet despite our discomfort with discord and disharmony, chaos appears to play an essential role in the process of growth. . . The crucial role of chaos is demonstrated in one of Dr. Jenny's

cymatics experiments with such grace and elegance that it completely changes the way one views disorder, beckoning you to accept disintegration as an ally, instead of resisting or fearing it. . . .

Volk observed that the beautiful, striking patterns seen in a small water sample under a microscope in experiments where the sound frequency gradually increased did *NOT gradually* change into more complex patterns. No, the striking pattern collapsed into *total chaos* and then would *suddenly* reappear in an even "more intricately structured form." Volk continues, "A sudden illness, the loss of a loved one – or ones' job for that matter – and chaos and disorder appear unexpectedly. How we view these things has a lot to do with how they impact on us. . . . We need not be swept up in the daily dramas, the cycles of creation and dissolution which are constantly occurring about us.[46]

Perhaps in life's chaos, God is making *us* more intricate! As I practiced the praise principle, I became better at praising God with my heart in addition to my lips. When my heart is right, I can even praise God for illnesses. I can see that they provided more opportunities for real soul stretching than almost anything else in life. I believe that learning to have gratitude, forgiveness, and praise *in all things* can help prepare a person for the prophesied calamities to precede the second coming of our Savior Jesus Christ. Where will our heart be on the map of emotion then?

---

[46] Jeff Volk, "Sound Insights" Kindred Spirit Magazine

~14~ Into the Unknown

I'm going to tell the reader something that I did not want to hear- and others may deny. It was not taught outright in any of the modalities I certified in. I share it for the benefit of others because truth is empowering. This information is too valuable for personal discomfort to get in the way. Truth can set us free! The learning curve I went through with my daughter drastically changed the way I look at illness, particularly mental illness. Variables are involved in disease which I had never considered pertinent today.

I was in the public library again, scouring the alternative health books. I picked up a book whose title intrigued me, *Remarkable Healings*. I thumbed through it and noticed references to evil spirits causing depression. I immediately thought "I don't want this book in my home." I was putting it back on the library shelf when I distinctly heard a whisper "Check the book out." I am extremely grateful that I listened to that prompting!

What I read astounded me. The author was a psychiatrist whose patients of widely diverse religions and cultures gave consistent information while under hypnotherapy: there were spirit entities attached to their energy fields. When this doctor treated the displaced spirit as a patient in need of help and prayed for help herself, what I will call "unwanted company" would leave her patients. Reading this book was very disturbing to me and I didn't know what to think of it at first! I hardly dared to speak of the book to anyone. *Why had I been prompted to read it?*

I kept reading, hoping that somehow the book would lead me to help for my daughter. I read cautiously and prayerfully. I was amazed that several things in the book fit in with my religious beliefs. Deceased relatives spirits looked young, the Bible had been changed, there was a war in heaven before we came to earth, and the importance of prayer was stressed. A list of evils to avoid that open a person up for disruption sounded like a Sunday School lesson, except for one thing on the list: "too much compassion."

I learned later that one can want to help *others* so much that they may harm themselves energetically. "Buying in" to every sad story without seeing gratitude for learning lessons is to be overly sympathetic to others. Thus, grounding to one's *own* circuit of energy is vitally important. This is a tendency I find in clients labeled with mental illness. It is *because* of their gifts, that they have vulnerabilities.

When my friend and I were introduced to this concept, it was difficult to accept that evil spirits had *anything* to do with the illnesses our children were experiencing. The knee jerk reaction is to say, that doesn't have anything to do with *my* kid! What a cruel thought when (s)he is *so sensitive and kind!* "In our deepest feelings of pain, we discover the depth of our capacity to love. . . .[With] perspective, our hurt may be considered to be a barometer of our ability to love, rather than a punishment for the choices we make."[47]

---

[47] Gregg Braden, *Secrets to the Lost Mode of Prayer,*

My husband was somewhat concerned about me, and the strange theory I had happened upon. He didn't seem to believe that there were such things as earthbound spirits. I noted that some of my LDS friends had the same belief and that NAMI held a firm stance that mental illness had *nothing whatsoever* to do with evil spirits. I was intrigued that this doctor's process immediately resolved many of her patient's mental illness symptoms. The author claimed it had worked with thousands of her patients and that beings of the light almost always appeared when she dealt with this. I mistakenly assumed that only the doctor's method of hypnotherapy could accomplish that.

I began to really ponder stories about healing in the Bible. Sometimes I "unpacked" scriptures a verse at a time. In *The Book of Mormon,* the prophet Nephi saw "multitudes of people who were sick, and who were afflicted with all manner of diseases, and with devils and unclean spirits . . . And they were healed by the power of the Lamb of God; and the devils and the unclean spirits were cast out." (1 Nephi 11:31) In decades of reading, I had somehow skipped right over that last phrase without thinking much about it.

As I reread verses, I felt I shouldn't have been so surprised that my daughter tried to drown, burn and cut herself given all of the biblical references about children afflicted by evil spirits that the Savior healed. Sometimes my daughter had said that she "didn't feel like herself." "No wonder!" I thought.

Once when my daughter didn't want to go to school she cried and told me that she was "tired of pretending to be herself." I didn't understand her at all back then. Now it made so much more sense. On more than one occasion my daughter explained, "I cut myself so I could know that I was real, Mom. I don't feel real." She had actually also said, "I feel like someone else is controlling me."

The author also said there were spirits who did not make their transition to the spirit world after the death of their physical body. They were so addicted to various things that they remained on the earth. The author said she found these were "the single leading cause of psychiatric problems, especially depression and its associated cluster of problems." [48] I still wondered why the Holy Ghost prompted me to check that book out. I asked God to help me find out if there was any truth in it or not.

Shortly after, I went to an RET appointment I had scheduled for myself. Sue was enthused to tell me about a book a friend had recently loaned her. She said it was written by a psychiatrist who helped over five hundred mental illness patients find great relief. The doctor's process was to pray and ask God to send help from angels to clear spirits from her patient's energy fields. I said, "Yes, I know that book, it is a really thick book." Sue looked at me oddly and said, "No, it's a tiny book titled *The Unquiet Dead.*" Sue said the author told how *the reader* could release such problems also, with prayer and God's help.

Sue had found a nearly identical book as the one in question! I felt this was a second witness that the strange library book had some truth in it. I was amazed at God's tender mercies in teaching me! Sue had read *precisely* the same story from a different author who had the same experience. I was relieved to have another witness, and this author said people who prayed could help.

I went home and realized that I had read of related occurrences in the book, *Return From Tomorrow* by George Ritchie. In George's near death experience he saw deceased spirits that were still addicted to

[48] Shakuntala Modi, M.D., *Remarkable Healings*, 460

alcohol entering mortal bodies. He wrote of a scene that Jesus Christ showed him, "the bright cocoon around the unconscious sailor simply opened up. It parted at the very crown of his head and began peeling away from his head, his shoulders. Instantly, quicker than I'd ever seen anyone move, one of the insubstantial beings who had been standing near him at the bar was on top of him. He had been hovering like a thirsty shadow at the sailor's side, greedily following every swallow...In the next instant the springing figure had vanished...." This scene was repeated twice more. I thought this certainly gave deeper meaning as to why alcohol is referred to and advertised as "spirits."

This scene from the book made so much more sense to me after learning about auras and chakras. I felt it must have been the crown chakra that opened up, allowing an earthbound spirit more influence on a physical body. Scriptures about light and armor suddenly made even more sense! I reread many scriptures to see exactly what God taught, *this time* with a very personal interest.

My mother sent a letter to me which included quotes from Duane Crowther's book *Life Everlasting* on the possibility of choosing and agreeing to our trials in the pre-existence. I read these with interest and bought my own copy of the book. I thrilled to find mention of healing with light in the future, of surgeries with no scalpels except light, of people vibrating at different levels. . . I loved all of that. I was even more in awe by what I found much later in the book: quotes from apostles and prophets on evil spirits affecting illness! I was really amazed when I read what Brigham Young taught at the funeral of his counselor Jedediah Grant:

> Do you not think that brother Jedediah can do more good than he could here? When he was here the devils had power over his flesh, he warred with them and fought them, and said that they were around him by millions, and he fought them until he overcame them. So it is with you and I. *You never felt a pain and ache, or felt disagreeable, or uncomfortable in your bodies and minds, but what an evil spirit was present causing it. Do you realize that the ague, the fever, the chills, the severe pain in the head, the pleurisy or any pain in the system, from the crown of the head to the soles of the feet, is put there by the devil?* You do not realize this, do you? I say but little about this matter.... When you have the rheumatism, do you realize that the devil put that upon you? No, but you say, "I got wet, caught cold, and thereby got the rheumatism." The spirits that afflict us and plant disease in our bodies, pain in the system, and finally death, have control over us so far as the flesh is concerned.[49]

Parley P. Pratt added his witness, "Many spirits of the departed, who are unhappy, linger in lonely wretchedness about the earth, and in the air, and especially about their ancient homesteads, and the places rendered dear to them by the memory of the former scenes."[50] After finding quotes like these, I felt *much* better about the previously unsettling library book!

Seeing my ill daughter improve required paradigm shifts in how I perceived illness and the world itself. I learned firsthand that scriptures about evil spirits afflicting the sick are literally true in our day, just as they were long ago. It is as if most of the world has blinders on and wants to pretend the problem with

---

[49] *Journal of Discourses* 4: 133, (emphasis added)

[50] Parley P. Pratt, Key to the Science of Theology, 117

evil spirits doesn't exist anymore in our modern age. We still face the same problem. Facilitators like Sue who understood the true nature of some of the "negative energy" they cleared offered the most help.

I will always remember the first time I had the courage to do something about this ancient and modern problem to help my daughter. It was yet another Monday morning that she refused to go to school. She wouldn't even get out of bed. I had witnessed a few different energy workers teach my daughter to command evil spirits out of her entire being. I knew it had helped. It finally dawned on me that I could exert faith myself. I really wanted my husband to use his priesthood authority to clear the unwelcome "company" from our daughter, but at that point in time he did not even believe that earthbound spirits existed around people. He felt that all spirits advanced to the next world when people died. I was on my own.

I knelt down to pray for strength. I must have asked for courage and added faith because I walked to my teenage daughter's bedroom, commanded devils and evil and unclean spirits to depart in the name of Jesus Christ, and ran upstairs. I hadn't been upstairs but minutes when my husband came rushing over exclaiming, "She is suddenly up and getting ready for school! What happened? Did you do something?" I told him all that I had done. My husband was in awe at the difference it made. Our daughter got out of bed, dressed, ate breakfast and left for school without *any* of the coaxing that usually required from us.

It takes great faith by people who follow Christ to perform such miracles. The wise consider every scripture outlining safety and guidelines. Be believing, pray and read scriptures daily, repent, have faith instead of fear, be sufficiently humble. . . No wonder the brethren plead for us to put on our shield of faith every day. Praying and reading scriptures daily are crucial structures in putting on the armor of God *daily*. I realized our shields of faith are shields of light! Those shields are more tangible and real than I ever suspected, for "All spirit is matter" (D&C 131:7).

There is so much not understood about mental illness that any bit of information I could find was something to mull over. I often wondered why behavioral health units in hospitals fill more beds at certain times of the year. Why was my daughter hospitalized near fall and Easter? An interesting comment by President Harold B. Lee was food for thought, "The influence [of Satan] is here. . . They are here all the time and they are directed by a mighty chieftain. I suspect every time we hold a general conference, he is holding a general conference too, and they are checking up to see about their gains and to consolidate their forces. I think they may have missionaries pretty well organized and I think they are watching each one of us." [51]

Speaking of mortal Nephi, 3 Nephi 7:19 says, "And in the name of Jesus did he cast out devils and unclean spirits." The scriptures teach us that there are many different kinds of spirits that afflict us. Here is just one of dozens of examples: "And behold there was a woman which had *a spirit of infirmity* eighteen years, and was bowed together, and could in no wise lift up herself. . . . And ought not this woman, being a daughter of Abraham, *whom Satan hath bound*, lo, these eighteen years, be loosed from this bond on the sabbath day?" (Luke 13:11,16 emphasis added).

---

[51] *The Teachings of Harold B. Lee*, 37

I have learned from experiences with myself and with my daughter as well as from years of working with clients that being afflicted by evil spirits is still the case for humanity. I learned from scripture this can make a difference for the suffering who request it. Evidence is laid out so obvious in scripture on what can truly be involved in illness, that it surprises me that the subject is not more openly discussed. Now my husband asks, "How can a problem be so rampant in Jesus' day, and spoken of often in the days of the restoration of the gospel, yet be *non-existent* in our day?" He has witnessed the benefits from learning about this help for families.

President George Q. Cannon explains, "God has reserved spirits for this dispensation who have the courage and determination to face the world, and all the powers of the evil one, visible and invisible, to proclaim the Gospel, and maintain the truth, and establish and build up the Zion of our God, fearless of all consequences." [52] One past General Young Men's Presidency was unusually frank:

> "In May of 1981 the Young Men Presidency of the Church stated, 'This generation of young men [and we may include young women] is going to do deeds never done before. You are going to accomplish the seemingly impossible because you are on His errand. Your generation will fight the greatest army of Satanic hosts ever assembled. You will be severely outnumbered. You will need a deep and abiding faith in Christ to survive--and you will survive. The Lord and His servants will triumph, we do know that' (Church News, 9 May 1981, 9)."[53]

The war that began in heaven is still going on and the enemy is *still* here! I do not allow myself to go into fear about all this. Opposition is part of God's plan for man. Light always wins over darkness. I know we can chase darkness with light. "I can do all things through Christ which strengtheneth me" (Philippians 4:13).

---

[52] George Q. Cannon qtd. in *Journal of Discourses* 11:230

[53] Jack R. Christianson, "Music: Apples or Onions?" *New Era*, April 1984

~15~ I Believe

"You are called to represent the Savior. Your voice to testify becomes the same as His voice, your hands to lift the same as His hands. . . So, your calling is to bless lives."[54]

All sorts of people have discovered portions of energy healing properties and principles, from atheists to believers. I came to the conclusion that premises underlying the energy work I was led to did fit with the gospel of Christ while there were other methods that do not follow scriptural teachings. I can't guarantee how others practice these methods, but I can make sure I do so within the gospel of Christ. Henry B. Eyring taught, "If you want to receive the gifts of the Spirit, you have to want them for the right reasons. Your purpose must be the Lord's purpose. . . . When we pray for the gifts of the Spirit—and we should—one for which I pray is that I might have pure motives."[55]

Sometimes I have changed the way I practice a modality to fit completely with my belief in scripture. I know with all my heart that this standard will never fail me. If I can find a principle in scripture, then it is true. As facilitators of Healing Arts, we must stay grounded on the rock of Christ, be "sufficiently humble" and work with pure intent. I found guidelines and safeguards in the scriptures. I wouldn't dream of working with another person's energy field before praying first and asking to be filled with the light of Christ. I desire a similar attitude when I seek a facilitator's help for myself and my family.

I believe answers to all of our questions can be found in the scriptures and words of modern prophets. "Whoso would hearken unto the word of God, and would hold fast unto it, they would never perish; neither could the temptations and the fiery darts of the adversary overpower them..." (I Nephi 15:24) I know this is true! I have applied it to my own questions about the field of Energy Medicine. What I found in this field greatly changed my life for the better. The research I did ended up helping me to understand scripture on a deeper level. Previously mysterious verses became clear. I felt that I was finding "hidden treasures" of knowledge during daily scripture study. The scriptures are my books of hope!

Each of us has the opportunity to choose what is right for ourselves when subjects are outside the scope of revealed topics. I felt relief whenever I found examples in the scriptures or words of modern day prophets to validate concepts I had been presented with. I kept getting nudged by the spirit to write down what I learned.

I believe that working in the Healing Arts is very Christ - centered. It ought to be so for every facilitator if credit is given where credit is due. My family paid a dear price to learn firsthand that the Savior's atonement is not just for sins, but also for the illnesses, pain and heartache we experience. I know help and healing is available today because of the atonement of Jesus Christ. "Surely, he hath borne our

---

[54] Elder Henry B. Eyring, "Rise to Your Call," *Ensign*, Nov. 2002, 76

[55] Elder Henry B. Eyring, "Gifts of the Spirit for Hard Times" CES Fireside, 10 Sep 2006, lds.org

grief and carried our sorrows" (Isaiah 53:4). He knows all of our mortal woundedness because He experienced it Himself when "He suffered the pain of all men" (D&C 18:11).

Jesus Christ is the source of all healing. I believe His universal life-giving light is the very reason that anyone heals. Therefore, this light-energy is paramount to any form of healing. I absolutely believe forgiveness heals! As a facilitator of Healing Arts, I find great joy in helping people make peace with their past, release unresolved emotions, clear generational patterns and bring light to dark places. Emotional patterns, dysfunctional beliefs and pain and disease are related to subtle energy imbalances that can be cleared with today's technology and ancient techniques. New York Times best-selling author Gregg Braden referred to spiritually-based techniques and raising one's consciousness as "internal technology" that a person can apply on their own to improve health. Larry Dossey, MD refers to some related principles as "Eternity Medicine" in his book *Reinventing Medicine*. I love the term he chose!

I believe that applying clearing techniques as well as principles of higher consciousness taught in them can help almost anyone with health challenges. I am blessed to see the wonderful and various benefits clients report. It is a true joy in life to know that the pain our family suffered in the past now pays dividends. If this book saves anyone else any angst, then our trials were all the more worthwhile.

I believe this field of medicine has truth in it because it was God that led me to it in the first place, or as one of you said in a class somewhere, "I didn't find energy healing. It found me." I have surely met some of the best people on earth in my learning journey! I am extremely grateful I was blessed to find out about the Healing Arts. Choosing to be open-minded about what may appear to be unusual methods of healing was a grand blessing. My family and I have benefitted tremendously. Learning about this field tremendously increased my faith. I desire that sharing these truths spreads hope and love in the world and that they will be a great blessing in preparing for the Savior's second coming.

It appears from decades of research that scientists are telling us the very things that prophets have told us all along; we literally are of light! I know that, "whoso believeth in God might with surety hope for a better world."[56] We can rely entirely on Him and our afflictions can be swallowed up in the joy of Christ. Knowing of the universal light of Christ, we are all, as it were, cradled in God's light and love. Rejoice!

[56]Ether 12:4

1

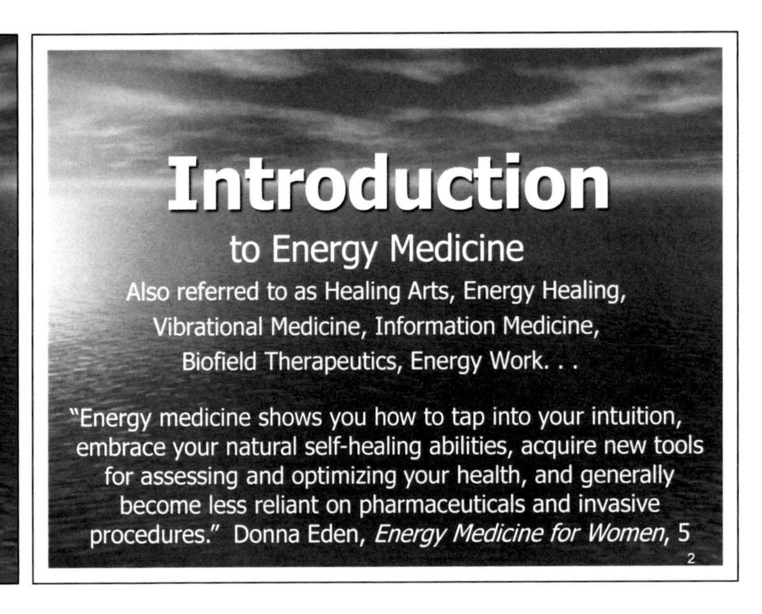

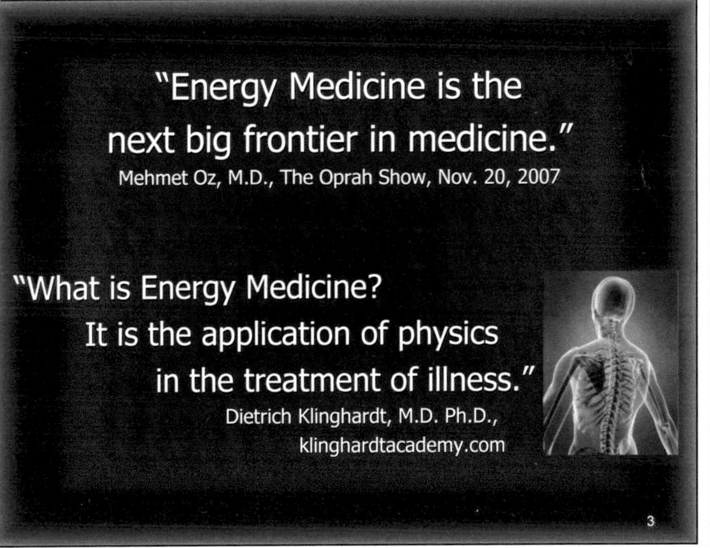

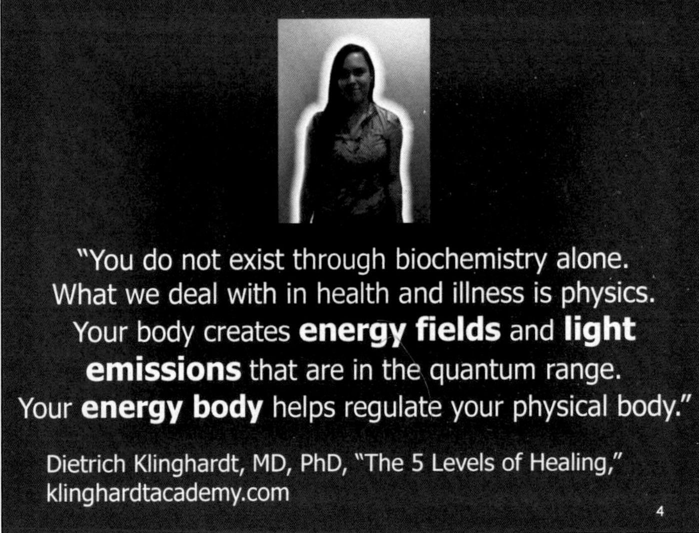

"An emerging trend of clinicians recognize that a far more powerful approach to healing is one that is based on physics and not on chemistry. Many natural health experts believe that **your body is not only made up of tissue, blood vessels and organs. It's also composed of energy, or chi** as it's called in traditional Chinese medicine. This **energy** is **circulated** through your body along specific meridians & when ... manipulated

5

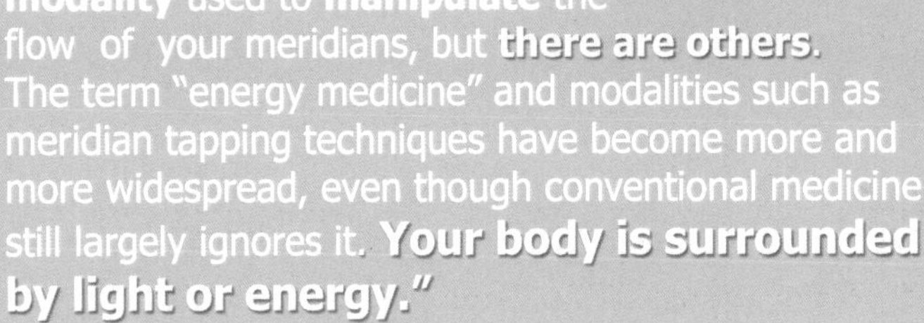

the **energy circulation** & your **internal organs** are **affected**. Acupuncture is one well-known **modality** used to **manipulate** the flow of your meridians, but **there are others**. The term "energy medicine" and modalities such as meridian tapping techniques have become more and more widespread, even though conventional medicine still largely ignores it. **Your body is surrounded by light or energy.**"

Joseph Mercola,M.D.; "Your Body Literally Glows with Light;" Aug. 15, 2009; articles.mercola.com

6

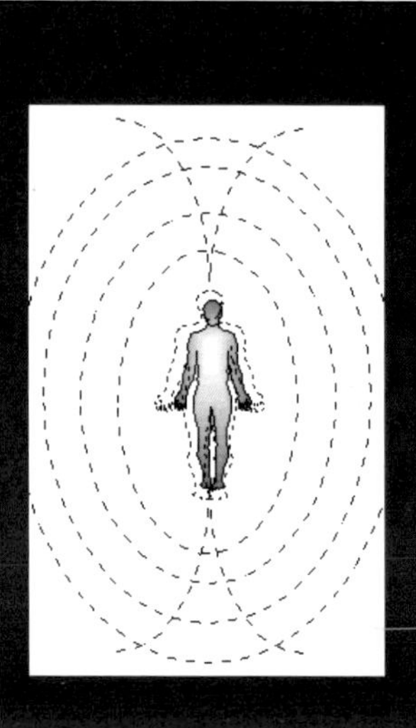

"Every thought, organ function, and physical movement involves masses of bioelectrical and biochemical signals coursing throughout your body.
All electrical activity generates electromagnetic fields.
A biomagnetic field is an electromagnetic field produced by a living being. Some of these fields are subtle and difficult to detect but this does not mean they are unimportant.

7

"The strongest human biomagnetic field is produced by the heart, which can be detected at a distance of more than 15 feet. The **energy** produced by healers and energy workers has also been measured by similar equipment and shown to be a significant **force** (Oschman and Pert 2000). . . . Every cell of your body is alive with bioelectrical activity that **produces biomagnetic fields.** Beneath this activity exist the **layers** of **subtle** and **spiritual energy fields** that comprise the human energy body."

Robert Bruce, *Energy Work*, 2

8

"Perhaps in discovering the **electromagnetic field,** scientists have merely found a way to detect and **measure** the **real energy** of the **spirit body** and the **intelligence** or **Light of Christ** which comprise it?"

Brent & Wendy Topp, *Glimpses Beyond Death's Door*, 254

9

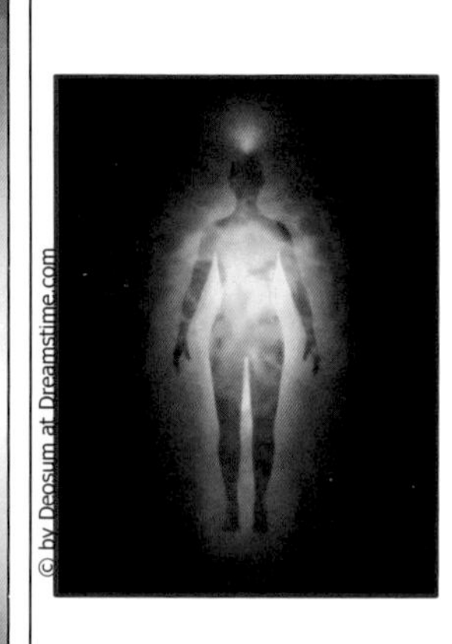

"There is an entire level of **subtle energetic anatomy** virtually unknown to physicians....
It is by **influencing** the **subtle energetic** pathways, which the **life-force** follows, that many alternative medicine practices are successful in affecting human illness."

Richard Gerber, M.D., *Vibrational Medicine*, 67-68

10

"When our human machinery is out of order, [God] understands all about it; and he is the **best physician** that can be employed.... He **imparts** to this machinery **his holy spirit** which **circulates through the whole body,** and **promotes health** and **strength** in the individual. But how apt are we to apply to inferior physicians."

Masterful Discourses of Orson Pratt, compiled by N.B. Lundwall, 490

11

"Einstein's Unified Field Theory states that all matter is organized **energy** & that **field reality** is one of the characteristics of the universe. . . . The deeper one probes material systems, the more one encounters field aspects or the substances' **underlying** **electrical** **pattern,** the very basis of the pattern itself.
Whether the **energy** is constellated as a cup, a tree, or a **human being,** **it has a field** associated with it."

Valerie Hunt, *Infinite Mind*, 47

12

"Cell biologist Bruce Lipton points out that '**Conventional medicine** works with the **iron filings**, whereas a **deeper** form of **healing** would attempt to influence the **magnetic field.** Most doctors don't see the field, so they're trying to figure out the relationship between the filings without even trying to incorporate the **energy field** in which they exist.'"

Dawson Church, *The Genie in Your Genes,* 152

13

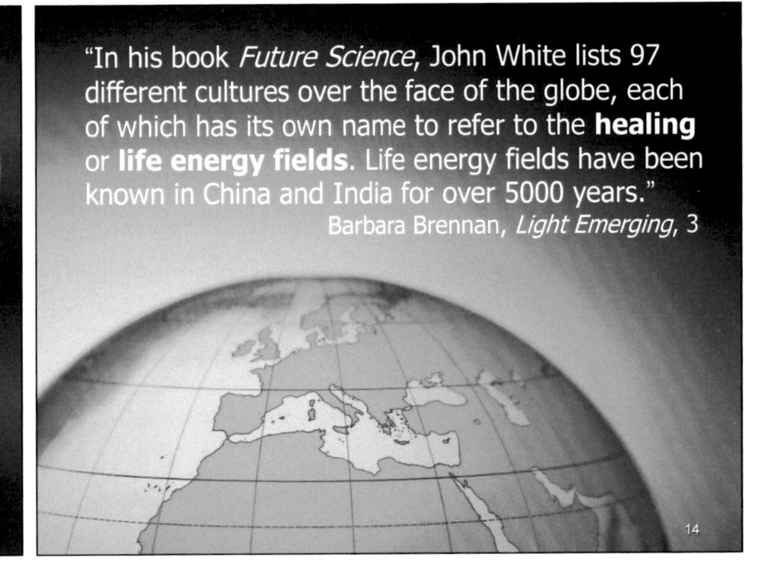

"One of the grand fundamental principles of 'Mormonism' is to receive truth, let it come from whence it may."

Teachings of the Prophet Joseph Smith, 313

15

"Numerous cultures describe a matrix of subtle energies that support, shape and animate the physical body, called *qi* or *chi* in China, *prana* in the yoga tradition of India and Tibet, *yesod* in the Jewish cabalistic tradition, *ki* in Japan, *baraka* by the Sufis, *wakan* by the Lakotas, *orenda* by the Iroquois, *megbe* by the Ituri Pymies, and the *Holy Spirit* in Christian tradition. It is hardly a new idea to suggest that subtle energies operate in tandem with the denser "congealed" energies of the material body."

Donna Eden, *Energy Medicine,* 16

16

" 'Mormonism,' so-called, embraces every principle pertaining to life and salvation, for time and eternity. No matter who has it. If the infidel has got truth, it belongs to 'Mormonism.'. . . 'Mormonism' includes all truth."

Discourses of Brigham Young, 3

17

"**Qi** (or ch'i), a word used to describe the dynamic **flow** of **life energy**. Qi defies exact description in our language. It refers to a **life force**, or a vital force, that permeates all living things, and departs when they die."

Susan Wagner M.D.,
A Doctor's Guide to Therapeutic Touch, 11

center image © by Deosum at Dreamstime.com

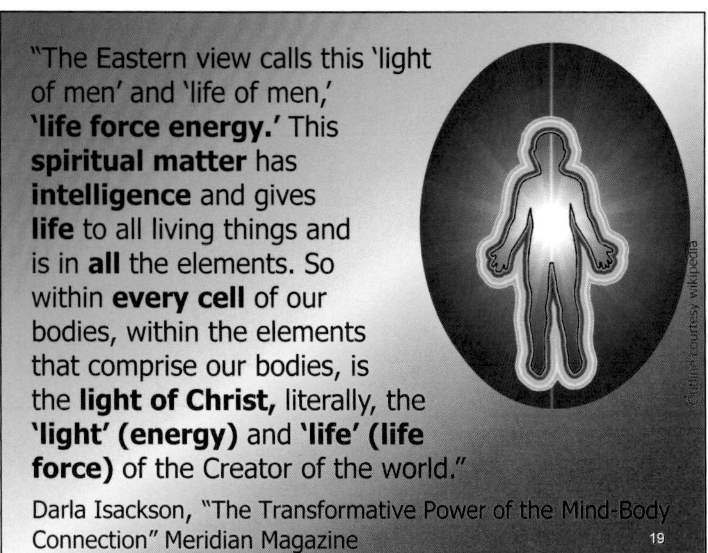

"The irony is that all people actually feel the life force within them every moment of every day. They just are not aware that they are feeling it. For most of us, the sensations of the life force energy can be analogous to the back-ground noise of the street where we live. We have grown so accustomed to it that we no longer notice it. We only notice the street noise if we stop and pay close attention to it. Sometimes, the most blatant and obvious things are the very last to be seen and acknowledged. Life force is just such a thing."

Richard Gordon, *Quantum-Touch,* 20

21

"Einstein showed through physics what sages have taught for thousands of years:

everything in our material world –
animate and inanimate –
is made of **energy,**
and everything **radiates** energy."

William Collinge
as quoted in
Donna Eden,
Energy Medicine, 20

22

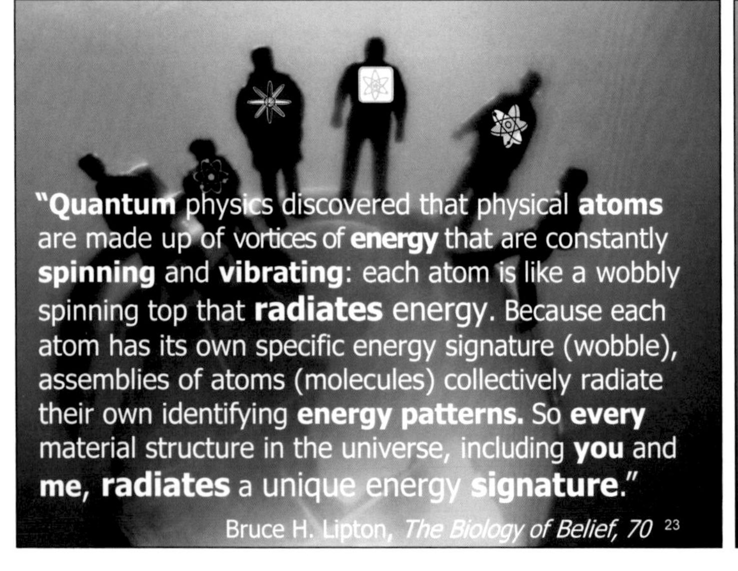

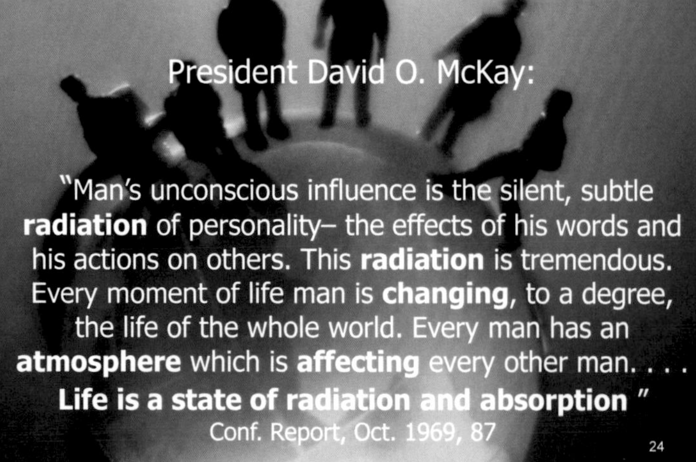

"You never change things fighting the existing reality. To change something, build a new model that makes the existing model obsolete."

R. Buckminster Fuller (1895-1983)

25

"Apparently, the control system of the body is not genes or chemistry, but *information* which is available in the body field."

Narrator, DVD
"The Living Matrix – The New Science of Healing,"(Hillsboro, OR: Beyond Words, 2009)

26

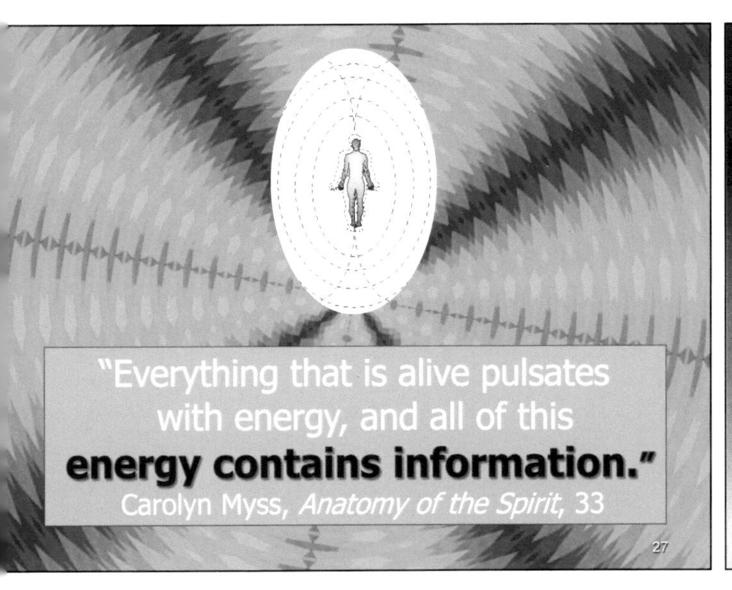

"Your body's abilities to heal a wound, fight off disease, cope with stress, respond to danger... reflect an astounding **intelligence** that is totally **independent of your mind.** This bodily wisdom is contained *not* primarily in the *neurons* of your *brain* but in **energy fields** that mobilize your cells into action, that coordinate the strategies used by your organs to maintain your **health.**"

Donna Eden qtd. in "Living a Better & Fuller Life with Energy Medicine," "The Life Connection" Sep. 2010, Vol. 26, No. 9, 8

28

"The true cause of negative emotions, it turns out, is not where everyone thinks it is. It is not where psychologists have been looking. That's why they haven't found it. The **cause** of all negative emotions can be found in the **body's energy system.** This is an important, **paradigm shifting concept**. The concept may seem strange to you, but the proof is in the results."

Gary Craig,
The EFT Manual, 42
"The Science Behind EFT"

29

"**Energy imbalance** is what was causing her **emotional intensity**. Tapping under her eyes sent pulses through the meridian and fixed the **disruption**. It balanced it out. Once the energy meridian was balanced, the emotional intensity--the fear--went away. Therein lies the most **powerful** thing you are ever going to learn about your **unwanted emotions**: They are **caused by energy disruptions."**

Gary Craig,
The EFT Manual, 46
"The Science Behind EFT"

30

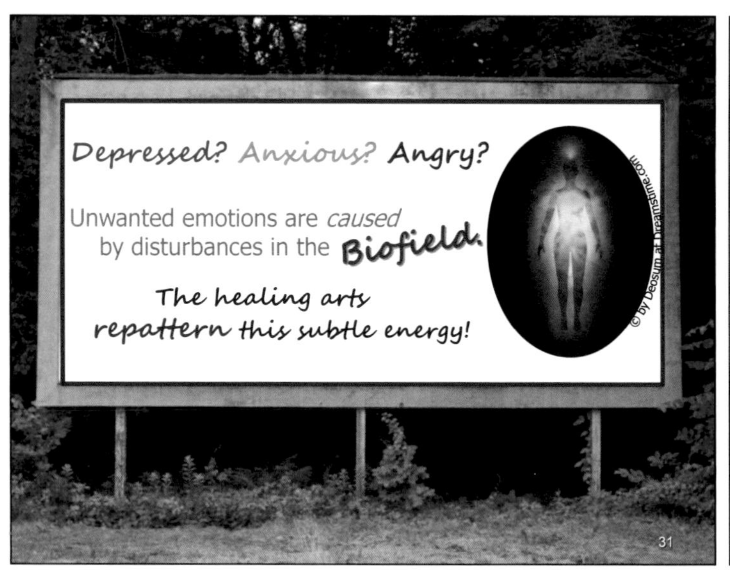

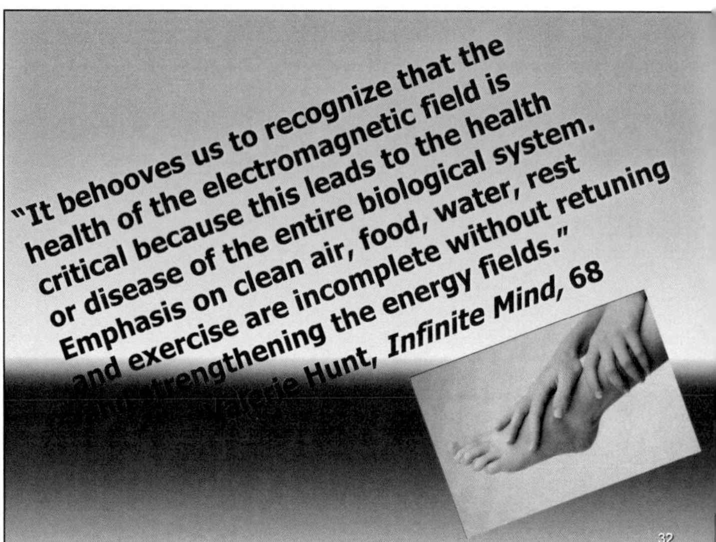

"**Today's medicine** still works on the **old paradigm** of physics which dates back to the time of Newton and the primacy of matter. Modern physics has long ago eliminated that paradigm and understands that **it is not matter** but **mind, or spirit,** which is **primary** - though it isn't defined as spirit, but as **energy fields**, as **intelligent energy fields.**"

Dietmar Cimbal, DVM, on DVD "**The Living Matrix-** The New Science of Healing,"(Hillsboro, OR: Beyond Words, 2009)

33

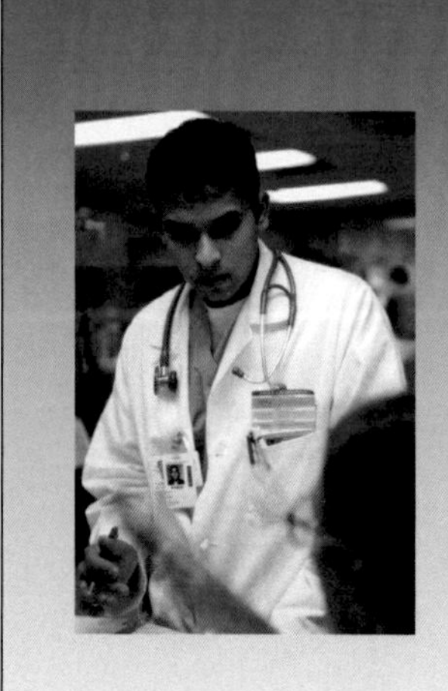

"The conventional medical establishment has not yet incorporated **quantum physics** into its research or medical school training, with tragic results."

Bruce H. Lipton, PhD, *The Biology of Belief*, xxviii

34

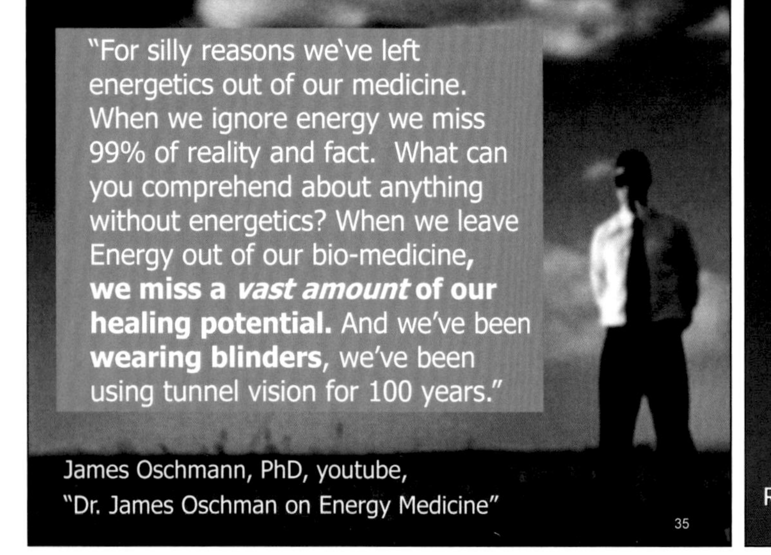

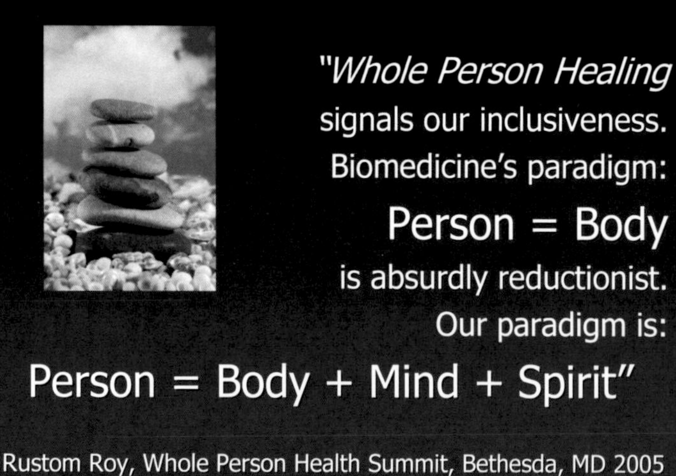

"**There is no scientific reason to leave spirituality out of medicine.** It's a **habit** our culture has gotten into ever since the 17th century philosopher Rene Descartes declared body and soul to be distinct ...
But... **the soul, mind, and emotions do play an important role in health.** What we need is a larger biomedical science to **reintegrate** what was taken out 300 years ago."

Dr. Candace Pert, *Molecules of Emotion*, 304

37

"According to energy medicine, the human **spirit** is a manifestation of **energy**. . . . The intention behind using Energy Medicine is to treat the **body and the spirit** equally."

Carolyn Myss, *Why People Don't Heal and How They Can*, x, xi

"Care not for the body, neither the life of the body, but care for the **soul,** and for **the life of** the **soul.**"
D&C 101:37

38

"Joseph Smith taught that man is organized from **matter**, **spirit** and **intelligence**. . . . 'The spirit and the body are the soul of man.' (D&C 88:15)
The **spirit** here referred to **may be compared** to the **ether of science, vibrating** with the force of **intelligence**, which is the first and highest of the many forces of nature. The body, similarly, refers to the grosser elements, also fired with the **universal energy-intelligence**.

39

The word Soul, in the above quotation means man as he is on earth and is used in Genesis. Man, according to this, is composed of matter; **the spirit** of which **may be likened to ether, and energy.**" John A. Widtsoe, *Joseph Smith as Scientist*, 63-64

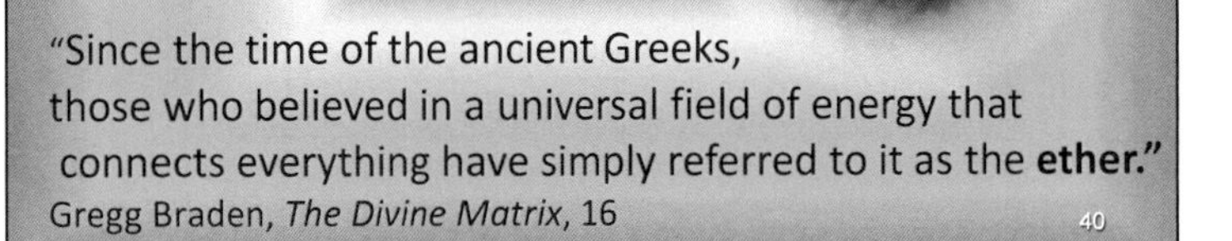

"Since the time of the ancient Greeks, those who believed in a universal field of energy that connects everything have simply referred to it as the **ether.**"
Gregg Braden, *The Divine Matrix*, 16

40

Boyd K. Packer: "I recently asked a doctor of family medicine how much of his time was devoted purely to correcting **physical** disorders. He has a large practice, and after thoughtfully considering, he answered, 'Not more than 20 percent. The rest of the time I seem to be working on problems that very much affect the physical well-being of my patients but **do not originate in the body.** These physical disorders,' the doctor concluded, 'are merely

41

symptoms of some **other kind** of trouble.' There is another part of us, not so tangible, but quite as **real** as our physical body. This **intangible part of us** is described as **mind, emotion, intellect, temperament**, and many other things. Very seldom is it described as **spiritual.** But there is a *spirit* in man; to ignore it is to ignore reality. **There are spiritual disorders, too,** and **spiritual diseases** that can cause intense **suffering**. The body and the spirit of man are bound together. Often, very often, when there are disorders, it is very difficult to tell which is which." "The Balm of Gilead," *Ensign*, Nov. 1977

42

"Interactions with our environment can be thought of symbolically as electro-magnetic **circuits.** These circuits run through our body and **connect us** to external **objects** and other **people**. . . At first, I thought of these energy circuits as symbolic, but I have come to believe that they are actually **real pathways** of energy. So often I hear people comment that they feel **'hooked'** on a **person** or an **experience** from their past. Some people remark that they feel **'drained'** after being with a certain person or in

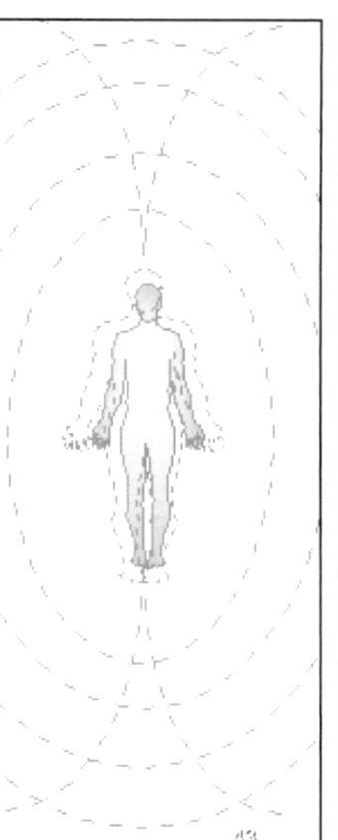

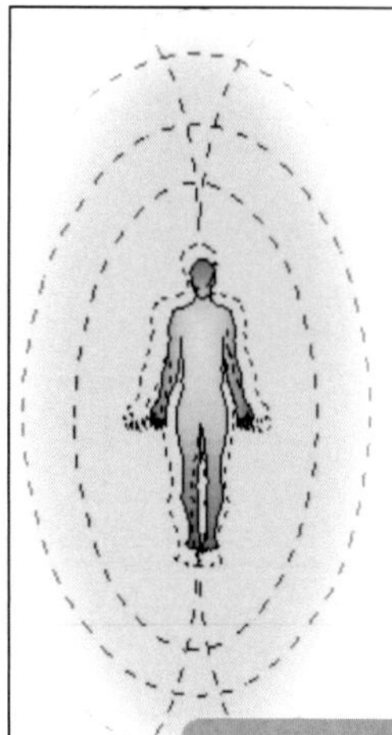

a particular environment. . . . I call such people *acquisitioners. . . .* As we learn more about our energy natures, we realize how much our **spirits** remain **attached** to negative **events**, and **thoughts,** past and present. **Remaining attached** to negative events and beliefs is **toxic** to our **minds, spirits, cell tissue** and **lives.**"

Carolyn Myss, *Anatomy of the Spirit,* 50, 228

"I Daniel was grieved in my spirit in the midst of my body." Daniel 7:15

"The things of the universe are, as it were, suspended in the ocean of ether. . . . Yet, the ether cannot be seen, heard, tasted, smelled, or felt. . . . To believe the existence of this ether requires a faith which is certainly as great as the greatest faith required by Mormon theology."

John A. Widtsoe, *Joseph Smith as Scientist*, 75

"Thanks to quantum physics, the Western world is now waking up to the fact that only 4% of the universe has form and is visible. The other 96% is **formless & invisible. But it is not empty**. It is a great seething ocean of **vibrating energy** that is **always available.** Western medicine usually focuses on the physical -- surgery and pills. **This is only 4% of the universe. We have access to the other 96% through energy medicine."**

Vivienne Verdon-Roe, PhD, "The Miracle of Qigong," The Life Connection, Sep. 2010, Vol. 26, No. 9, p 10, 11

"**Techniques** from **Energy Medicine** and **Energy Psychology** can alleviate chronic diseases, shift autoimmune conditions, and eliminate psychological traumas with an **efficiency** and **speed** that conventional treatments can scarcely touch."

Dawson Church, Ph.D.,
The Genie in Your Genes, 29

"Physics has found that by periodically **introducing energy** into chaotic systems they can be **pulled back toward order**. Because the human energy field is so resilient, manipulation **techniques** such as **hands-on healing, subtle energy devices**, and **body therapies introducing subtle energy** into the **system** can **more** effectively preserve health than those therapies using chemical or mechanical intervention. Controlling **chaos anywhere** in the body **via the field will be faster** and **more enduring** than testing specific biological subsystems."

Valerie Hunt, *Infinite Mind*, 56

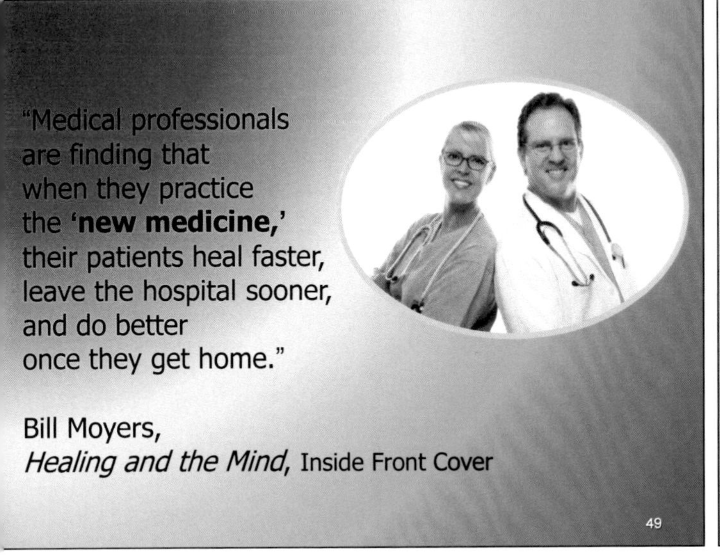

"Western medical science tends to focus on the **chemical** nature of the body and has not paid much attention to these **subtle, but powerful, energy flows** until recent years. However, they *do* exist and are attracting an expanding group of researchers. . . . **A growing number of health practitioners are finding ways to use this vital energy system to help physical healing.**"

Gary Craig, *The EFT Manual*, "The Science Behind EFT"

51

"**I'm not against mainstream, conventional medicine.** The Chinese have a saying about the wisdom of walking on both feet," which means **using the best of Eastern & Western procedures. That's what I want to see us do.** There is no single approach that works for all people, or with all conditions. This goes for alternative medicine as well. . . . **There may be many underlying factors influencing your health-** nutritional deficiency, poor digestion, toxicity from environmental pollutants, or mental and emotional stress....What's good for Harry is not necessarily good for Mary. **You are biochemically unique** .... You need only to find the right therapies. Be well!"

Burton Goldberg, *Alternative Medicine*, xxxviii

"**All truths are compatible** and will blend perfectly whether they are from sacred temples, secular universities, or even from what we would consider foreign cultures.... As we become... an international church – 'They [who are gathered into the church] shall bring forth their rich treasures unto the children of Ephraim, my servants.' (D&C 133:30)

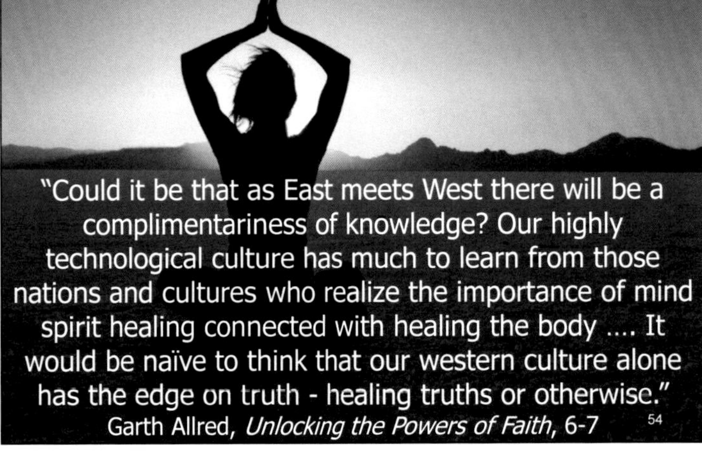

"Of course, caution must be encouraged as we seek for proper healing principles and practices for our spirits, minds and bodies. The spirit of discernment and wisdom is vital as we sift and sort through new ideas and techniques for healing."
Garth Allred, *Unlocking the Powers of Faith*, 7

"He that answereth a matter before he heareth it, it is folly and shame unto him." Prov. 18:13

55

"Rather than judge the Church and its programs against the principles of our profession,
we would do well to set the Church and its accepted program as the rule,
then judge our academic training against this rule."
Elder Boyd K. Packer, *A Dedication - To Faith*,
BYU Speeches of the Year, Provo, 29 Apr. 1969, 6

56

President Harold B. Lee, "Find the Answers in the Scriptures,"*Ensign*, Dec. 1972

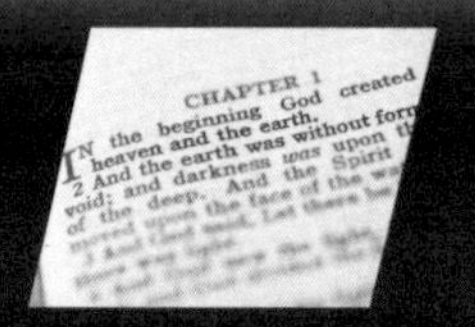

"We need to teach our people to find their answers in the scriptures. If only each of us would be wise enough to say that we aren't able to answer any question unless we can find a doctrinal answer in the scriptures! And if we hear someone teaching something that is contrary to what is in the scriptures, each of us may know whether the things spoken are false -- it is as simple as that."

57

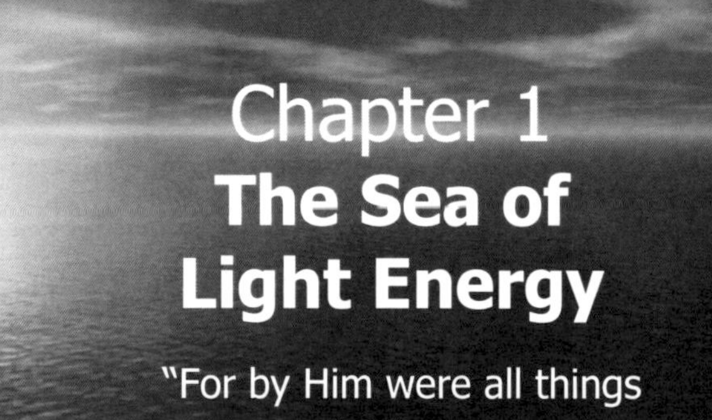

Chapter 1
The Sea of Light Energy

"For by Him were all things created, . . . visible **and invisible.**"
Col. 1:16-17

58

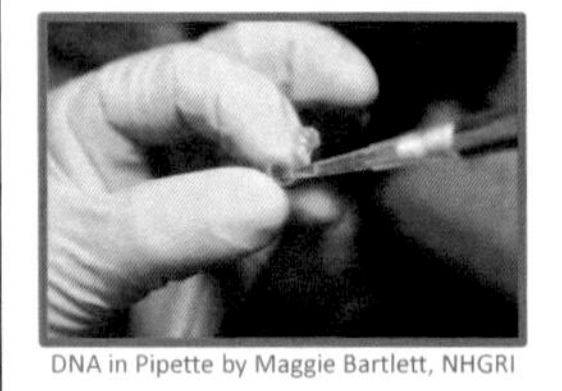

DNA in Pipette by Maggie Bartlett, NHGRI

"3 Experiments That Change Everything"

1. Poponin- 'DNA Phantom Effect'
2. Army 1993- DNA Long Distance
3. Heartmath- DNA Coherent Emotion

*A previously unrecognized type of energy exists.
*DNA influences matter through it.
*Emotion has a direct influence on DNA.
*Distance is of no consequence.

"We believe this discovery has tremendous significance for the explanation and deeper understandings of the mechanisms underlying subtle energy phenomena including many of the observed **alternative healing phenomena.**"
Vladimir Poponin qtd. in Gregg Braden, *The Divine Matrix,42,43*

WORLD VIEW:

"In the 20th Century, modern science may have rediscovered **the Spirit of God** as a **field of energy** that's different from any other form of energy. It appears to be **everywhere**, always, and to have existed since the beginning of time."

Gregg Braden,
Secrets of the Lost Mode of Prayer, 2

60

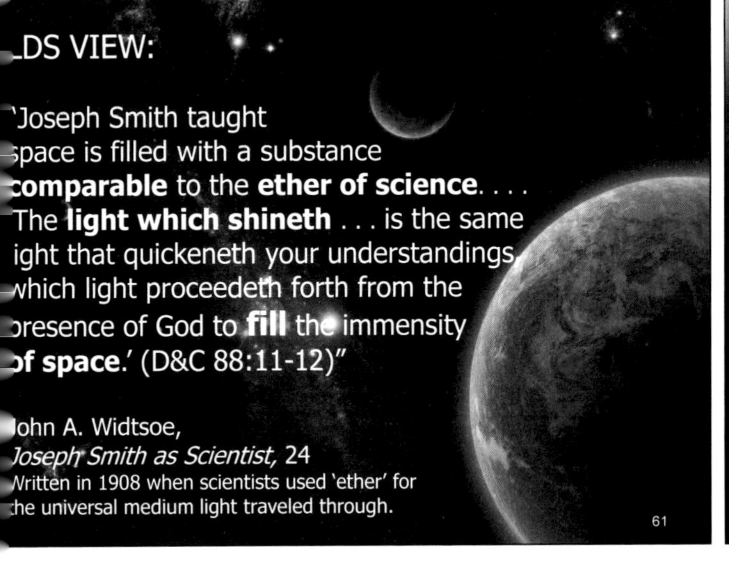

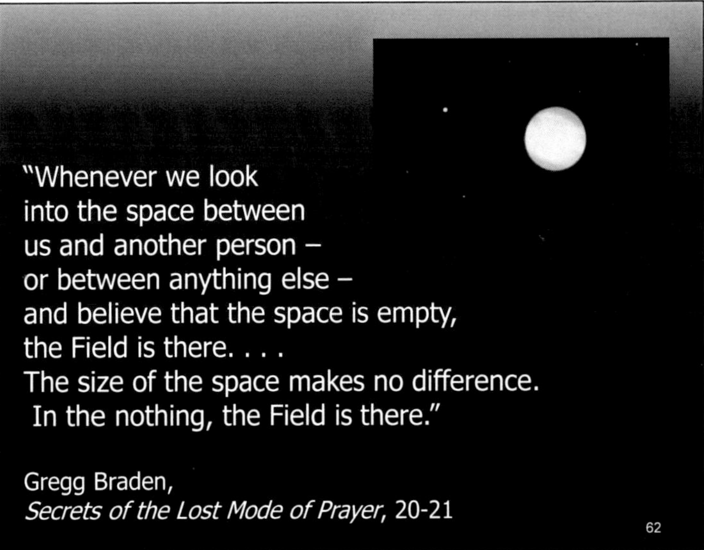

"Our understanding of creation indicates that it is mostly vacant space. Even those things we consider as solid, firm, tangible, when viewed at enormous magnification in the Heavens or in minute matter, **are mostly vacant space** that God, our Father, perfectly **controls and uses** for His exalted purposes."

Elder Richard G. Scott,
Truth: The Foundation
of Correct Decisions,"
Ensign, Nov. 2007, 91

63

"It is an energy inherent in space itself. Because [this background energy] exists and keeps atoms moving even at the coldest possible temperature of zero degrees, it has become dubbed the "zero point energy" or simply ZPE." (see calphysics.org/zpe)

John Pratt, "Science and the Light of Christ," Meridian Magazine, 2006

64

"It may be the
Zero Point Field
that is constantly supplying energy to the atom to support it. If so, then... **Zero Point Energy** may actually be what allows matter even to exist. That seems to match very closely the Lord's description of the **Light of Christ.**"

John Pratt, "Science and the Light of Christ," Meridian Magazine, 2006

65

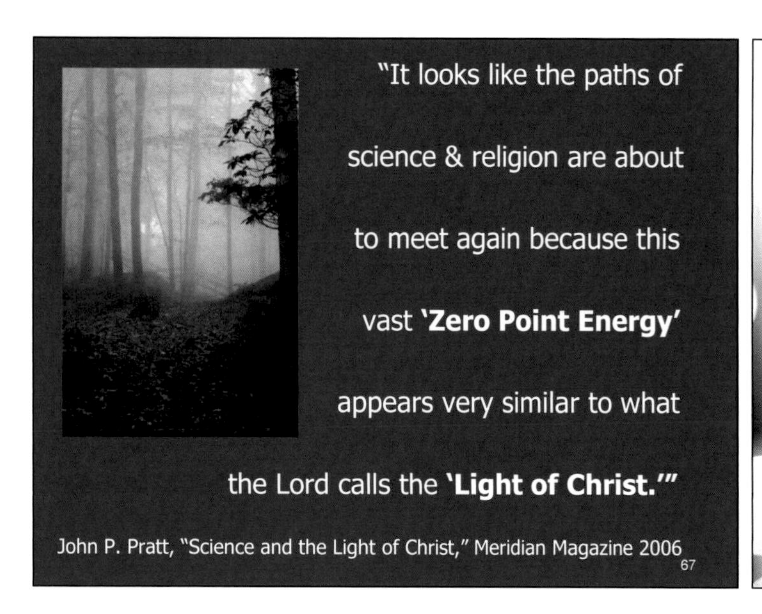

"The idea of The Field might just offer a scientific explanation for many meta-physical notions, such as the Chinese belief in the life force, or qi, described in ancient texts as something akin to an energy field. It even echoed the Old Testament's account of God's first dictum: 'Let there be light,' out of which matter was created." Lynn McTaggart, *The Field*, 24

Note that Genesis 1 speaks of 'light' and 'lights'.

68

Photo courtesy of NASA

"This substance is widely diffused among the elements of space.... This is the great, positive, **controlling element** of all other elements... which organizes and puts in motion all worlds and which, by the mandate of the Almighty or any of his commissioned agents, performs all the wonders, signs and miracles."

Parley P. Pratt, *Key to the Science of Theology*, 39

70

"Because awareness of this field is so new, scientists have yet to agree on a single name for it. It's identified in research papers and books by names ranging from the Quantum Hologram and Nature's Mind, to the Mind of God, and often, simply the 'Field.'"

Gregg Braden, *Secrets to the Lost Mode of Prayer*, 20

Latter-day Saints also use several names for it!

71

"From the presence of these Divine Beings proceeds an essence or substance (perhaps like unto ether) variously called **'spirit,' 'light,' 'light of truth,' 'light of Christ**,' corresponding somewhat to what other teachers regard as **'vital force**' or '**energy**' which permeates all nature and constitutes the immanence of God in the universe."

B.H. Roberts

Comprehensive History of the Church, Vol. 2, 399

72

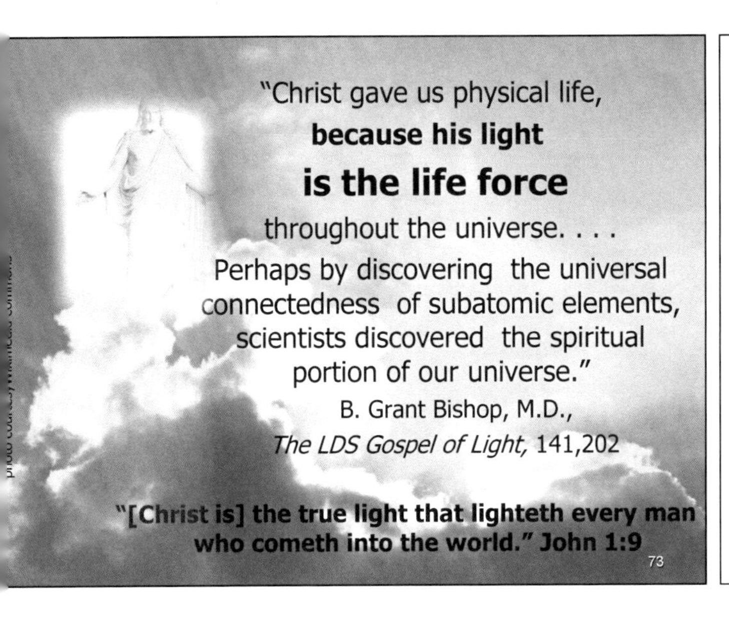

"It **is not** the Holy Ghost who in person lighteth every man who is born into the world, but **it is** the **light of Christ**, the **Spirit of Truth**, which proceeds forth from the source of intelligence, which permeates all nature, which lighteth every man and fills the immensity of space. **You may call it the influence of God's intelligence** that permeates the universe and gives to the spirits of men understanding, just as Job said. (Job 32:8)"

Pres. Joseph F. Smith, *Gospel Doctrine*, 73-74

74

"Scientists have called this field of intelligence the 'unified field of intelligence,' or the 'unified field of consciousness.' This field holds the **power** to orchestrate Nature; therefore, it contains all **the laws** of Nature."

Dr. Christine Horner, *Waking the Warrior Goddess*, 215

"The light which is in all things, . . . which is **the law** by which all things are **governed.**" D&C 88:13

75

"This holy spirit with its infinite sound and light is known by various names in scripture: the light of Christ, the Light of Truth, the Light of God, the Spirit of God, the Spirit of Truth, even the Voice of God, as well as *holy spirit* written here in lower case to distinguish it from . . . *the* Holy Spirit."

M. Catherine Thomas, *Light in the Wilderness*, 39-40

76

"Behind the physical ability to see... behind the physical ability to hear... exists a matrix of Primal Light and Primal Sound resonating unconditional love. The closer we become to achieving resonance with this matrix, the closer we are to achieving our freedom."

Dr. Sari Y. Suttka,
Layers of Light Ldrshp Retreat, Park City, UT 20

77

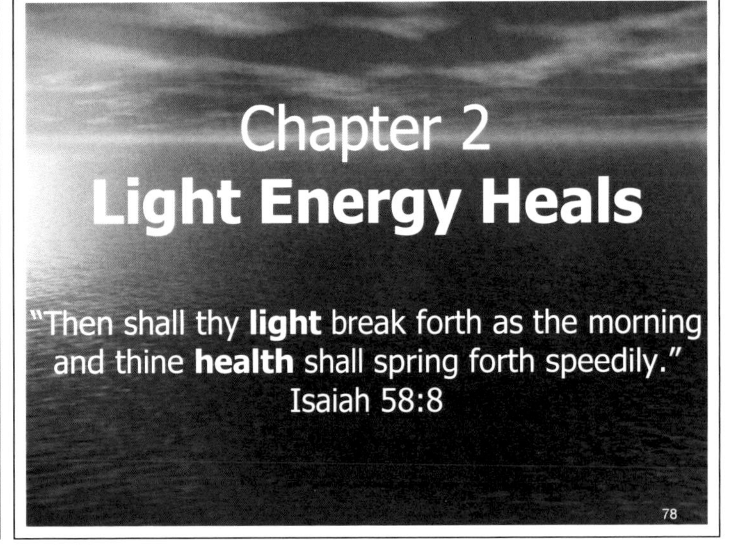

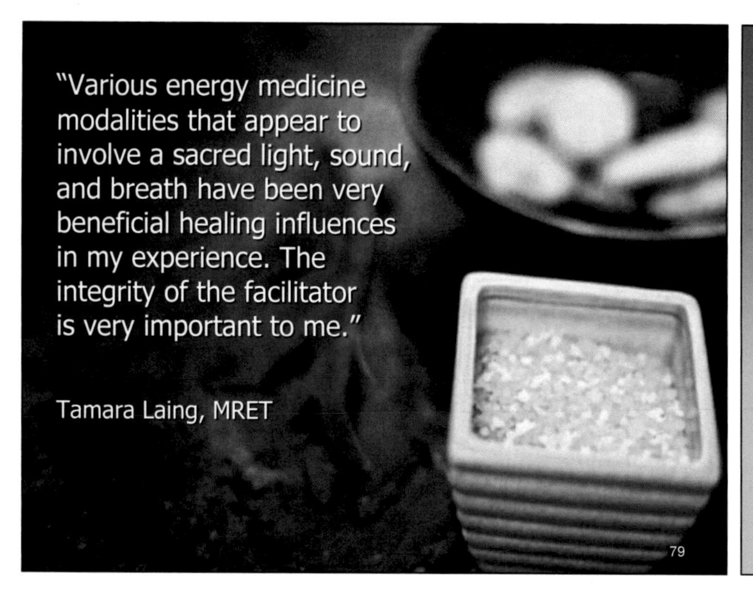

"Therapeutic Touch is grounded in the idea that a human being is a **system of energy**, and that we can **direct this energy** in a specific way to **help** one another."

Susan Wager, M.D., *A Doctor's Guide to Therapeutic Touch*, 3

This is true for all Energy healing modalities.

80

"Energetic (vibrational) medicine operates on the premise that the body is made up of **energy patterns** that are **invisible** to the human eye and that interface with, underlie, and influence our physical cells, organs, and systems. Techniques as varied as traditional Chinese medicine, acupuncture, homeopathy, therapeutic touch, and electromagnetic and sound therapies **all work with the body's energy and energy fields.** A growing body of evidence shows that when we alter the flow of energy or change energetic patterns, we see corresponding changes at the **physical, mental** and **emotional** levels."

Margaret Ruby, *The DNA of Healing*, 18-19

81

"Anyone who claims to be able to heal others is either ignorant, mistaken, arrogant, or delusional. All they are doing is **providing** the **resonant energy** to allow others to **heal themselves**."

Richard Gordon, *Quantum Touch*, 18

82

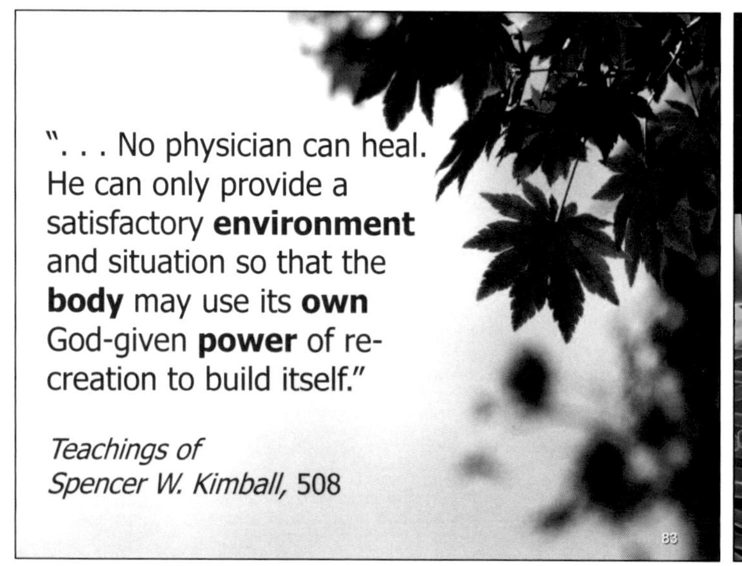

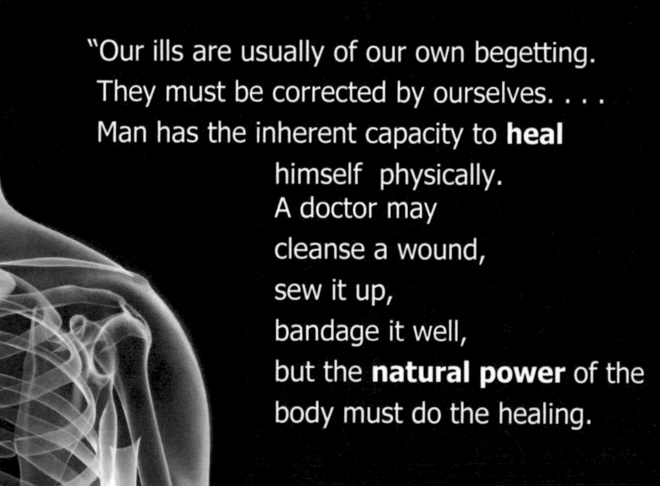

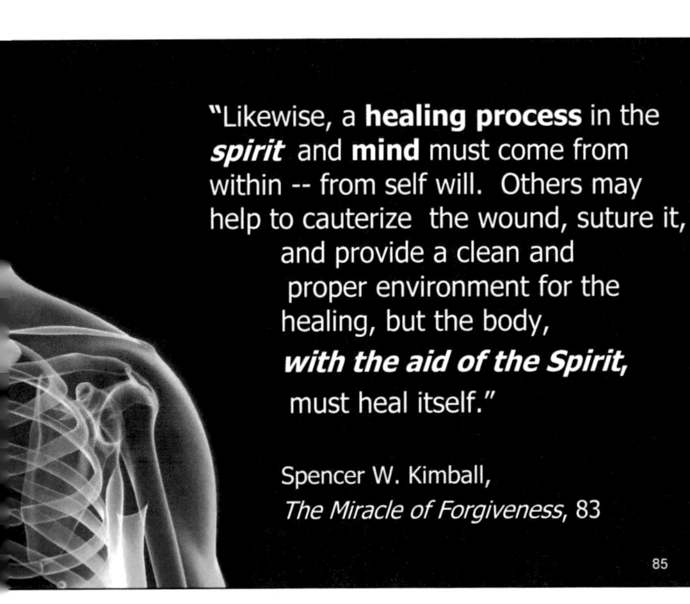

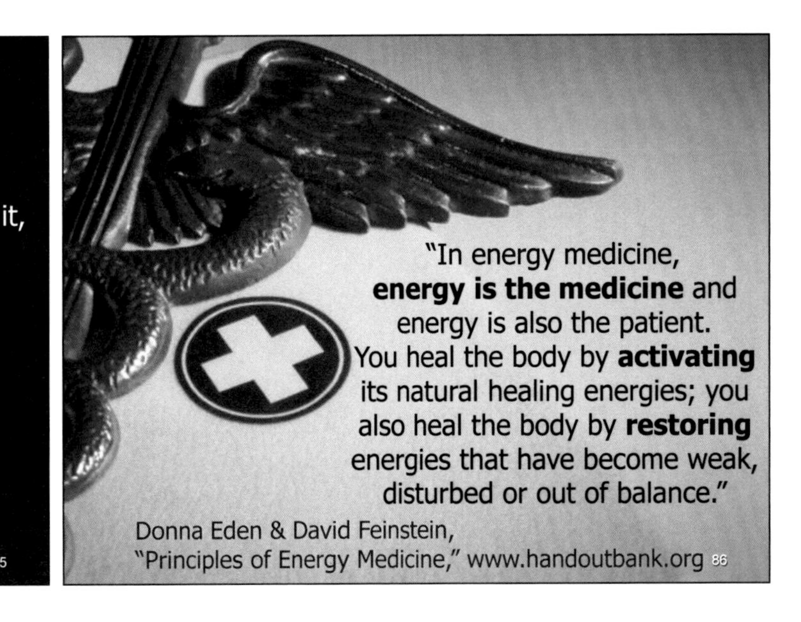

"There are **several** of these **subtle, invisible substances** but little understood as yet by man, and their existence is only demonstrated by their **effects** Some of them are recognized under several terms, electricity, galvanism, magnetism, animal magnetism, spiritual magnetism, essence, spirit, etc. The purest, most refined and subtle of all these substances, and the one least understood, or even recognized, by the less informed among mankind, is that **substance called the Holy Spirit**. . . . This substance is widely diffused among

87

the elements of space. . . . This is the great, positive, **controlling element** of all other elements. It is **omnipresent** by reason of its infinitude of its particles, and it **comprehends** all things. It is the agent or executive, by which God organizes and puts in motion all worlds, and which, by the **mandate** of the Almighty, or any of his commissioned servants performs all the mighty wonders, signs and miracles ever manifested in the name of the Lord, the dividing of the sea, the removing of a mountain, the raising of the dead, or the **healing of the sick.**" Parley P. Pratt, *Key to the Science of Theology,* 39-40

88

"The **spiritual or holy fluid** conveys itself, through certain channels, from **one body to another** in accordance with certain legitimate laws. The usual **channel** for all spiritual fluids whether holy or impure, in their operations upon the human system, or **in their passage from one animal body to another** is the **nerves**. A person **commissioned of Jesus Christ** and **filled** with this spiritual substance, **can impart of the same to another**, provided there is a preparation of **heart** and **faith** on the part of the receiver."

Parley P. Pratt, *Key to the Science of Theology,* 11[illegible]

89

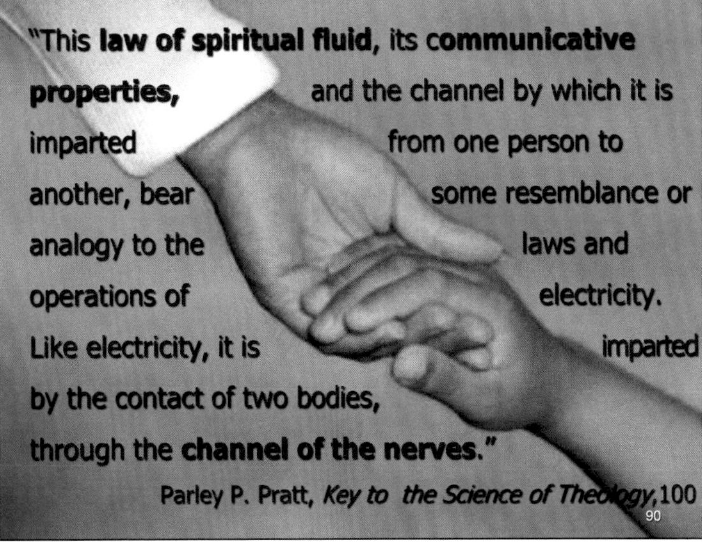

"So well acquainted with this principle was the prophet Elisha, that he sent his servant to lay his **staff** upon a dead child, in order to raise it from the dead; but in this instance, the undertaking **failed**. The prophet could only resuscitate the child by **placing** face on face, eye to eye, mouth to mouth, hand hand, etc., so as to **give** the greatest possible **effect** to the **imparting of the spirit of life.**"

Parley P. Pratt,
Key to the Science of Theology, 110-111, see 2 Kings 4

91

"And the whole multitude sought to touch him: for there **went virtue out of him**, and **healed** them all." Luke 6:19 "And Jesus, immediately knowing in himself that **virtue** had **gone out of him**, turned him about in the press, and said, Who touched my clothes?.... But the woman fearing . . . came . . . And he said unto her, Daughter, **thy faith** hath **made** thee **whole**." Mark 5:30-34

92

"The **minds** of the Latter-day Saints [have] the same **power** and **authority** to exercise **faith** in God which the Former-day Saints had; so that all the saints, in this respect, have been, are and will be, alike until the end of time; for **God never changes,** therefore His attributes and character remain forever the same. ... **All** men have had and will have an **equal privilege**."
Joseph Smith, *Lectures on Faith*, 4:19

93

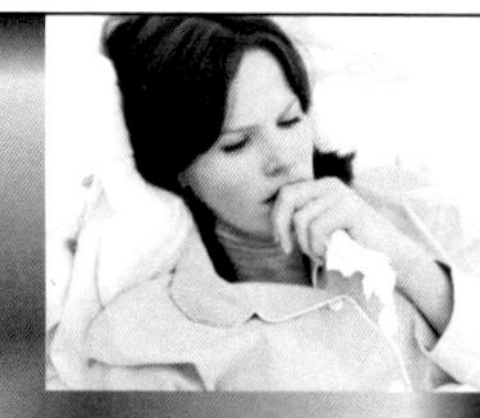

Brigham Young:

"When I lay hands on the sick, I expect the **healing power and influence** of God to **pass through me to the patient**, and the disease to give way. . . . When we are **prepared,** when we are **holy vessels** before the Lord, **a stream of power** from the Almighty can **pass through** the tabernacle of the administrator **to the system of the patient,** and the sick are made whole; the headache, fever or other disease has to give way. My brethren **and sisters**, there is **virtue in us if** we will do right; **if** we live our religion we are the temples of God wherein he will dwell." *Journal of Discourses* 14: 72-73

94

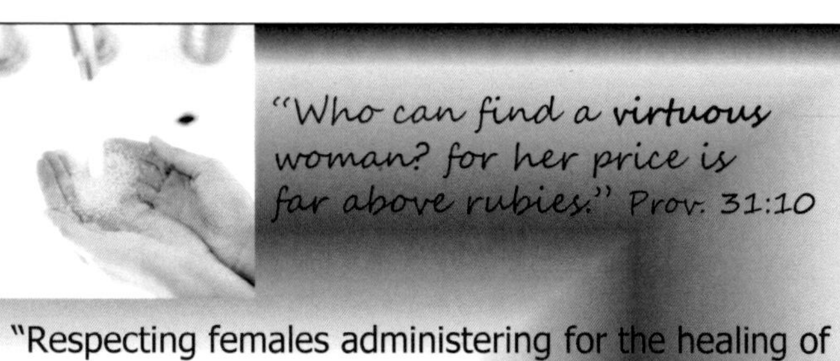

"Who can find a **virtuous** woman? for her price is far above rubies." Prov. 31:10

"Respecting females administering for the healing of the sick, he further remarked, there could be no evil in it, for if God gave His sanction by healing; that **there could be no more sin in any female laying hands on and praying for the sick, than in wetting the face with water;** it is no sin for anybody to administer that has **faith . . .**"
Teachings of the Prophet Joseph Smith, 224-25

95

"Because Latter-day Saint women have received the gift of the Holy Ghost, they can seek and be blessed by **spiritual gifts** such as 'the gift of tongues, prophecy, revelation, visions, **healing,** interpretation of tongues, and so forth.' Throughout the history of the Church, L.D.S. women have received gifts of the Spirit and used them to bless their families and others."

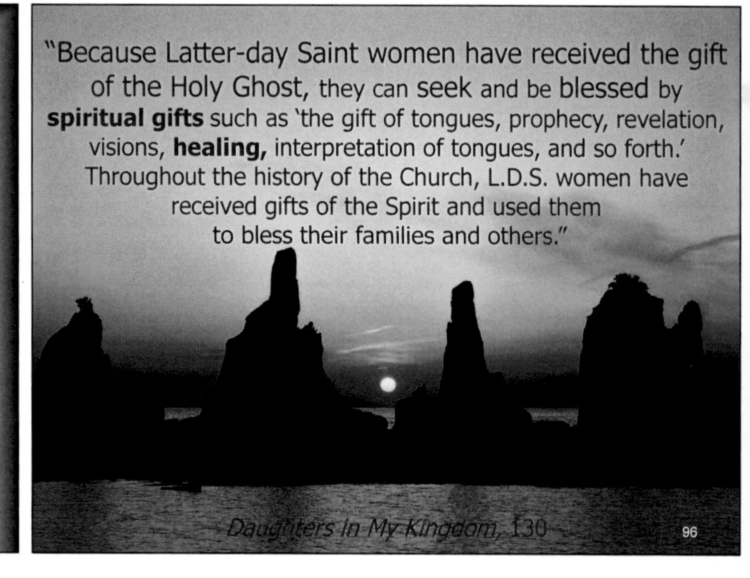

Daughters In My Kingdom, 130

96

"We have and live with an inseparable connection to the priesthood. The Prophet Joseph Smith put the sisters in the position to receive all the gifts, blessings, and privileges of the priesthood. . . . The priesthood is God's power. It is His power to create, to bless, to lead, to serve as He does. . . . Don't confuse the power with the keys and the offices of the priesthood. God's power is limitless and it is shared with those who make and keep covenants. . . . There is a power of godliness that comes to each of us in each of those ordinances. That power is our goal. . . . God's power should be in, and around, and through our lives every moment." Julie B. Beck, BYU Women's Conference 2011

97

"There is the **prayer** that is unlike the [priesthood] administration; it makes request to the Lord to heal and may be offered by **any** soul who has a desire to do so and is **not an ordinance** in the same sense. The **prayer** is a request for the Lord to act, **whereas** the **blessing** or the **administration** is given by the **brethren** in the name of Christ."

"President Kimball Speaks out on Administration to the Sick," *New Era*, Oct. 1981, 46

98

Parley P. Pratt:

"There are **eyes** which can **discern** the most refined particles of elementary existence, there are **hands** and **fingers** to whose refined touch **all** things are **tangible**. . . . To **impart** a portion of the Holy Spirit by the touch . . . or to impart a portion of the element of life, **from one** animal body **to another** . . . is as much in accordance with the laws of nature, as for water to seek its own level." *Key to the Science of Theology*, 45

99

"Deny not the **gifts of God**, for they are **many** and they come from the same God. And there are **different ways** that these **gifts are administered**. But it is the same God who worketh all in all, and they are given by the ...Spirit of God unto men, to profit them;...to one is given **great faith** and to another the **gifts of healing**."

Moroni 10:8-11

100

"Because the priesthood has been restored, we also share equally in the blessings of **spiritual gifts**. The Lord gives us these gifts for our **own** benefit (D&C 46:26) and to **help each other** (D&C 46:12)." Julie B. Beck, "An Outpouring of Blessings," *Ensign*, May 2006, 12

"The individual should be allowed to exercise his inborn gifts." John A. Widtsoe, *Rational Theology*, 137

101

"Chi... is translated as **energy.** Chi represents an invisible **flow of energy that circulates** through plants, animals and people as well as the earth and sky. It is what **maintains** physiological functions and **health**." Karen L. Fontaine, *Absolute Beginners Guide to Alternative Medicine*, 37

"That he might be in all and through all things." D&C 88:6

"Without this **light of life,** the planets would not stay in their orbits, vegetation would not grow, men and animals would be devoid of the **breath of life**" (Gen. 2:7), and life would cease to exist. (D&C 88:50)."

Bruce R. McConkie, *Mormon Doctrine*, 447

102

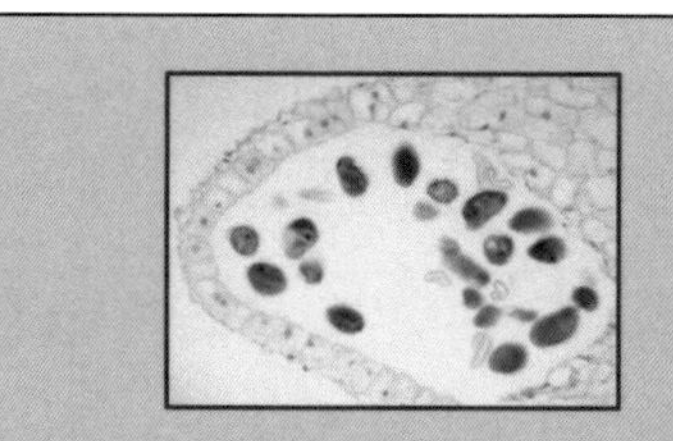

"Progressive health practitioners are embracing **Chi** as a **major** [factor] in their holistic programs. **Chi** is an electronic energy that can be measured using sensitive electro-acupuncture machines. **It is thought that Chi originates at the level of a single cell...** Trillions of cells in the human body make electronic energy simultaneously with chemical energy in the tiny energy factories called mitochondria.

103

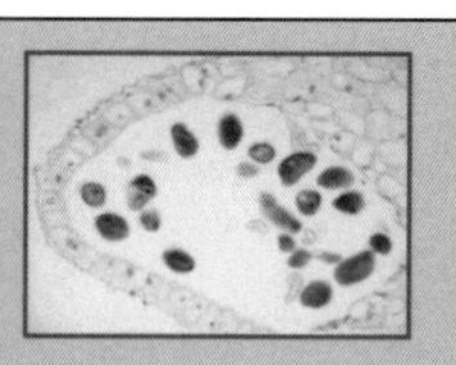

The Chi energy leaves the single cells and moves out of the tissue, then travels through the organs and the entire body, as measured via acupuncture meridian points.... **Our cells make the sparks of Chi.**"

Quoting Parris M. Kidd, Ph.D., in Farley M. Anderson, *Nature's Answer*, 37-38

"In him was life; and the life was **the light of men**." John 1:4

104

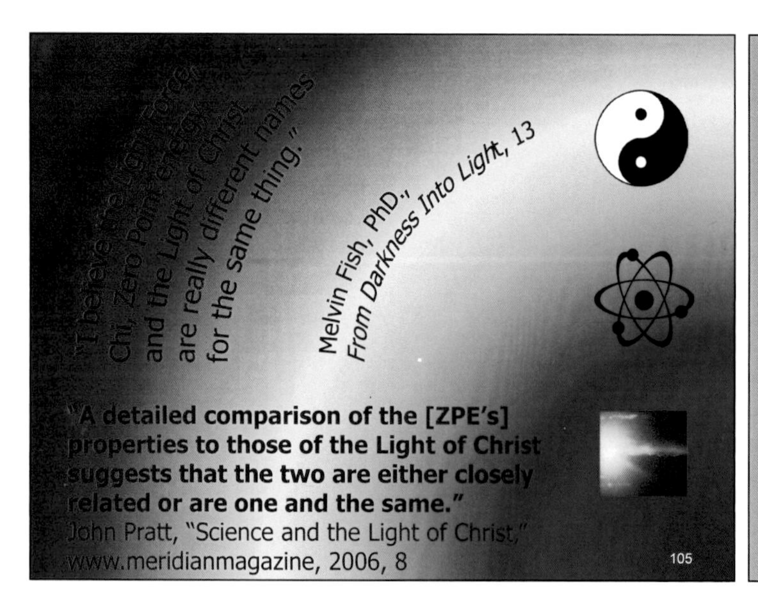

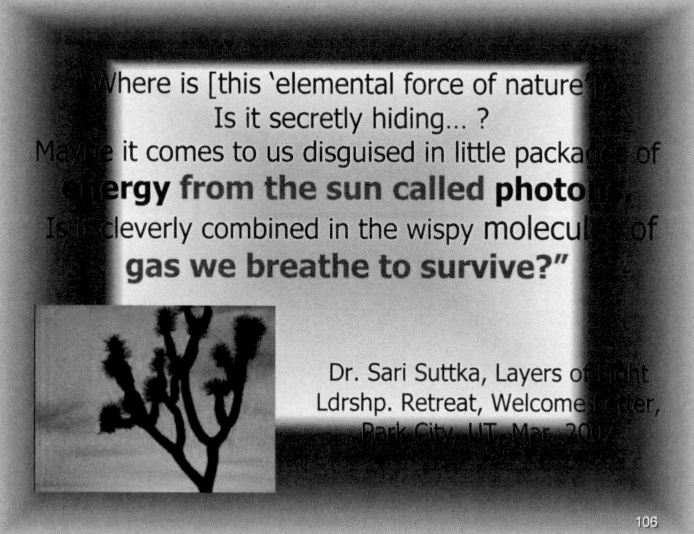

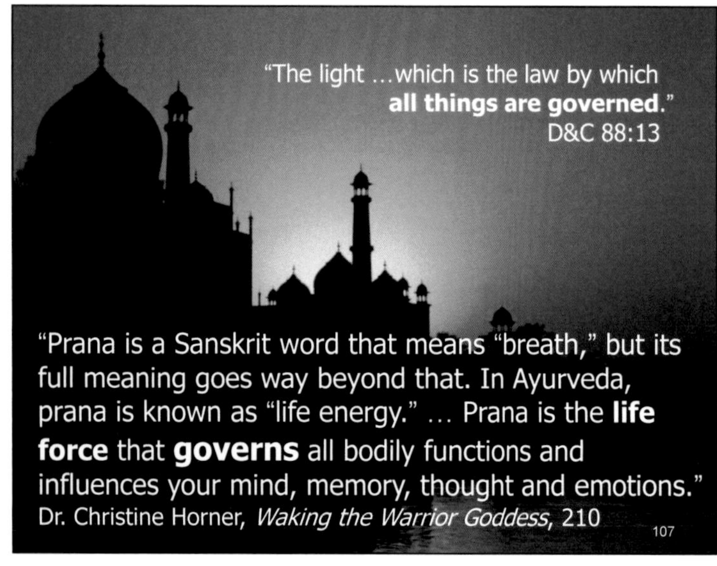

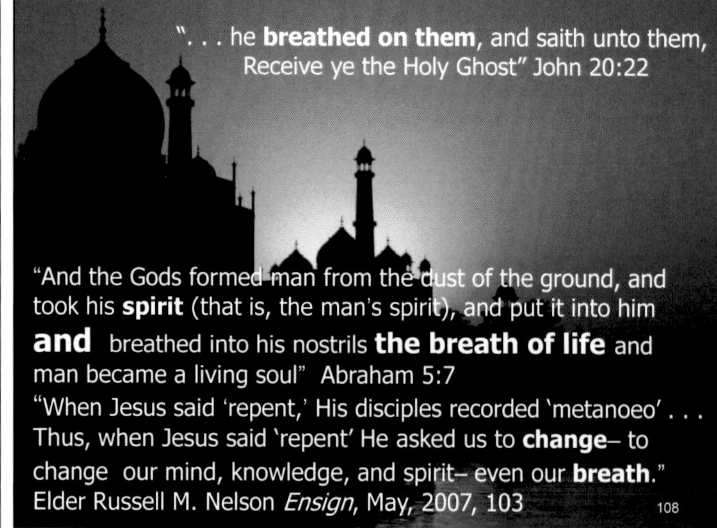

Woman at the Well by Carl Bloch

Rivers of Energy
called Nadis
from India

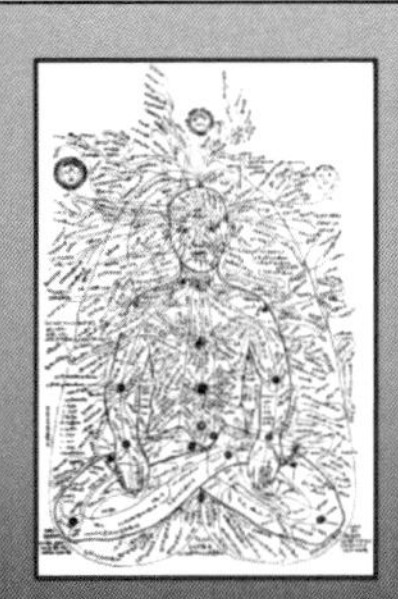

"He that believeth on me, as the scripture hath said, out of his belly shall flow rivers of living water. (But this spake he of the Spirit, which they that believe on him should receive: for the Holy Ghost was not yet given...)" John 7:38 -39 "The water that I shall give him shall be in him a well of water springing up into everlasting life." John 4:14

109

"The Egyptian associated life, light, air, breath, and everything good in a single symbol, the *nfr*-sign, showing the heart and respiratory passages, including the aesophagus, for the breathing pipes were also the way of nourishment: in a single intake one absorbs life, breath, nourishment, health, vigor – everything good."

Hugh Nibley,
"What is 'The Book of Breathings'?", BYU Studies, 5-6

110

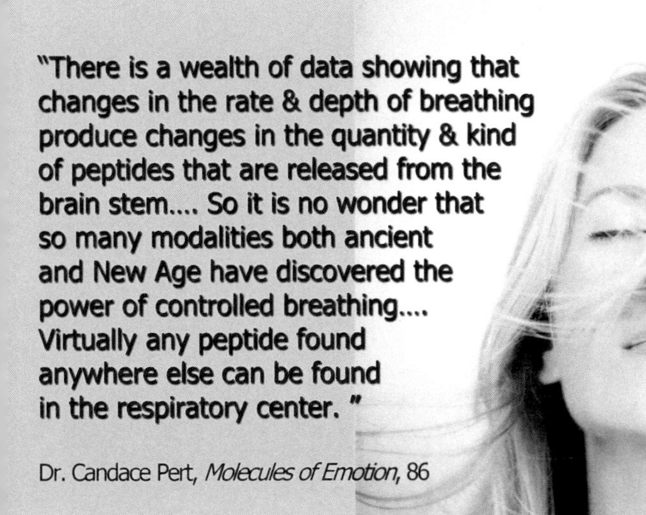

"There is life in all matter, throughout the vast extent of the eternities; It is in the rock, the sand, the dust, in water, air, the gases, and in short in every description and organization of matter, whether it is solid, liquid, or gaseous, particle operating with particle."

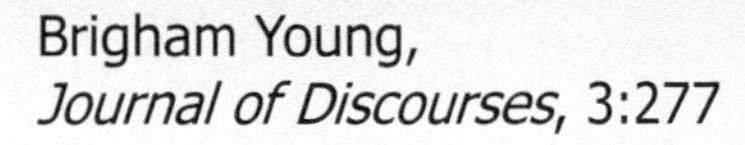

Brigham Young,
Journal of Discourses, 3:277

112

"If you look at platinum crystal under a field ion microscope, you see bubble formations which form **pyramid shapes of Light** going from every stage of geometry all the way through the immediate **field** of the crystal. If you look at blood crystals under an electron microscope, you can find the shape of the pyramidal field in the crystal forms of blood. . . . **The pyramid shows that the Universal Mind is all present**, not only in **every molecule** ... but in **every vibration of consciousness flow**. . . . A close examination of the pyramidal units in hydrogen atoms will further reveal the **geometry** of a Star of David as a **life-giving form.**"

JJ Hurtak, PhD, PhD
An Introduction to the Keys of Enoch, 27

by Erwin W. Mueller, Penn State

113

"The footsteps of divinity are deeply impressed upon the whole creation accessible to man. **It is as if God was inscribed in living characters of light, upon every department of the universe.** All things proclaim, in silent grandeur, the magnificence of his glory, the fullness of his wisdom, the eternity and omnipotence of his power."

Masterful Discourses of Orson Pratt, 470

by Erwin W. Mueller, The Future Science Foundation

114

"Every atom of matter; every particle of ether is endowed with a form of **intelligence**. . . . The explanations of the mysteries of nature will be **greatly simplified** when the 'Mormon' doctrine of the position of **intelligence in universal phenomena** is clearly **understood by scientific workers."**

John A. Widtsoe,
Joseph Smith as Scientist, 130

115

"It was clearly comprehended by the Prophet and his associates that **intelligence** is **the** vivifying force of all creation - **animate or inanimate -** that rock and tree and beast and man, have ascending degrees of intelligence. The **intelligence** spoken of by the prophet **corresponds fully with the energy of science."**

John A. Widtsoe,
Joseph Smith As Scientist, 141

116

". . . According to 'Mormon' doctrine, there is no special life force. The intelligence residing in a stone is in quality, as far as it goes, the same as the intelligence possessed by man. But, man is so organized that a greater amount of intelligence, a fullness of it, centers in him, and he is as a consequence, essentially and eternally different from the stone."

John A. Widtsoe
Joseph Smith as Scientist, 65

117

"All matter originates and exists only by virtue of a **force** which brings the particles of an atom to **vibration** and holds [the] atom together....
We must assume behind this **force** the existence of a conscious and **intelligent Mind. This Mind is the matrix of all matter."**

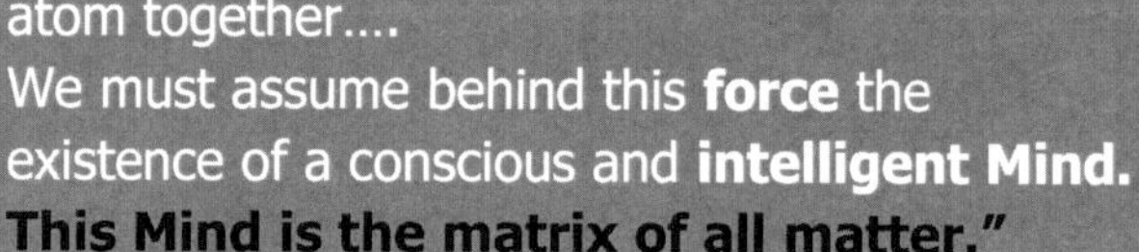

Max Planck, speech in Florence, Italy, 1944
"The Essence/Nature/Character of Matter"

118

"British Physicist, David Bohm, theorizes there is an invisible field that holds all of reality

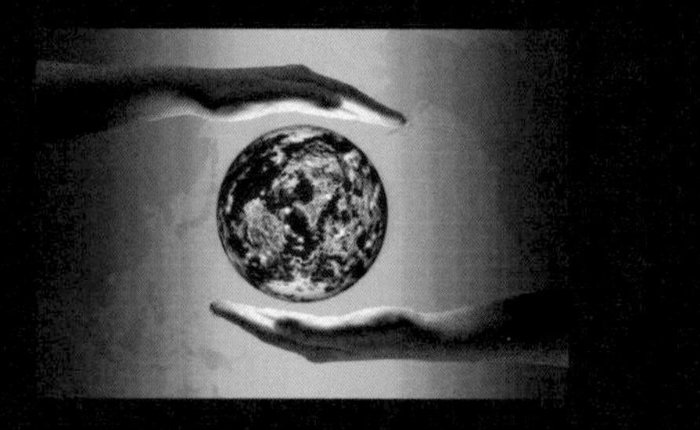

together, a field that possesses the property of knowing what is happening everywhere at once."
Deepak Chopra, *Quantum Healing*, 104-105

119

"The holy spirit vibrates with intelligence; it takes up the word and will of God as given by him or by his personal agents and transmits the message to the

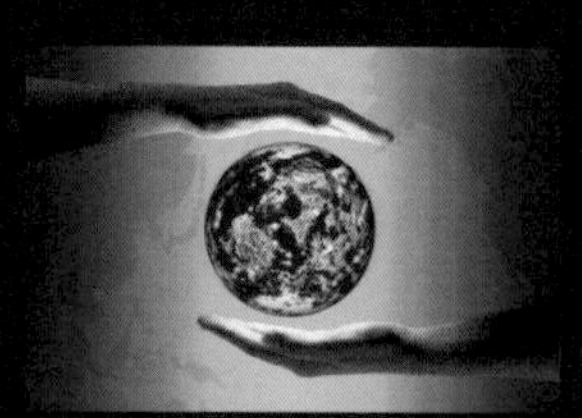

remotest parts of space. By the intelligent domination and infinite extent of the holy spirit the whole universeis **held together** and **made as one whole**."
John A. Widtsoe, *Rational Theology*, 69

120

"I'm going to explain to you how nature is – and if you don't like it, that's going to get in the way of your understanding it. . . . The theory of QED [quantum electrodynamics] describes nature as absurd from the point of view of common sense. And it agrees fully with experiment. So I hope you can accept Nature as She is– absurd. I'm going to have fun telling you about this absurdity, because I find it delightful. Please don't turn yourself off because you can't believe Nature is so strange. Just hear me out, and I hope you'll be as delighted as I am when we're through."

Richard P. Feynman,
Physics Nobelist
QED-The Strange Theory of Light and Matter, 10

121

"In the form of matter, what we see as individual parts, including people are but the organized *physical* part of a larger universal *spiritual* whole. We are **spiritually connected** with all other parts in the universe, including with each other. One electron is no more independent from the universe than one cell is independent from the whole body." B. Grant Bishop, *The LDS Gospel of Light*, 27-28

Photo courtesy of NASA

122

"Of even greater importance in daily work is the fact that every intelligent being affects every other intelligent being. **Every person affects every other person.** Through the operation of the Holy Spirit **all things are held together.** Good or evil may be **transmitted from personality to personality."**

John A. Widtsoe, *Rational Theology*, 126

123

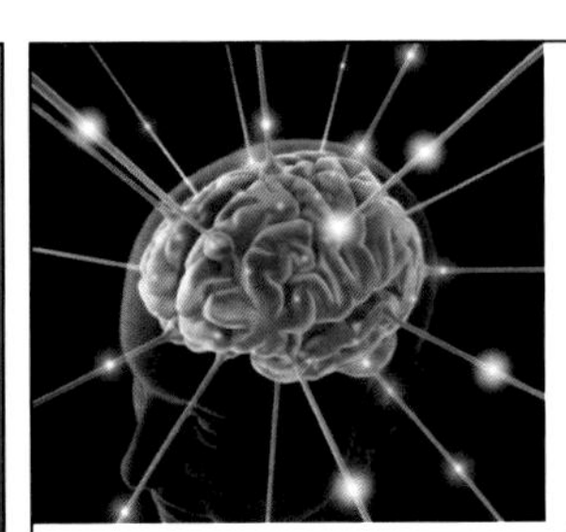

"As Fritz Albert Popp theorized, molecules speak to each other in oscillating **frequencies.** It appeared that the **Zero Point Field** creates a medium enabling the molecules to speak to each other **nonlocally** and virtually **instantaneously**. . .

Information

is not dependent on time or space, as is matter and energy."

Lynn McTaggart *The Field*, 68,

124

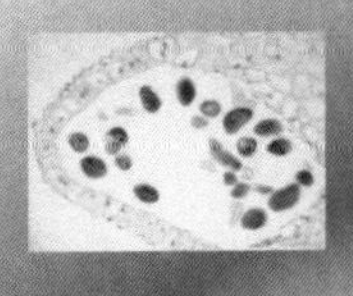

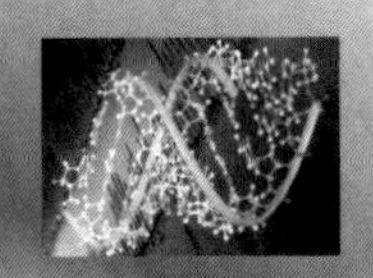

"Cells & DNA communicate through **frequencies.** The brain perceives and makes its own record of the world in pulsating **waves**. A **substructure underpins** the universe that is essentially a **recording medium** of everything, providing a means for **everything** to **communicate** with everything else.... Living **consciousness**... increases order in the rest of the world... [and] has **incredible powers, to heal** ourselves, to heal the world." Lynne McTaggart, *The Field*, 224-225

125

"Our mechanistic notions of cause and effect in time and space operate on a very limited range of the spectrum of what is possible. Though we see ordinary examples of distributed nonlocal consciousness every day, such as schools of fish that turn in tandem, or flocks of birds that band and swoop in perfect coordination,

126

our collective medical brain still has trouble with the idea that things far apart in space and time can affect each other, and medical treatment is prescribed as though only what is here and now has meaning."

Dawson Church, *PhD*,
The Genie in Your Genes, 210

127

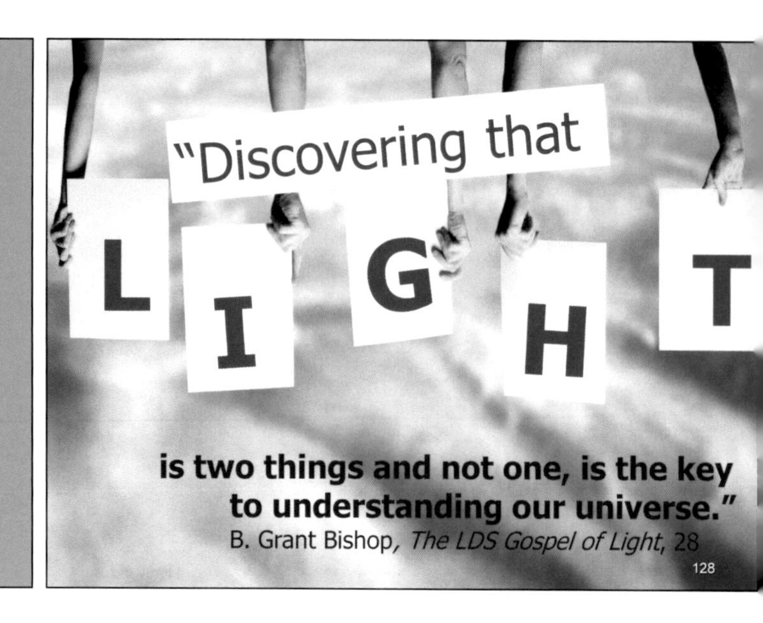

"There are philosophical and spiritual implications to energy healing. If we are all interconnected by **energy and consciousness** as proposed by Einstein and Planck, and supported experimentally by contemporary scientists, such as Radin and Sheldrake, then there are **vast implications** for how we **practice medicine** as well as how we live our lives."

Gary E. Schwartz, PhD,
The Energy Healing Experiment-Science Reveals our Natural Power to Heal, 227

129

"The **mind**, like **light**, does not need to be helped along by anything else. It is genuinely present everywhere in space and time. Since it is already everywhere, it has no need to "go" or be "sent." We can think about the **MIND** as if it were some sort of **FIELD**."

Larry Dossey, M.D.,
Reinventing Medicine, 28

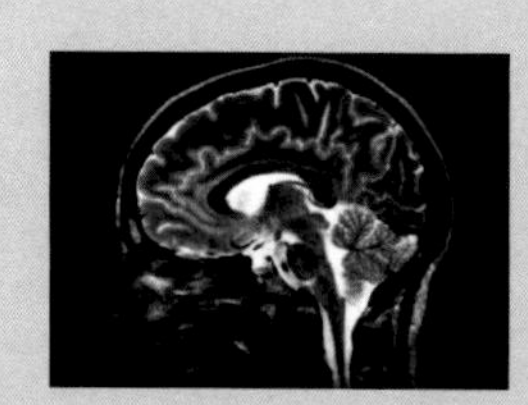

"Memory, thinking and the mind are all phenomena outside the Physical Body; they are not happening in the brain. The Mental Body is an energetic field." Dietrich Klinghardt, M.D., PhD quoted in Stephanie Marohn, *Bipolar Disorder*, 64

130

"The mind is more than a brain. It can do things brains can't do, such as acting remotely from the body and venturing outside the present. . . . 'Nonlocal' or 'infinite' describes a natural part of who we are. Its expressions include sharing of thoughts and feelings at a distance And this part of your MIND can be used today in healing illness and disease. Many studies reveal that healing can be achieved at a distance. These findings reveal some part of our mind… [can] act anywhere regardless of distance."

Larry Dossey, M.D., *Reinventing Medicine*, 24

131

"Laying on of hands is not the only means of **communicating** the gift of **healing**. A **word spoken**, **a mandate issued**, or even a handkerchief, …worn or touched by a person **full of this Spirit** and conveyed to another, has, according to sacred history and also the experience of the present age, proved sufficient to **communicate** the spiritual fluid **between MINDS** of *strong* and *mutual faith*."

Parley P. Pratt,
Key to the Science of Theology , 110

132

by Paolo Veronese

Matthew 8:5-10,13

"There came unto him a centurion ... saying, Lord, my servant lieth at home sick of the palsy... Jesus saith unto him, I will come and heal him. The centurion answered and said, Lord I am not worthy that thou shouldst come under my roof, **but speak the word only**, and my servant shall be healed. . . . When Jesus heard it he marveled, and said to them that followed, Verily, I say unto you, **I have not found so great faith**, no, not in Israel... and his servant was healed in the selfsame hour."

133

"Ye know the things that ye must do in my church; for the works which ye have seen me do, that shall ye also do; for that which ye have seen me do, even that shall ye do." 3Nephi 27:21

134

John Pratt, "Science and the Light of Christ," 5-6

"**Non-local events** are well known in quantum mechanics. Those are events where two entities "know" something about each other much faster than a light signal could be sent between them. These are the essences of many psychic phenomena, and they might be explained by the ZPE [zero point energy field]. Thus, such observations are **not beyond science at all**, but rather **are predicted** by the best and **most** modern science that **we know.**"

135

"And God wrought special miracles by the hands of Paul: so that **from his body were brought unto the sick** handkerchiefs or aprons, and the diseases departed from them, and the evil spirits went out of them."

Acts 19:11-12

136

"How much would you give for even a cane that Father Abraham had used? Or a coat or ring that the Savior had worn? The rough old boxes in which the bodies of Joseph and Hyrum were brought from Carthage, were made into canes and other articles. I have a cane made from the plank of one of those boxes, so has Brother Brigham and a great many others, and we prize them highly, and esteem them a great blessing. . . . The day will come when there will be multitudes who will be healed and blessed through the instrumentality of those canes, and the devil cannot overcome those who have them, in consequence of their **faith** and **confidence** in the

137

virtues connected with them. . . . In England, when not in a situation to go, I have blessed my handkerchief, and asked God to sanctify it and fill it with life and power, and sent it to the sick and hundreds have been healed by it. In like manner I have sent my cane. Dr. Richards used to lay his old black cane on a person's head and that person has been healed through its instrumentality, by the power of God. I have known Joseph, hundreds of times, send his handkerchief to the sick, and they have been healed. There are persons in this congregation who have been healed by throwing my old cloak on their beds."

Heber C. Kimball in *Journal of Discourses* 4:294

138

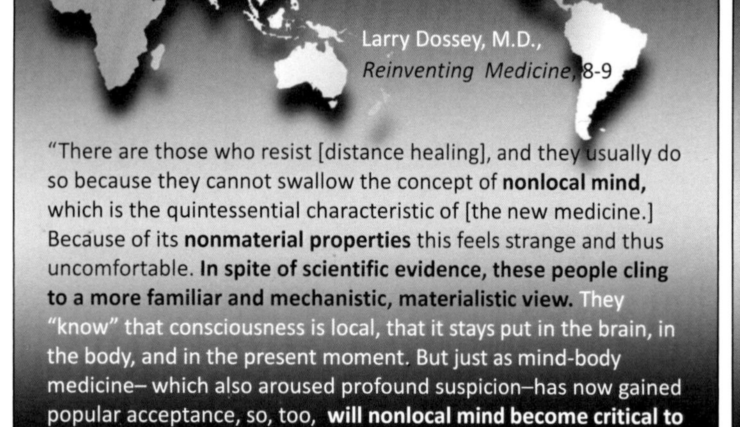

"I've spent years searching for a suitable term for the unbounded ways in which **consciousness** displays itself in space and time. I've bumped into dozens of expressions that have been used in the past– extended mind, cosmic consciousness,... universal mind, Christ consciousness, collective consciousness, the collective unconscious, and on and on. . . . Nonlocal is a term used by physicists. . . . I chose to adopt the physicists term. . . . No other term describes **consciousness** so well as *nonlocal mind*."

Larry Dossey, M.D., *Reinventing Medicine*, 8-9

140

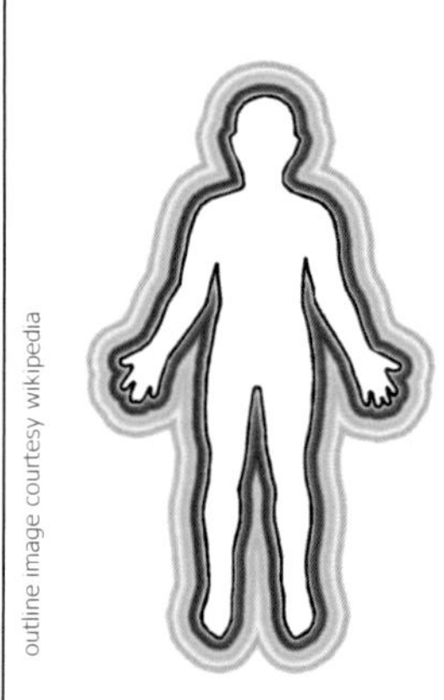

outline image courtesy wikipedia

"Every living person has an **electro-magnetic energy field** which radiates six to twelve inches off the body. People who **see** this field call it an **aura**. Even though I can't see it, **I certainly can demonstrate it,** so I prefer to call it an **energy field.**"

Dr. Jan Graf, booklet
"Graf Stress Management," 17

"All spirit is matter, but it is more fine or pure, and can only be discerned by purer eyes." D&C 131:7

142

"Those with **second sight** have observed that **everything shines with heavenly light**. Knowing that that's true, we too can see it, that **divine invisible spirit** which seems to bring to our hearts a feeling of security. As our **hearts** expand, there is so much more to **'see.'** Our **spiritual senses** open, and we touch the **sacred** many times a day." M. Catherine Thomas, *Light in the Wilderness*,109

143

"I shall come in a cloud with power and great glory." D&C 34:7

"I have heard this [spiritual] body described in many different terms. . . . a mist, a **cloud**, smoke-like, a vapor, transparent, **a cloud of colors,** wispy, **an energy pattern**, and others which express similar meanings." Raymond Moody, Jr. MD, *Life After Life*, 50

". . . the angel of the Lord appeared unto them; and he descended as it were in a cloud . . ." Mosiah 27:11

144

"The electromagnetic components of the human energy field can be detected with special electronic instruments. The pool of electromagnetic energy or corona, **invisible to most people**, is seen at times as a **halo or light-colored mist around a human body."**
Dr. Valerie Hunt, 1989

Outline courtesy wikipedia

Colossians 1:16-17
*"For by Him were all things created, . . . visible **and invisible**."*
*D&C 84:45 "Whatsoever is light **is spirit**, even the Spirit of Jesus Christ."*

145

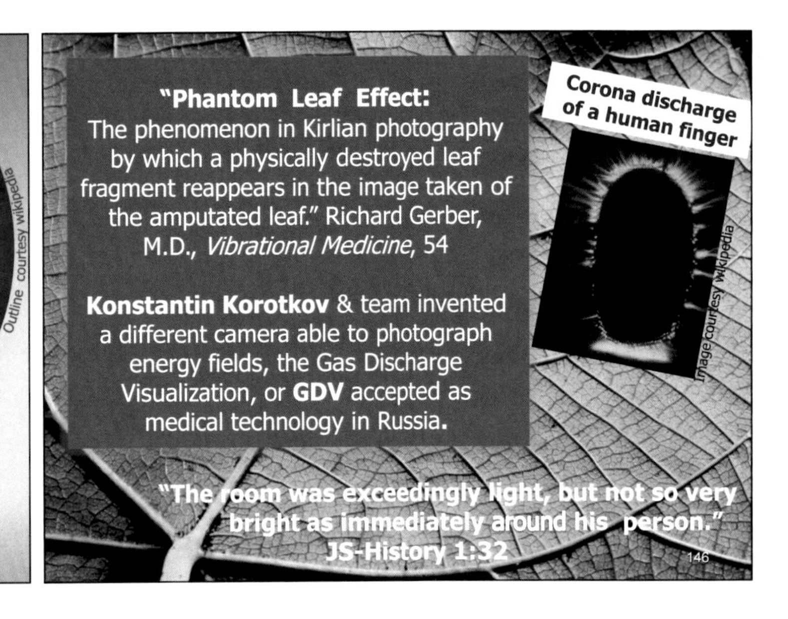

"The human body literally glows, emitting a visible light in extremely small quantities at levels that rise and fall with the day. Past research has shown that the body emits visible light, 1,000 times less intense than the levels which can be seen with the naked eye. In fact, virtually all living creatures emit very weak light. . . . . The existence of the biophoton field was scientifically proven by Dr. Fritz - Albert Popp in 1974."

Dr. Joseph Mercola, "Your Body Literally Glows with Light," Aug. 15,2009, articles.mercola.com

147

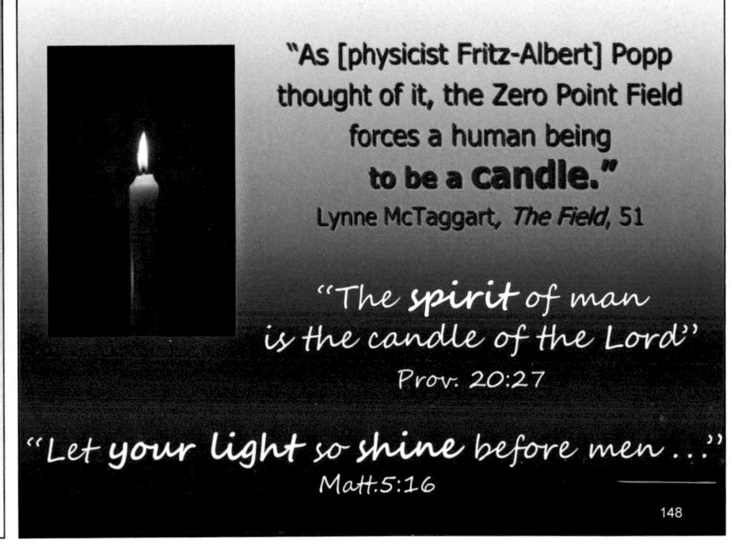

"Light, energy and mass are related as expressed in Einstein's famous equation. Energy equals the mass of physical matter times the speed of light squared. In other words, **energy and matter are two forms of the same thing**. That is important. Light is energy and energy can be changed into matter. **That means everything in the universe is a variation of light."**
B. Grant Bishop, M.D., *The LDS Gospel of Light*, 19

"Spirit is matter and matter is **full of spirit**."
Parley P. Pratt, *Key to the Science of Theology*, 44

149

"I believe **subtle energy** is a kind of universal **life force** that flows to us from the **divine.** According to Eastern wisdom, everyone has an **aura,** a field of this energy surrounding the physical body, and flowing through it as well, travelling along lines called **meridians** by the Chinese or radiating out from the seven body centers called **chakras** by the practitioners of yoga. Westerners even have a version of it in Christianity, as the **halo** surrounding the **crown of the head,** often depicted on saints and angels in medieval art. But you don't have to be a saint, an angel, or a yogi to acknowledge this subtle energy. **It's in everyone and can be a force for healing."** Brian Seaward quoted in Candace Pert, *Molecules of Emotion*, 307

150

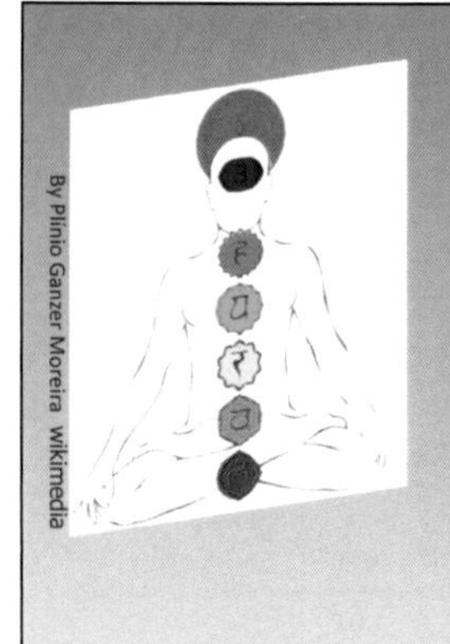

"If one cannot see the **aura** and discussion of it is couched in unfamiliar language from other cultures, one doubts its value. Ancient writings claiming that **chakras are the auric field source** with **meridian** pathways the circulation route do not fit snugly into the current understanding from structural anatomy. Nonetheless, the few who have chosen to research this unchartered human field discover facts unique to living fields that also correspond to universal laws. The **human field** looms as primary to life."

Valerie H. Hunt, *Infinite Mind*, 65

151

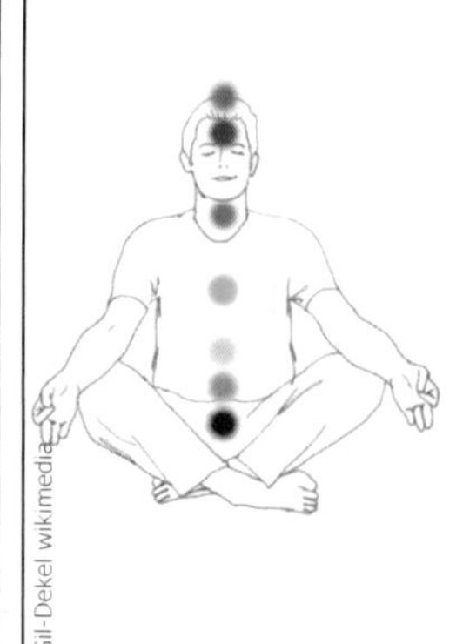

"CHAKRA: An **energy center** in the body which is a step down transformer for **higher frequency subtle energies.** The chakras process subtle energy and convert it into chemical, hormonal, and cellular changes in the body."

Richard Gerber, M.D.
Vibrational Medicine, 556

152

"I will give unto you a **pattern in all things**, that ye may **not be deceived**." D&C 52:1

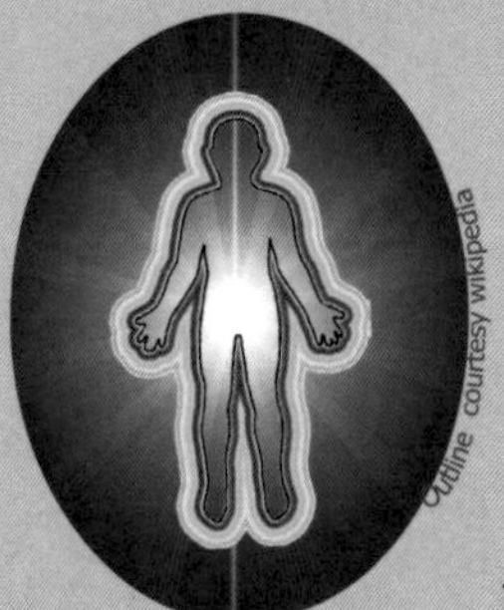

Psalms 5:12

"For thou Lord, wilt bless the righteous; with favor wilt thou compass him as with a shield."

153

The Bible speaks of 'wheels,' which in Sanskrit is 'chakras.' In Ezekiel 1, the prophet saw creatures in the likeness of a man with **wheels** of **colored light**going **up and down**. The brightness was as a **RAINBOW.**

"The **spirit** of God like a **fire** is burning."
William W. Phelps, *Hymns* #2

"**Light shall on us beam** the **Spirit's** heavenly **flame.**" Parley P. Pratt,
"Father in Heaven We Do Believe, *Hymns*, #180

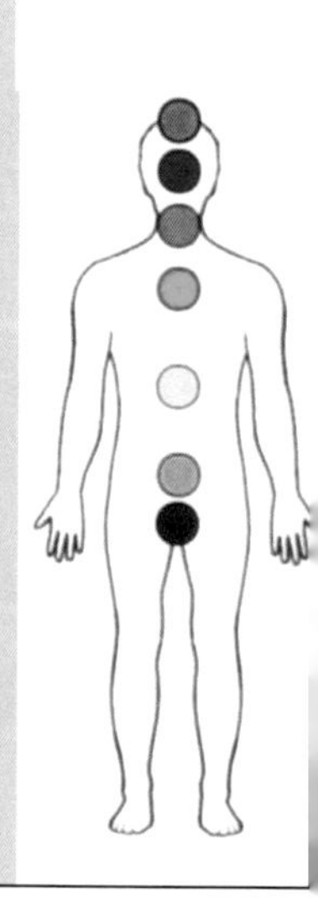

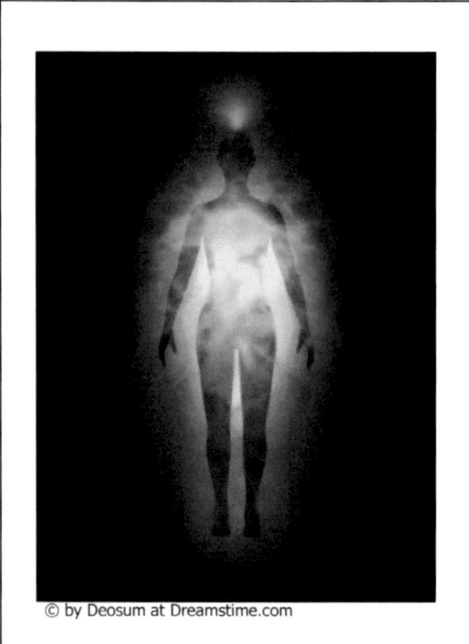

"**. . . the spirit of the living creature was in the wheels"** like **burning** coals of **fire** or lamps.

Ezekiel 1:20 and repeated in 1:21

155

The body's seven main Chakras
Crown
Brow
Throat
Heart
Solar Plexus
Sacral
Base

Ezekiel Chapter 1

- Above their head it was the color of the **terrible CRYSTAL,**
- Above the firmament over their heads it was the color of a **Sapphire stone (deep BLUE.)**
- One wheel was **GREEN**
- **AMBER** was above the loins
- From the loins down "I saw as it were the **APPEARANCE of FIRE."**

"*I will cause* that your bosom shall ***burn within*** you." D&C 9:8
"And they saw angels ... in the midst **of fire**; and they came down and encircled those little ones about, and **they** were ***encircled*** *about* ***with fire.***" 3 Nephi17:24

156

"Joseph described the descending light. In dictating the account, he sought the proper word. He first used the word **fire.** That is crossed out in favor of **spirit** or **light**. The word he finally settled on and used most often was **glory**. It refers to the emanating and **radiating spirit** and **power** of God. But the word **fire** is important to notice. Orson Pratt . . . says that the young prophet expected to see 'the leaves and boughs of the trees consumed.' In other words, he thought he was seeing descending fire, the kind that burns and consumes.... The Prophet indicates in the 1835 account that **he was filled** with **that light**, but also **surrounded** by it, that it **filled** the Grove." Truman Madsen, *Joseph Smith the Prophet*, 11

see also Exodus 3:2 JST

157

"Or ever the **silver cord** be loosed, or the **golden bowl** be broken, or the pitcher be broken at the fountain, or the **wheel** broken at the cistern. Then shall the **dust** return to the earth as it was: and the **spirit** shall return unto God who gave it." Eccles. 12:6-7

"And the spirit giveth light to every man that cometh into the world" D&C 84:46

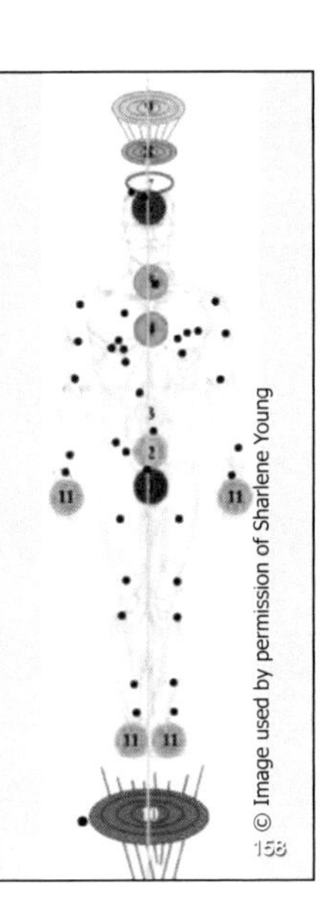

© Image used by permission of Sharlene Young

158

Ezekiel said the **rings** he saw were **so high** they were *"tall and awesome."* Holy Bible New Revised Standard Version Ezekiel 1: 18

"Grounding to your unique point **in the center of the earth** **and being open to receive through** your body **to [God]** creates your **complete circuit** of **energy."**
Sharlene Young,
Clearing Your 12 Chakras, 10

Center image © used by permission of Sharlene Young

"If therefore the light that is in thee be darkness, **how great** is that darkness!" Matt. 6:23

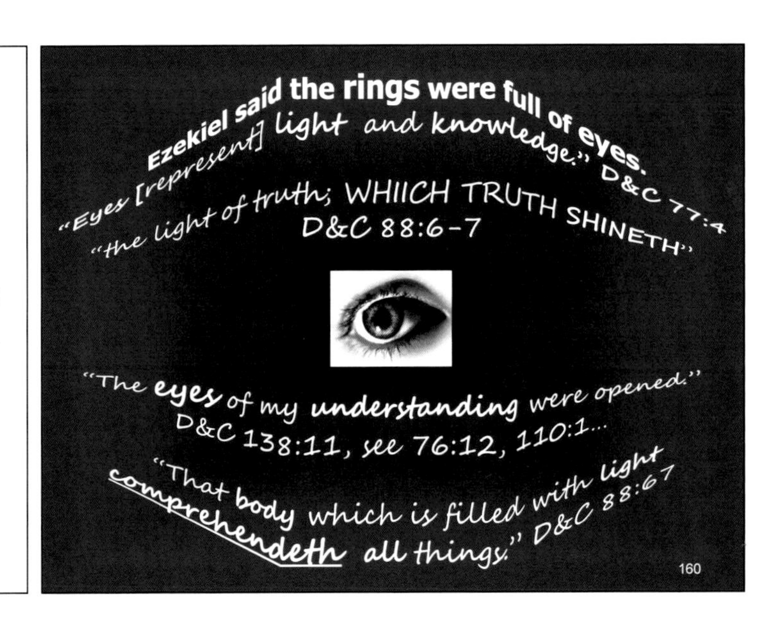

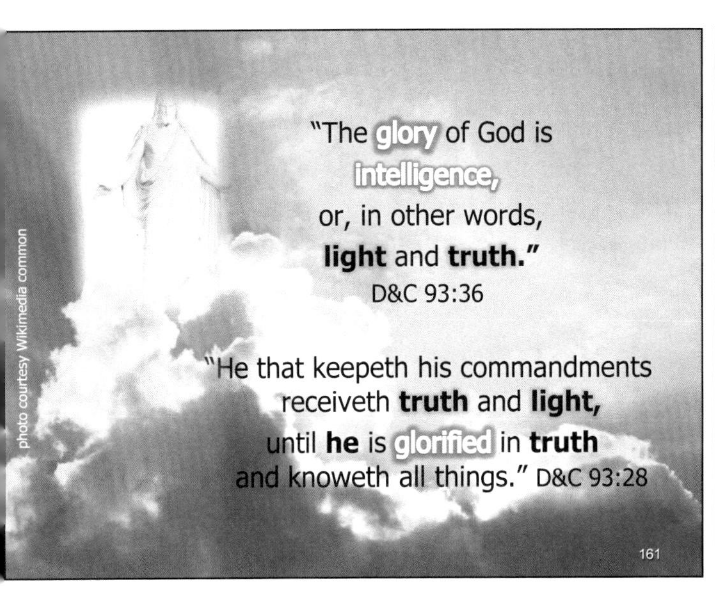

by unknown artist courtesy wikipedia

"The purest, most refined and subtle of all these substances, and the one least understood,... [is] called the Holy Spirit. . . . This is the true light, which in some measure **illuminates all men.** It is, in its less refined particles, the **physical light** which reflects from the sun. . . and in its **higher degrees**, the **intellectual light** of our **inward and spiritual organs**, by which we reason, discern." Parley P. Pratt, *Key to the Science of Theology*, 39,41

"...and the **light** which did **light up** his [king Lamoni's] **mind**, which was the **light of the glory** of God..." Alma 19:6

162

"If we are not grounded in our 10th chakra we may experience an inability to deal with stress or cope with everyday realities, maintain boundaries or think clearly. We may experience difficulties in separating our feelings or perceptions from those of others.... [and] problems with avoidance issues, feeling spacey or out to lunch, paranoia or schizophrenia, and other neurosis or disassociation of some sort."

Sharlene Young, *Tenth Chakra*, 5

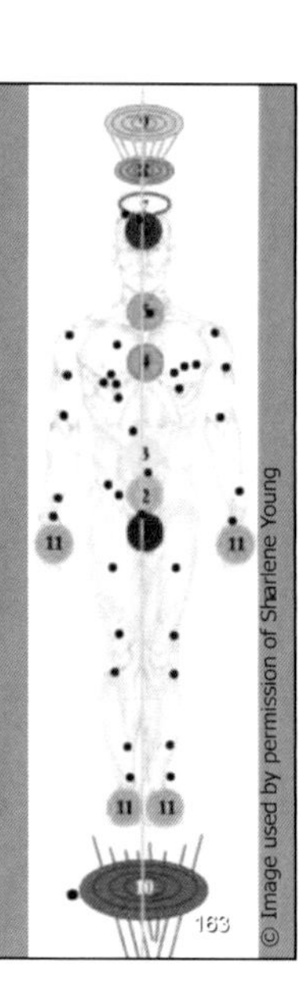

© Image used by permission of Sharlene Young

163

"People in Western cultures, whose **crown chakras are wide open** are more likely to receive psychiatric medication than the arduous training that would help them to become more **balanced** and **grounded**."

Donna Eden,
Energy Medicine, 1998, 163

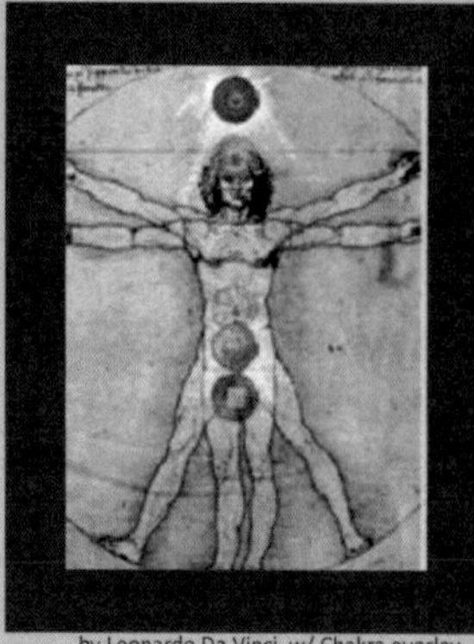

by Leonardo Da Vinci w/ Chakra overlay

There are also grounding essential oils as well as Rapid Eye Technology's grounding scripts & CDs.

164

Elder Boyd K. Packer: "If all you know is what you see with your natural eyes and hear with your natural ears, then you will not know very much." quoted in Elder David A. Bednar, "Quick to Observe," *Ensign,* Dec 2006

"And there is no other one item that will so much astound you, when your eyes are opened in eternity, as to think that you were so stupid in the body."
Brigham Young, *Journal of Discourses* 8:30

165

Chapter 4
The Light of Consciousness

"For as he thinketh **in his heart**, so is he."
Proverbs 23:7

166

Pres. John Taylor: "He is the light of the stars and the power by which they were made. He says it is the **same light** that enlightens the understanding of men. What, have we a **mental light** and a **visual light,** all proceeding from the **same source?** Yes, so says the scripture, and so says science when rightly comprehended."

Journal of Discourses
18: 327-328

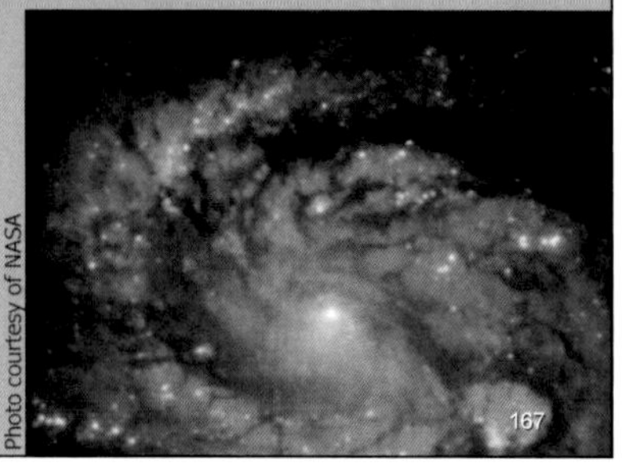

Photo courtesy of NASA

167

"Whatever we choose to call it, this **energy** appears to be the living canvas upon which the events of our lives are **inscribed**."

Gregg Braden,
Secrets to the Lost Mode of Prayer, 20

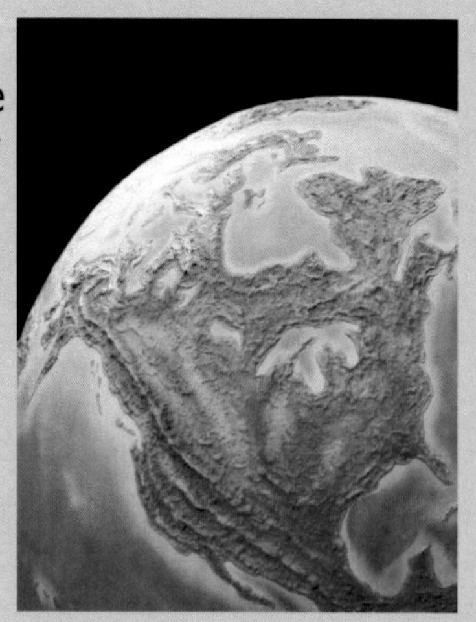

168

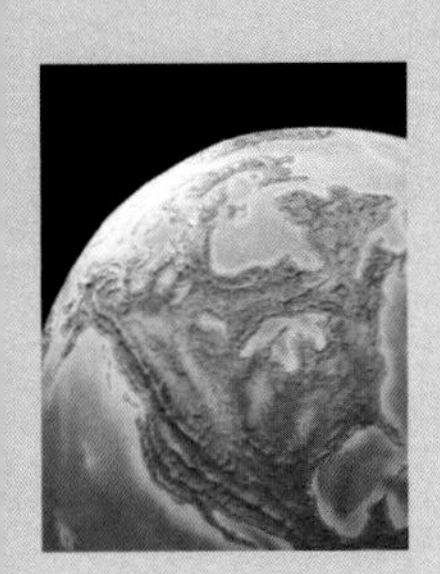

"So thoroughly permeated with the holy spirit is the immensity of space that **every act** and **word** and **thought** is **recorded** and **transmitted** everywhere, so that all who **know** how to read **may read.** Thus we make an imperishable **record** of our lives. . . . He who has the receiving apparatus, in whose hands the key is held, may **read** from the record of the holy spirit, an imperishable history of all that has occurred during the ages that have passed in the world's history."
John A. Widtsoe, *Rational Theology, 70*

169

"A generation ago it was thought that the concept of **matter & energy** was the basis for understanding all phenomena.

Bob Gottesman
as quoted in Candace Pert,
Molecules of Emotion, 256

Today the concept of **information** is **replacing energy and matter** as the common denominator for understanding all biological life and even environmental processes."

170

"Energy and information exist everywhere in nature. In fact, at the level of the quantum field, there is nothing other than energy and information.... This quantum field is influenced by intention and desire."
Deepak Chopra, *The Seven Spiritual Laws of Success*, 67

"The ultimate stuff of the universe is consciousness."
The Institute of Noetic Sciences, "Scientific Positivism: the New Dualism"

"Conscience is a manifestation of the Light of Christ."
True to the Faith, 40

171

"Since intelligence is everywhere present, all the operations of nature, from the simplest to the most complex, are the products of intelligence. **We may even conceive that energy is only intelligence, and that matter and intelligence, rather than matter and energy, are the two fundamentals of the universe!"**
John A. Widtsoe, *Rational Theology*, 13

172

"Like the atom's electrons, which vibrate to give off an electrical field, so too does the **human body** produce an oscillation and **energy field** which Bentov refers to as subtle energy. . . . This subtle energy . . . constitutes various layers of human consciousness."

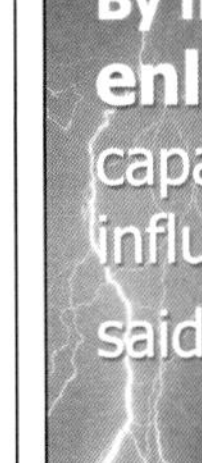

Brian Luke Seaward, ***Managing Stress***, 175
(referring to Itzhak Bentov)

173

"The Spirit of God which emanates from Deity may be likened to electricity, or the universal ether..., which fills the earth and the air, and is everywhere present. It is the power of God ..., By means of this Spirit every man is enlightened, ... each in accordance with his capacity to receive the light; and this Spirit or influence which emanates from God may be said to constitute man's **consciousness."**
Joseph Fielding Smith, *Gospel Doctrine*, 61

174

"It is imperative to understand that your feelings and your thoughts are energy; your FEELINGS and your THOUGHTS are *matter*. And according to what physics has taught us, matter cannot be destroyed. The form of matter CAN be altered, but matter itself is indestructible."

Karol Truman, *Feelings Buried Alive Never Die*, 10, emphasis in original

"There is no such thing as immaterial matter. All spirit is matter. . ."
D&C 131:7

175

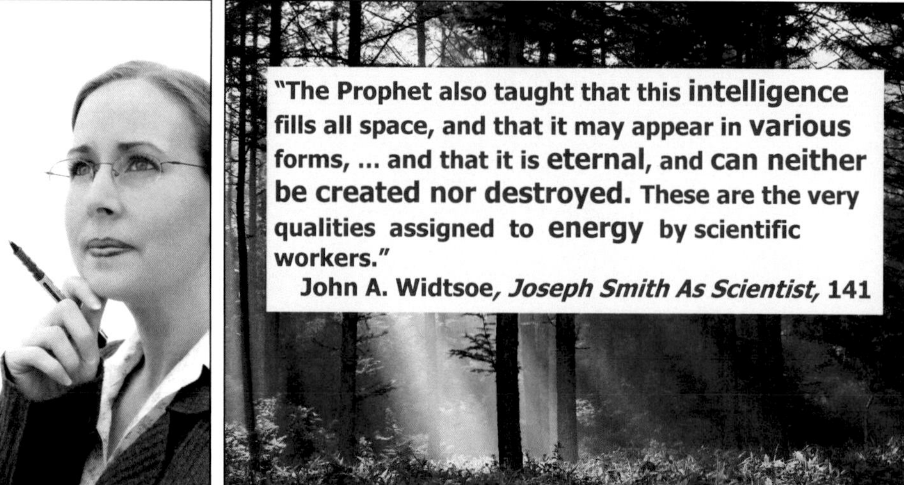

From a Near-death experience:
"I saw how a person's **words** actually **affect the energy field** around him. The very words themselves- the **vibrations** in the air- attract one type of energy or another.... We **create** our surroundings by the thoughts we think. **Physically**, this may take a period of time, but **spiritually**, it is instantaneous. If we understood the awesome power of our words, we would prefer silence to almost anything negative.... We can always replace negative with positive. Because our thoughts **attract this eternal energy,** they are the source of creation. All creation begins in the mind."
Betty J. Eadie, *Embraced by the Light*, 58

177

"Stunning new scientific discoveries about the brain's functioning show that all the cells of your body are affected by your thoughts."
Bruce H. Lipton,
The Biology of Belief,
back cover

"Your biography - that is, the experiences that makeup your life – becomes your biology."
Caroline Myss, Ph.D.
Anatomy of the Spirit, 34

178

**"Every thought, every feeling, every emotion and every belief that we have, has its own vibration! . . . .
All those... have been recorded in the DNA of the cells of your glands, your blood, your lymph system, your organs and your muscles... in your flesh."**

Karol Truman, *Feelings Buried Alive Never Die*, 82

179

"The book of life is the record of the acts of men . . . **written** in their own **bodies.** It is the **record** engraven on the very bones, sinews, and **flesh** of the mortal body. That is every **thought**, **word**, and **deed** has an **effect** on the human body; all these leave their **marks.**"

Bruce R. McConkie, *Mormon Doctrine,* "Book of Life," 97

180

"The thought
in your mind
at this moment
is contributing,
however infinitesimally,
almost imperceptibly
to the shaping of your soul,
even to the lineaments of your countenance . . .
even passing and idle thoughts leave their impression."

Pres. David O. McKay quoted in Spencer W. Kimball, *The Miracle of Forgiveness,* 105

181

"The **show of their countenance**
doth **witness** against them,
and doth **declare** their sin
to be even as Sodom,
and they **cannot hide it.**" 2 Nephi 13:9

"Our bodies can be changed as we retrain our thinking."
Bruce Lipton, *The Biology of Belief*, Inside Front Cover

"A man's wisdom maketh his face to shine." Eccles. 8:1

182

"They [your thoughts] will make you handsomer, young man - more beautiful, young woman - **because your thoughts modify your features**. They may not be the handsomest, but they will **radiate** that which makes handsome young men, and beautiful young women."

David O. McKay, *Treasures of Life*, 402, as quoted in Rex A. Wadham, Dept. of Educ. BYU, "The Nature of Brain Chatter," 5

183

"Directly under the physical world is the dimension of the universal life energy fields in which the aura... exists. This level is the **energetic framework** or grid structure upon which the physical world rests. Everything that is created in the physical world must **first** exist or be created in the world of life energy."

Barbara Brennan, *Light Emerging*, 13

184

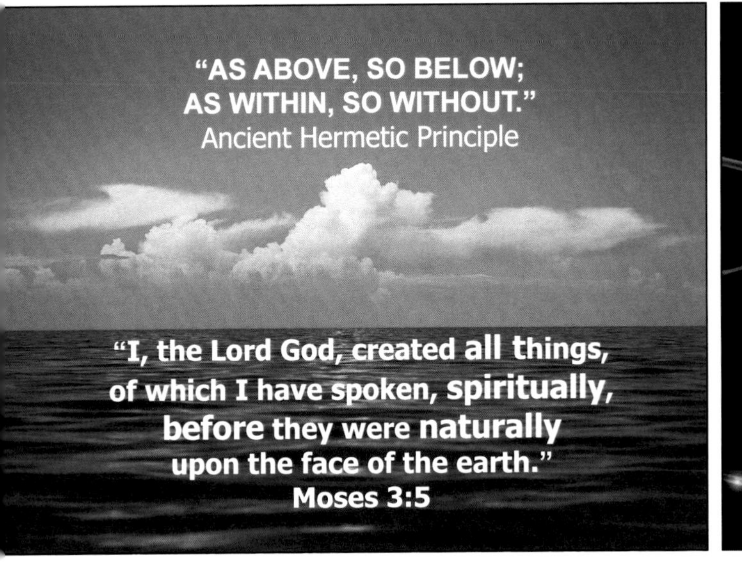

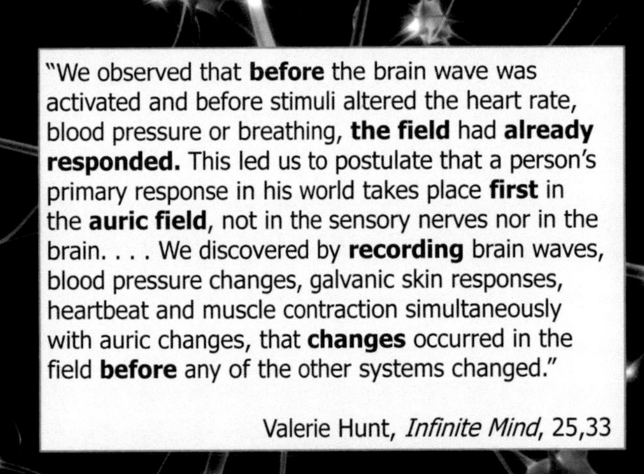

186

"**The holographic model** is **exciting because** it can clarify **why** there **had** to be a **spiritual creation before** a **physical creation**, why we were organized spiritually before physically, and why the world was organized in its spiritual wave form first before it was organized in its physical particle form. All matter, whether animate or inanimate would have been organized the same way."

B. Grant Bishop, *The LDS Gospel of Light,* 203

187

"**Changing energy patterns** *before* they manifest as disease works at a level of cause that is of a **higher order than matter**. . . . Modern research is now giving us an understanding of the **genetic changes** that occur in response to **changes in energy** and **consciousness.** This opens up the prospect of using **consciousness** deliberately, as a **planned** medical **intervention."**

Dawson Church, PhD, *The Genie in Your Genes,* 320

188

"Behavioral kinesiology is the first line of prevention. You **examine your body at an energy level**, long before physical problems develop."

Jerome Mittelman, DDS (quoted below)

"All illness **starts** as a problem on the **energy level**, a problem that may exist for many years before it **manifests** itself in **physical** disease. It appears that a generalized reduction of body energy leads to energy imbalances in particular parts of the body. **If** we **become aware** of these **energy imbalances** when they first occur, we have... primary **prevention**."

John Diamond, MD, *Your Body Doesn't Lie,* 18, 27

189

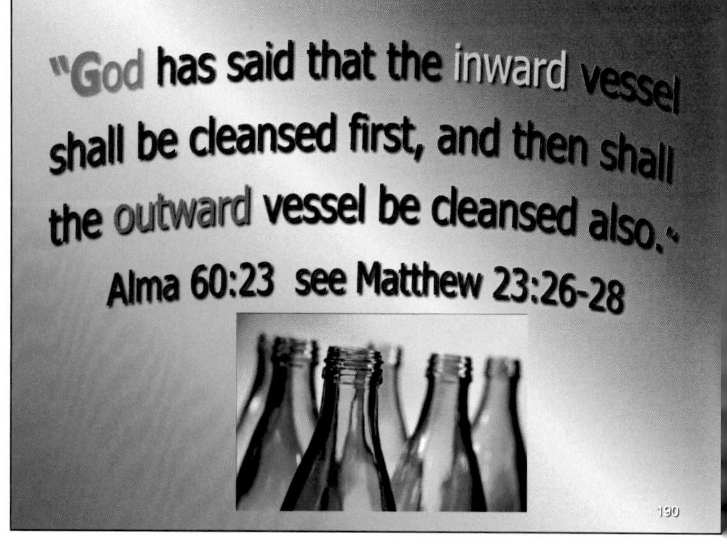

Inward → Outward

"When he saw their faith, he said unto the sick of the palsy, Son, thy sins be forgiven thee. . . . Is it easier to say to the sick of the palsy, Thy sins be forgiven thee; or to say Arise, take up thy bed and walk? . . . And immediately he arose, took up the bed and went forth before them all." Mark 2:5

191

"The Lord works from the inside out. The world works from the outside in. The world would take people out of the slums. Christ takes the slums out of the people, and then they take themselves out of the slums. ... Christ changes men, who then change their environment. The world would shape human behavior, but Christ can change human nature"

Ezra Taft Benson, "Born of God," *Ensign,* Nov. 1985, 6

192

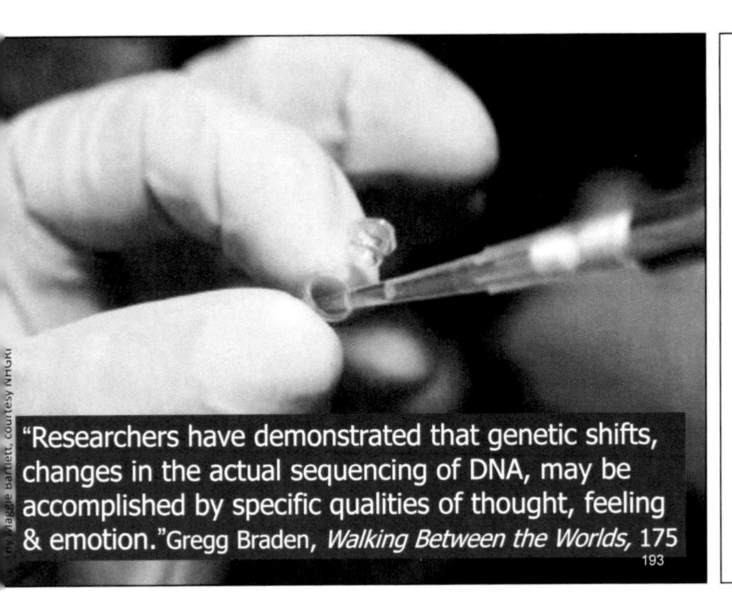

"Researchers have demonstrated that genetic shifts, changes in the actual sequencing of DNA, may be accomplished by specific qualities of thought, feeling & emotion." Gregg Braden, *Walking Between the Worlds,* 175

193

"This is a thought-form universe. A thought - as nearly as can be described - is a globular, encapsulated, magnetized image of anything that can be conceived by mind. It can exist by itself or be related to clusters of thought forms - each contributing their bit to any whole idea of feeling. Without thought forms or mental images, there can be no awareness of being. In the absence of thought forms, there would be no consciousness."

Harold Sherman, *How to Picture What You Want,* 218 as qtd. in Rex Wadham, "The Nature of Brain Chatter," 3

194

"**Thoughts are things.** Your body is in fact a very powerful electromagnetic transmitter and receiver of energy. Every thought you have can have a **powerful impact** on the **cells** in your body. **Positive high vibration** thoughts can **rid** your body of disease. **Negative, stressful, low vibration** thoughts can **give** your body disease."

Kevin Trudeau, *Natural Cures- What* They *Don't Want You to Know,* 109

195

"Every thought that one permits through his mind leaves its trace. **Thoughts are things.** Our lives are governed a great deal by our thoughts." *Teachings of Spencer W. Kimball,* 154

"Faith is the **substance** of things hoped for." Heb. 11:1

196

"If you first gain power to **check your words**, you will then begin to have power to check your judgment, and at length actually gain power to check your **thoughts and reflections**."
Brigham Young, in *Journal of Discourses* 6:98

"That which cometh **out** of the man, that **defileth** the man, for from **within** out of the **heart** of man, proceed **evil thoughts**, ... covetousness, an **evil eye**, ... pride, foolishness. All these evil things come from **within**, and **defile** the man." Mark 7:20-23

197

"You may not think that you can **'talk'** to your DNA..., but in fact, you do continually.... Thinking happens at the level of DNA." Deepak Chopra, *Quantum Healing,* 234

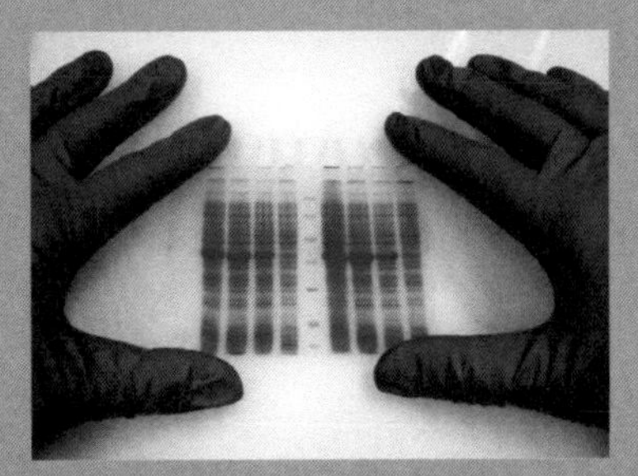

"We **communicate** with the **field** through the language of **emotion**." Gregg Braden, *The Divine Matrix,* xxi

198

"Clients have come to me after having been diagnosed with a condition, saying: 'I am a diabetic',…'I am overweight,' 'I am depressed'… and many other physical mental and emotional ailments. They have taken this diagnosis and **made it** part of their identity. **By saying "I am"** they are **directing** their **body and all its cells,** to **confirm** that this is my identity, so **act accordingly**…. **'I am'** statements are the most powerful expression of telling our bodies what we believe our identity is." Carol Tuttle, *Remembering Wholeness*, 69

199

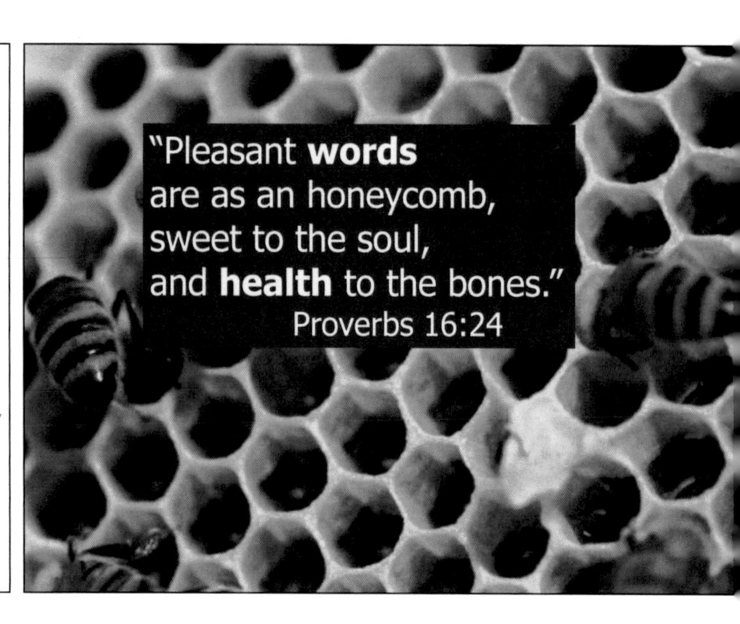

"When a man works by faith he works by **mental exertion** instead of physical force….Faith then, works by **words**."
Joseph Smith,
Lectures on Faith 7:3

"Surely as I have **thought**, so shall it come to pass, and as I have proposed so shall it stand." Isaiah14:24

"Faith is your positive inner self-talk."Carolyn Ringger, *Faith Unpuzzled*,5

201

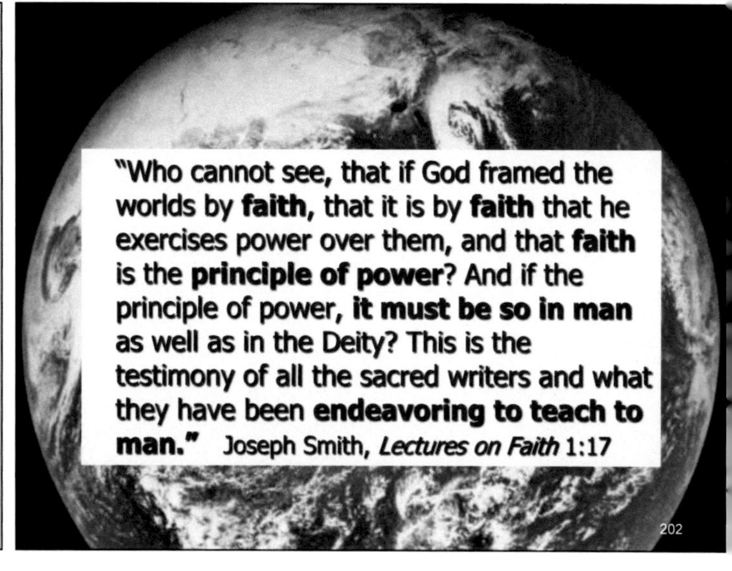

"Sometimes the Elders will get that **faith**, and the sisters will often lay hands on their children and have faith and confidence in themselves that God will answer their ***prayers***, and **say** to fevers and pains, "Be ye **rebuked** and stand far off from this the afflicted," and it is done. But you have to attain to this **power** by your **faithfulness and confidence** in yourselves, that **God will answer** your ***prayers***.
We know that the Lord often heals the sick … but will He because we ask Him to? That is the question, and we are often doubtful about it."
Brigham Young in *Journal of Discourses* 4:284

203

"If you are thinking, feeling or expressing in negativity, you will connect to negative fields of energy that amplify what you are experiencing. You will attract more of the same energy. This is also true if you are expressing positive thoughts and feelings." Sharlene Young, *Clearing Your Twelve Chakras*, 8

"Remove from thee all doubting; And question nothing at all when thou asketh anything of the Lord." 2 Hermas 9:1, *The Lost Books of the Bible*, 221

205

"**Refrain from repeatedly thinking or saying negative words about yourself**. . . . When plagued by the **thought** that you are inadequate, **confidently** say, **"I can do all things through Christ that strengtheneth me."** (Philippians 4:13) . . . **Avoid** wasting time and energy reliving the past."

Elder Anthony D. Perkins, *Ensign*, Nov 2006, 77

206

"A **double minded** man is unstable in all his ways." James 1:8

"Sanctify yourselves that your mind**s** become single to God." D&C 88:68

"If we FEEL in our heart that we are not worthy of something we THINK in our brain that we want in our life, we will generally not receive it. We may THINK in our brain we are not worthy, but unknowingly FEEL in our heart that we are. In this case, what we are FEELING will win. (John 16:33 see D&C 50:41). . . . After we align the **THINKING** and the **FEELING** so they are the **same**, we become **single-minded**." Karol Truman, *Feelings Buried Alive Never Die*, 57-58

"Answers often come immediately when we are **single-minde**d in our requests. This explains why some people receive answers to prayer and others do not. The people who receive answers are single-minded. They not only THINK God will answer, they FEEL He will answer, which adds up to KNOWING. Everyone who asks **with the heart** gets answers. Being able to do this unlocks an unlimited force in our life!"

Karol Truman, *Feelings Buried Alive Never Die,* 57-58

208

"When I administer to somebody, I say, "Father, bless this person," and probably it is my fault that I say it that way for not being in tune as much as I should be. . . . Because, if I were fully in tune and had the spirit of inspiration I would do what Peter did. I would stand in the place of Christ and act as though I were Christ, because I am his agent and have his authority. . . .

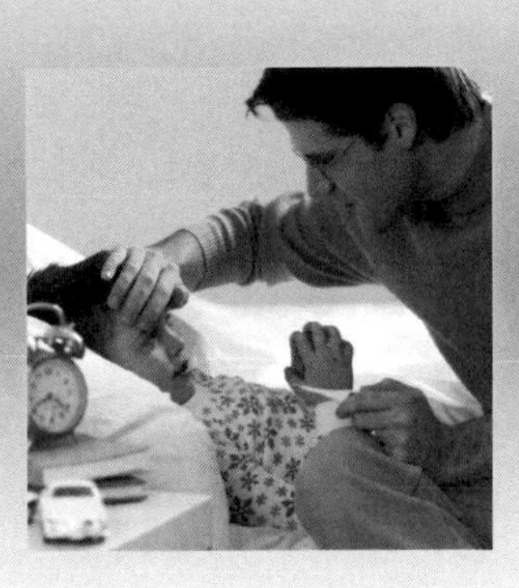

209

"The best administrations are those where you say, "I rebuke the disease," "I command the organs of your body to function," "I say unto you, in Christ's name, rise up." Ordinarily you do both of them in an administration, and pray, because you are struggling and trying to figure out what to do. So you pray over him, and try to get in the mood to get the inspiration and learn what ought to be said directly."

Dennis Horne, *Faith to Heal and To Be Healed, 184-5*

210

"Thirty-six natives came to the mission home... all relatives and said they all wanted a **blessing**. I said "That is quite a job..." They answered, 'We don't want you to put your hands on us– **just stand up in front of us**," the spokesman said. 'Many years and generations ago one of the chiefs put a curse on our family, and every generation since someone would produce a leper, & the last one in the last few days has been taken off to the leper colony. We want you to stand up & **rebuke that curse** & take away that leprosy.' There was no doubt in my mind when those people spoke. I blessed them and **commanded** the power of God to **cleanse** that family of that **curse**; and I know as well as I am standing here there will never be another leper in that family."

Henry A. Smith, *Matthew Cowley- Man of Faith*, 140

211

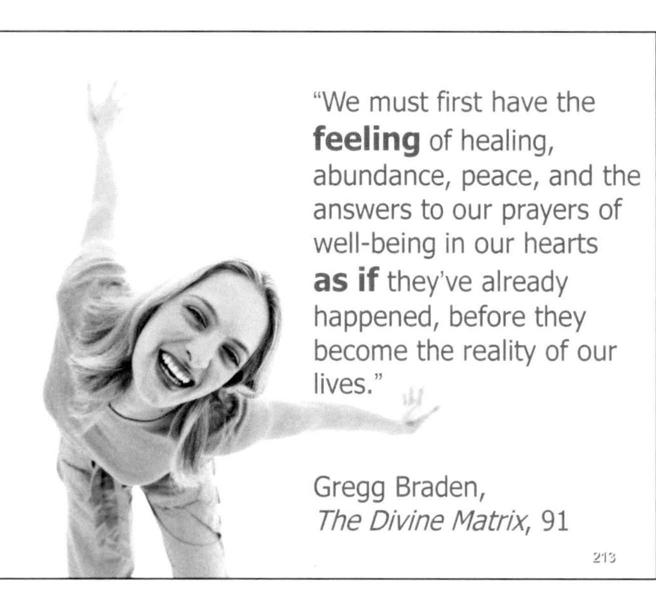

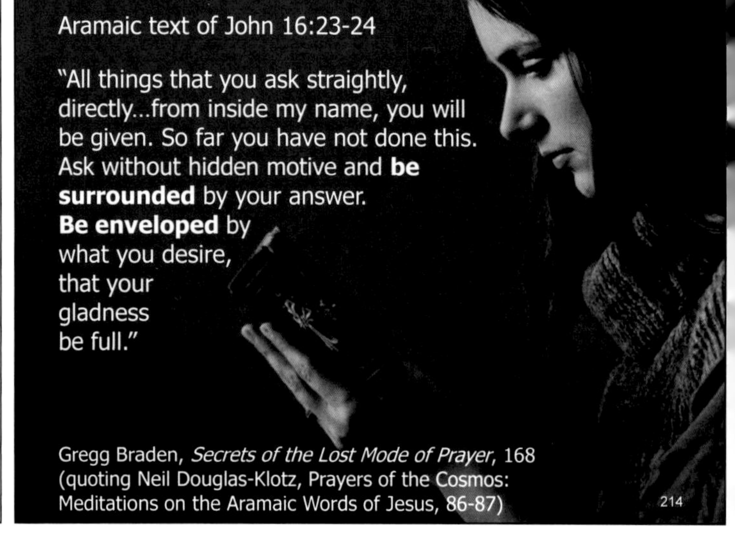

An example:

By Carl Bloch

"Then they took away the stone from the place where the dead was laid.
And Jesus lifted up his eyes, and said,
Father, I thank thee that thou hast heard me.
And I knew that thou hearest me always...
And when he had thus spoken,
he cried with a loud voice, "Lazarus come forth.
And he that was dead came forth." John 11:41-44

215

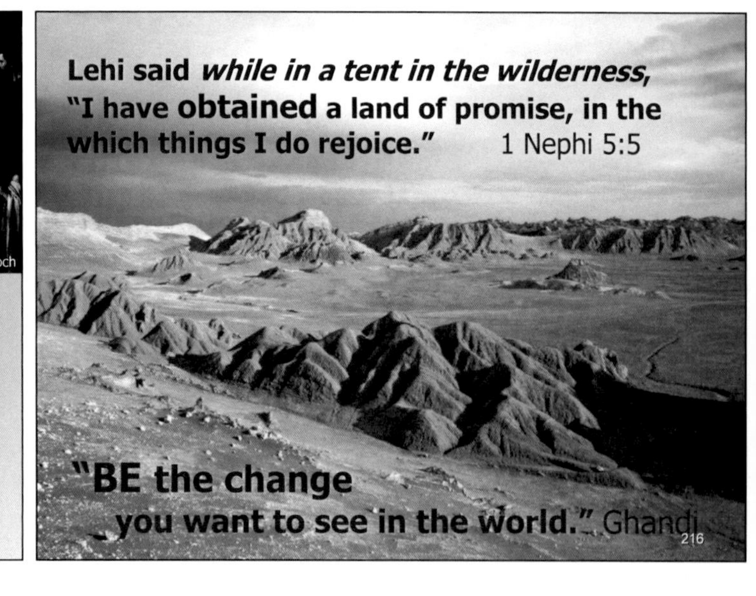

"**Consciousness** creates reality... **Expectation** decisively influences outcome... **Awareness, attention, and intention** should be as much a part of **health care** as drugs, radiation and surgery."

Deepak Chopra, *Quantum Healing*, preface

217

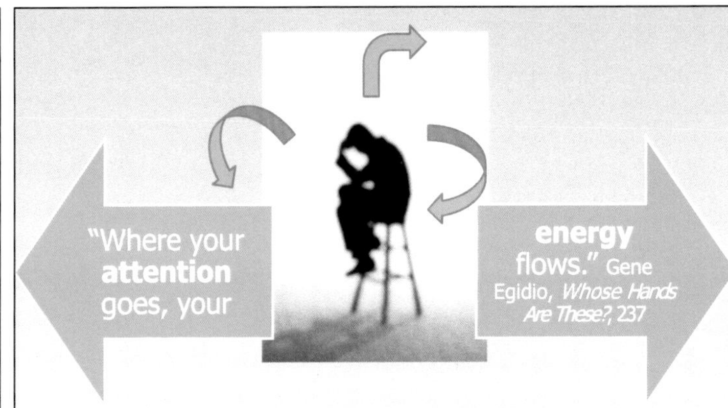

"It can be very self-instructive to listen carefully to what we are **thinking** and what we are **saying**. When emotions, judgments and discouragement are allowed to govern our thoughts, our bodies reflect the results." Stan Gardner, M.D., "Thinking Ourselves to Better Health," Meridian Magazine

218

"**I wasn't questioning my thinking. I believed everything I thought.** . . . It was very deep mental illness. Since then I've come to see that **anyone who doesn't question their thoughts** is suffering from mental illness. No one has to suffer that kind of pain when life can be so simple." quoting Byron Katie in "Truth Seeker," Pacific Sun, May 22-28, 2002

"**The Work** is simply four questions that, when applied to a specific problem, enable you to see what is troubling you in an entirely different light. As Katie says, "It's not the problem that causes our suffering; it's *our thinking* about the problem." . . . "**Suffering is optional**." . . . After doing **The Work**, many people report an immediate sense of release and freedom from **thoughts** that were making them miserable." Byron Katie with Stephen Mitchell, *Loving What Is*, inside front cover, x, xiii

219

"In its most basic form, The Work consists of **4 questions and your turnarounds**. For example, your statement might be '[Name] doesn't listen to me.' Find someone in your life about whom you have had that thought, take that statement and put it up against the four questions and turnarounds of **The Work.**

1. **Is it true?**
2. **Can you absolutely know that it's true?**
3. **How do you react, what happens, when you believe that thought?**
4. **Who would you be without the thought?**

Turn around the concept you are questioning, and be sure to find at least three genuine, specific examples of each turnaround." Byron Katie, thework.com

220

"Studies have shown that the patient's **mental images** have a direct effect on the functioning of the **immune system.** One study demonstrated that cancer patients who used relaxation techniques, as well as their **creative imagination**, could stimulate lymphocyte production and enhance the activity of their natural killer (NK) cells, both of which play active roles in the body's destruction of cancer cells."

Susan Wagner, MD, *A Doctor's Guide to Therapeutic Touch*, 40

221

"**Attention creates connection**. When you allow your mind, consciously or unconsciously, to experience energy and information, this process promotes connections not only within your body, but between your body and the environment."
Gary E. R. Schwartz,
quoted in Dr. Eric Pearl,
The Reconnection, xv

"**Energy moves by intention.**"
Carolyn Cooper,
LDS Holistic Living Conf. 2011

"On the subatomic level of the particle, sometimes we cannot find the mass and particles seem essentially empty. We find only a wave of energy without dense form. **At the quantum level** of **matter, things don't exist until they are observed.** Probably both the wave and particle concepts are essential to represent reality fully." Valerie Hunt, *Infinite Mind*, 41

"And the Gods **saw** that they were obeyed ...and the Gods **watched** those **things which they had ordered until** they obeyed." Abr. 4:10,18(12, 21...)

223

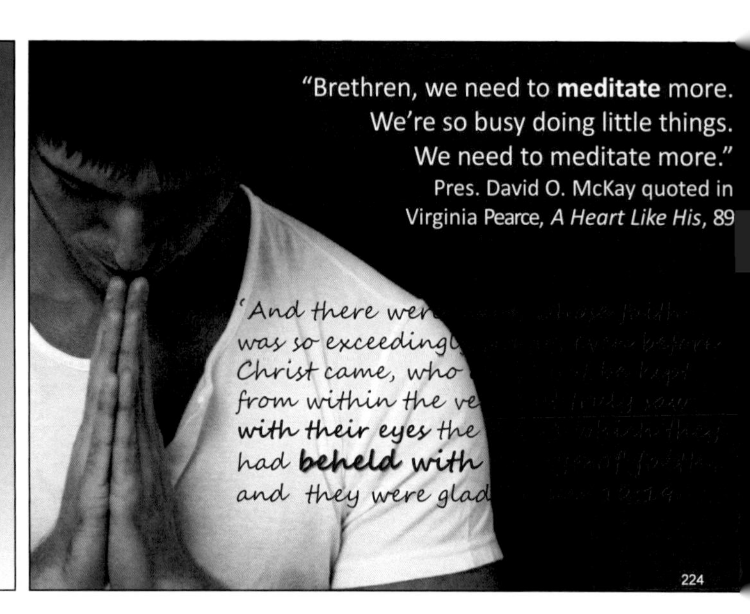

"The understanding that **consciousness affects matter** through the function of life-force would have a profound impact."
Richard Gordon, *Quantum-Touch*, 204

"The act of focusing our consciousness is an act of creation. Consciousness creates!"
Gregg Braden, *The Divine Matrix*, 62

225

"From the implicate order of creation, Primal **Light** manifests into electricity and Primal **Sound** manifests into magnetism creating a dynamic enfoldment of Infinite energy patterns that can oscillate into and out of the dimension of Space-time reality.

From the potential field of **thought** into the manifest field of Creation, **consciousness creates** and connects all matter with unconditional love, "
Dr. Sari Suttka, Layers of Light Leadership Retreat, Park City, UT, Mar. 2006

226

"Be ye transformed by the renewing of your mind."

Romans 12:2

"...View **faith** [not only] as a thought or feeling, but also a **power** with which we can control or even **change** the **circumstances** of this world."
F. Enzio Busche, *Yearning for the Living God*, 268
(see Ether 12:14, Mosiah 27:14)

227

"**Human emotion** determines the actual patterning of **DNA** within our bodies. DNA determines how patterns of light (matter) surround our bodies. . . . The arrangement of matter (atoms, bacteria, viruses,

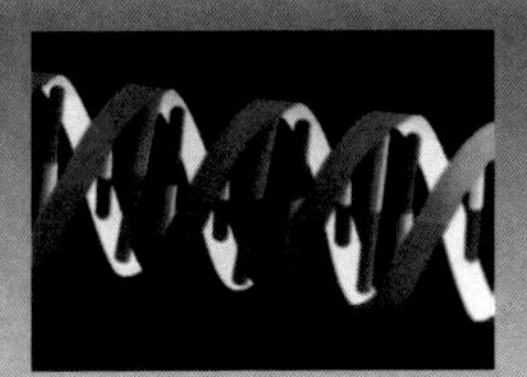

climate, even other people) surrounding your body, is directly linked to the **feeling** and **emotion** from within your body."

Gregg Braden, *Walking Between the Worlds*, 161

229

"What you may not realize is that when negative feelings are not resolved as they occur, these feelings remain very much alive in your physical energy field (body) and these feelings affect each day of your life. In other words, unresolved FEELINGS BURIED ALIVE NEVER DIE!"

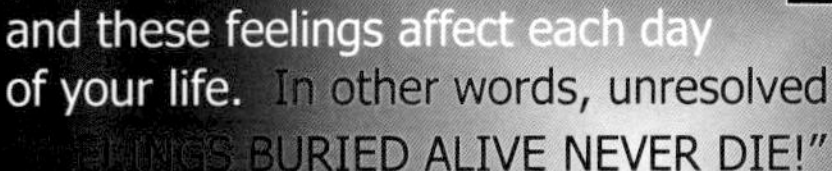

Karol Truman, *Feelings Buried Alive Never Die*, 2

"Do not let any of us imagine that we . . . lose in the grave all our sins and evil tendencies. They will be with us. They will be **with the spirit** when separated from the body."
Elder Melvin J. Ballard, "*Three Degrees of Glory,*" 14

230

Dr. Brian Luke Seaward:

"The body becomes the battlefield for the war games of the mind. All the unresolved thoughts and emotions, the negativity we hold on to, shows up in the body and makes us sick."
As quoted in Candace Pert, *Molecules of Emotion*, 306

". . . Strong emotions that are not processed thoroughly are **stored at the cellular level**." Candace Pert, 290

231

"**Emotions** that we have not faced, **accepted** nor **dealt with** are **stored** as repressed emotional energy, waiting for a future time when we can learn from them. . . Since they are **filed in our bodies** in places of which our conscious mind is not aware, they keep us reminded of their **existence** in a variety of negative ways. They can **cause** pain, illness, disease, & malfunctions on any and all levels- physical, mental, social, emotional and spiritual."

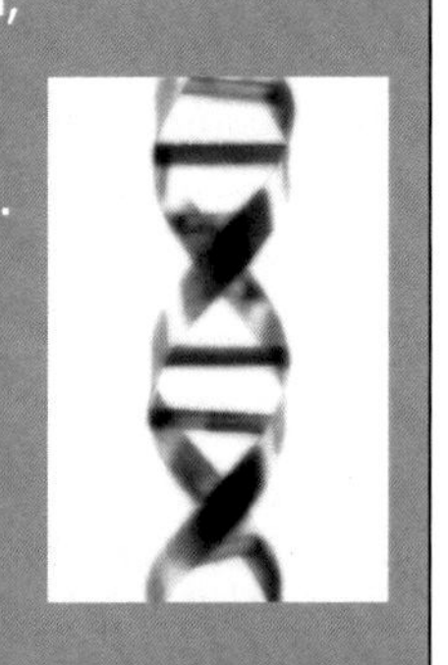

David Stewart, PhD,
Healing Oils of the Bible, 116-117

232

"The body is the unconscious mind! Repressed traumas caused by *overwhelming emotion* can be *stored* in a body part, thereafter affecting our ability to feel that part or even move it." Candace Pert, *Molecules of Emotion*, 141

"Most everyone understands that symptoms such as ulcers and high blood pressure can be related to stress. Few people are aware that a **knee pain** or **shoulder pain may also be stress induced,** or possibly related to diet. Even fewer know that ulcers, high blood pressure [or pain] **may be due** to a **memory** of a past experience or a **feeling** that their bodies have been **programmed to respond to."** Dr. Bradley R. Wilde, *The Safe Box of Health*, iv

233

"**What is one of the most common causes of illness** which is not only invisible, but is something that has gone completely undiscovered by the medical profession? . . .

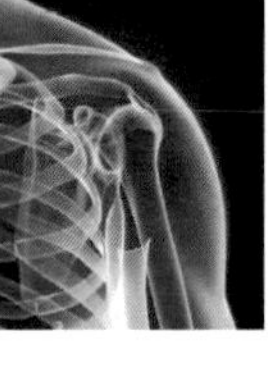

Trapped Emotions. . . . When you experience an intense negative emotion, such as anger during an argument, or a deep feeling of depression or sadness, the "energy" of that emotion may become "trapped" in the body, creating **physical** symptoms that range from aches and pains to cancer, and **creating self-sabotage** and **all manner of relationship difficulties**. In many years of clinical practice, I found that these trapped emotional energies

234

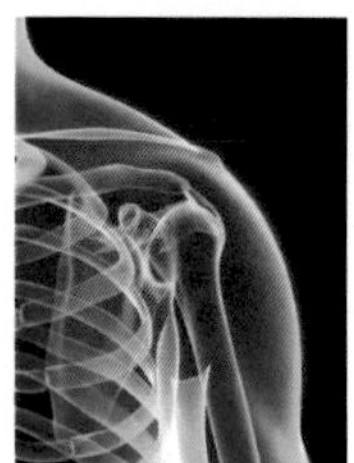

were present in every disease process, in every person I treated. Oftentimes, the **trapped emotions** people had were the major, and sometimes the ONLY underlying cause of their **physical** symptoms, and they are ALWAYS present in **any kind of emotional problem or relationship issue.** Trapped Emotions are an epidemic that is unseen and unknown."

"The release of trapped emotions have consistently helped patients to overcome depression."

Dr. Bradley Nelson, e-mail message and *The Emotion Code*, 115

235

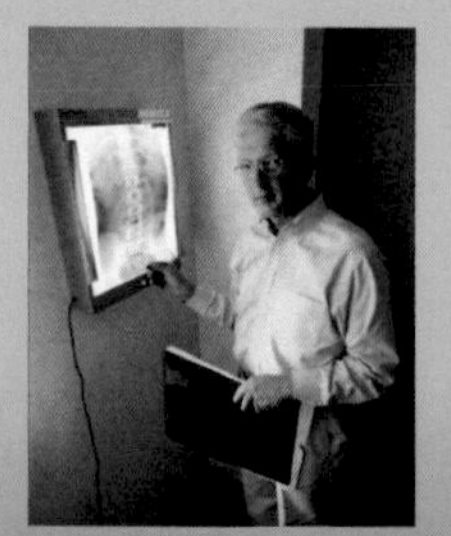

"Our **bodies** will let us know when we are out of balance. A **physical** imbalance is a message that there are **emotional and mental disharmonies** that need to **be cleared**. If you only try to fix the **physical body** without **clearing** the more **subtle disharmonies**, they will continue to reside & grow within you and manifest in another **physical disease**."

Carol Tuttle, *Remembering Wholeness*, 69

236

"The symptoms in the body are often the only way that our soul can get our attention. Covering up our symptoms with external 'cures' prevents us from healing the parts of our lives that need attention & change."

Christiane Northrup, M.D.

***Women's Bodies Women's Wisdom*, 45**

237

"If you are driving your car, and your oil light goes on, you wouldn't say:

'My oil light is on. I need to get my oil light to go off. I know what I'll do. I'll unscrew the bulb! Ah! The oil light is no longer illuminated.'

You haven't solved the problem have you?

You got rid of the symptom."

Kevin Trudeau, *Natural Cures* They *Don't Want You To Know About*, 112

238

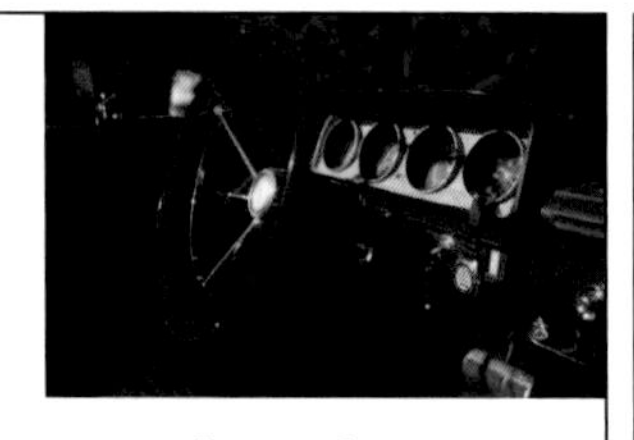

"Symptoms are messengers to get our attention that a problem exists so we can deal with it. Allopaths mistake the messenger for the problem. Instead of trying to interpret the messenger and address the root of the problem, they kill the messenger."

David Stewart, PhD, *Healing Oils of the Bible*, 45-46

239

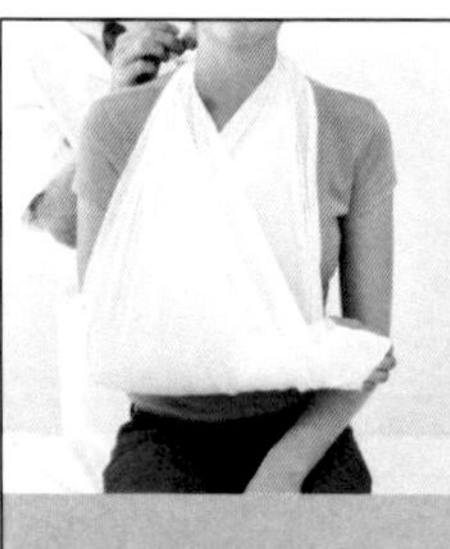

"When symptoms are suppressed the [depressed] patient may act and feel more normal. But the underlying brain rhythms are unaffected. Antidepressant drugs are masking their symptoms without removing them. This is like taking a painkiller when you have a broken arm. You might feel better, but your underlying condition remains unchanged."

Dawson Church, *The Genie in Your Genes*, 232, emphasis in original

240

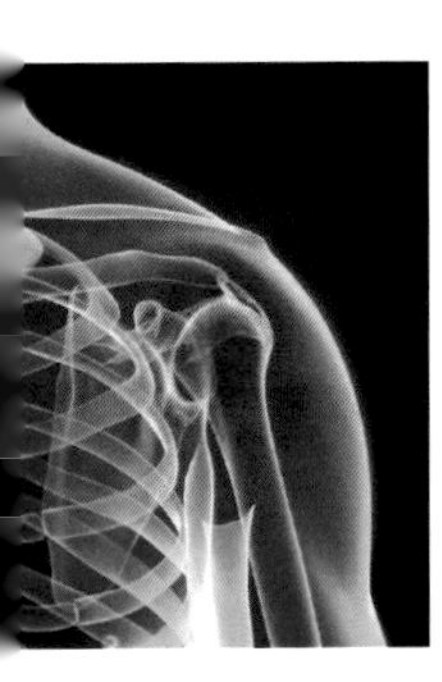

"Now that I know my body has **wisdom**, this calls for a new kind of **responsibility**. I can no longer act like a dumb machine and wait to be fixed by the mechanic - otherwise known as the doctor. I have the potential to **consciously** intervene in the system myself, to take an **active** role in my own healing. I'm both more powerful and more responsible in creating the health I experience than the dumb machine I used to think I was."

Candace Pert, *Molecules of Emotion*, 262

241

"It is this problem of unhealed feeling, the accumulation of bruised and broken emotions, that most people stagger under without ever saying a word, that the mainstream medical model is least effective in dealing with. . . . I believe the complementary therapies are a form of professional help much less likely to do harm and more likely to do good than conventional approaches."

Dr. Candace Pert,

Molecules of Emotion, 265, 323

242

"**The emotions** exist in the body as informational chemicals... They also exist in another realm, the one we experience as feeling, inspiration, love - beyond the physical. The **emotions** move back and forth, flowing freely between both places, and, in that sense, **they connect** the physical and nonphysical. **Perhaps** this is the **same thing** that Eastern healers call the **subtle energy**, or **prana - the circulation of emotional and spiritual information** throughout the bodymind."

Candace Pert, Molecules of Emotion, 307

243

"**Spirit** is **intelligence,** or the light of truth that filleth all things. Its several **emotions** or affections such as love, joy, etc., are but so many **actions** or motions of these elements... By these **actions or emotions** the **elements manifest** their eternal **energies, attributes** or **inherent powers.** . . . [Space, time, element or intelligence] constitute the energies which act and the things acted upon."

Parley P. Pratt, *Key to the Science of Theology*, 45

244

"**Emotions** rising up during Quantum-Touch sessions are not uncommon. I find it fascinating how the specific emotions that bring on cathartic experiences seem to consistently be the emotions that had **been suppressed, oppressed or repressed.** So often, the act of courageously allowing these emotions to be fully experienced is exactly what is necessary for relieving or transforming **physical** conditions. I'm convinced that the biggest human blockage is the unwillingness to fully experience the intensity of our emotions."

Richard Gordon, *Quantum-Touch*, 183

"Dr. [Geerd]Hamer found that all disease originates from emotions, which creates noticeable changes in your brain in areas corresponding with the afflicted area of your body."

Dr. Joseph Mercola, mercola.com

245

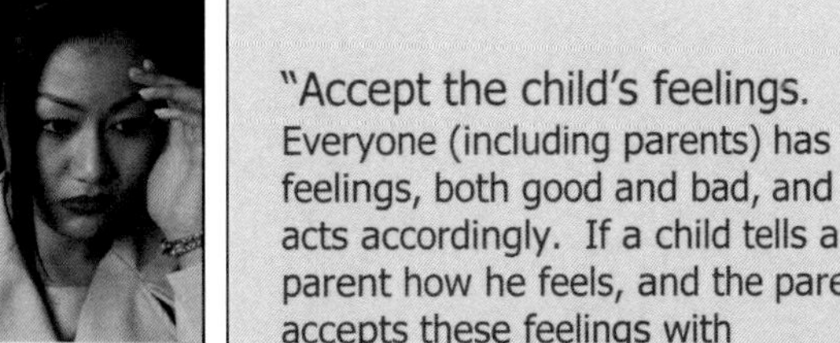

"Accept the child's feelings. Everyone (including parents) has feelings, both good and bad, and acts accordingly. If a child tells a parent how he feels, and the parent accepts these feelings with understanding, without condemning the child for having them, the parent has successfully passed the first step in helping the child change a negative feeling to a positive one. Rebuking the child for his feeling of resentment, telling him how wrong it is to feel that way, what a good person the brother or sister is - - these reactions will not change his resentment to love for the other child. Rather, it will probably make the situation worse."

"Attack the Problem Not the Child," *Family Home Evening-Love Makes Our House a Home*, 221

246

"Trapped emotional energy will always lodge somewhere in the physical body, and the body tissues that lie within that sphere will tend to fall into **resonance** with the **vibrational energy** of the trapped emotion. In other words, **those tissues will actually be experiencing that emotional vibration on a continual basis. Suppose you have a trapped emotion of anger.** You've carried it around for years, not even knowing it was there. As a result, **whenever you come into a situation where you *could* become angry, it's much more likely that you *will* become angry, because in a fascinating and literal way, part of you is *already* angry."**

Dr. Bradley Nelson, *The Emotion Code*, 5

247

Scriptures refer to our 'hearts' and 'inward parts' as 'tables of flesh' that are **written** on.
Jesus speaks of 'storing' emotion in the body:
"Bring them hither and I will heal them for I have compassion upon you; my **bowels** are **filled with mercy**." 3 Nephi 17:7
"Put on therefore, as the elect of God . . . **bowels** of mercies, kindness, humbleness of mind, meekness . . ." Col. 3:12
"Your **inward part** is full of ravening" (greed) Luke 11:39

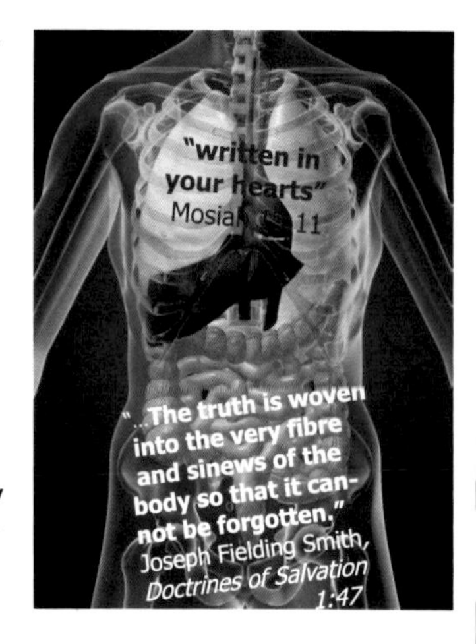

248

"The **mental thought patterns** that **cause** the most **disease** in the body are **criticism, anger, resentment and guilt...**
Criticism... will often lead to diseases such as arthritis. Anger turns into things that boil and burn and infect the body. Resentment long-held festers and eats away at the self and ... can lead to tumors and cancer. Guilt always seeks punishment and leads to pain."
Louise Hay, *Heal Your Body*, 7
(uses forgiveness statements)

"Anger is a **thought** sin."
Spencer W. Kimball,
The Miracle of Forgiveness, 112

249

"It is so much easier to **release** these negative **emotional** and **mental patterns** with the **clearing technologies** and **healing arts** we have available to us today, when we are healthy, than to wait until we are in a physical crisis and our body has deteriorated considerably." Carol Tuttle, *Remembering Wholeness*, 68-69

250

"In the Indian worldview, pranic flow responds to an individual's **thoughts** and **emotions.** Positive thoughts and emotions **increase** the **amount** of **prana** available to the body, which in turn improves **physical** health. Maintaining **psychological** health, therefore, becomes an important way to promote **physical** health." Susan Wagner, M.D.,
A Doctor's Guide to Therapeutic Touch, 12

251

Level
Enlightenment 1000

	Level	
P	Peace	Constructive ↑
O	Joy	
W	Love	
E	Reason	
R	Acceptance	
	Willingness	
v	Neutrality	
s	Courage 200	
	Pride	← Destructive ↓
F	Anger	
O	Desire	
R	Fear	
C	Grief	
E	Apathy	
	Guilt	
	Shame 20	

Dr. David R. Hawkins'

Map of Consciousness

from 20 years of investigation.

"All attitudes, thoughts, feelings, associations, entities, or historical figures below [200] make a person go **weak**- those that calibrate higher make subjects go **strong**."

© David Hawkins, PhD,
Power Vs. Force, 68-70

252

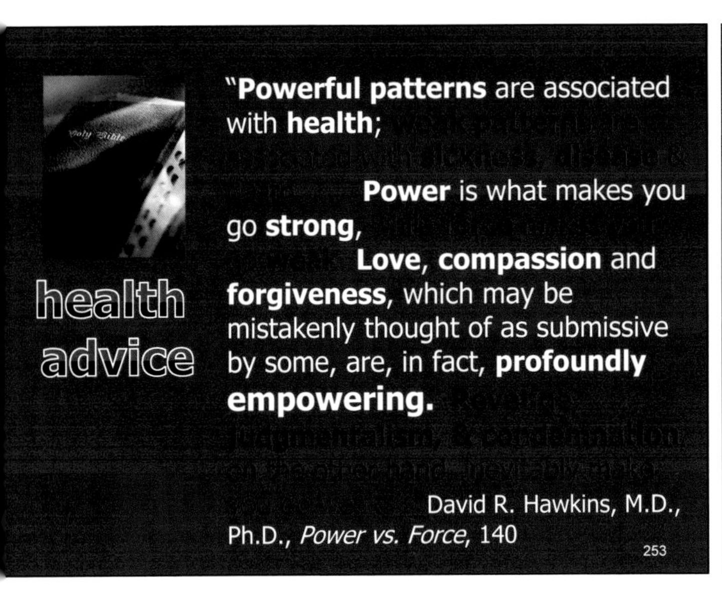

"We are not warranted in assuming that all bodily ills are the result of culpable sin; and against such a conception stands the Lord's **combined instruction and rebuke** to those who, in the case of a man born blind, asked who had sinned, the man or his parents to bring so grievous an affliction upon him, to which inquiry our Lord replied that the man's blindness was due neither to his own sin nor to that of his parents. In many instances, however, disease is the direct result of individual sin." James E. Talmage, *Jesus the Christ, 192*

254

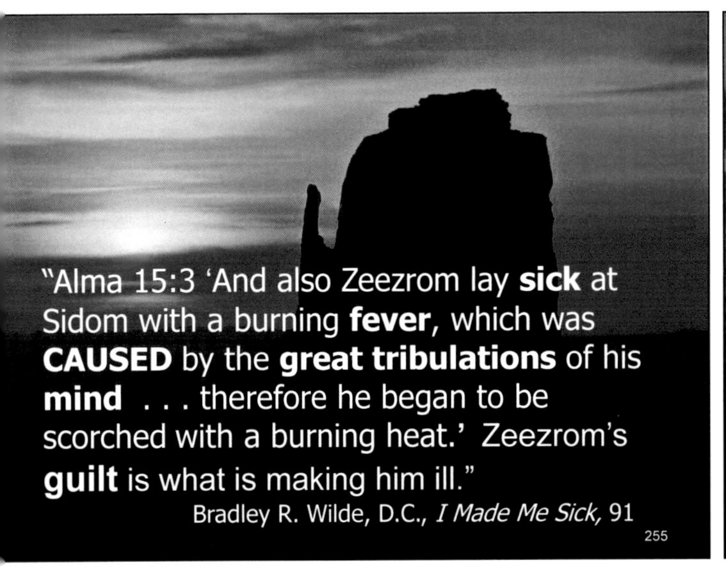

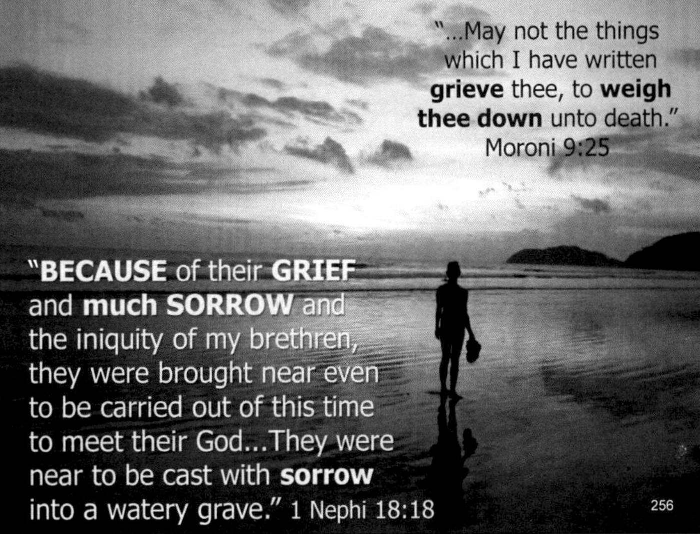

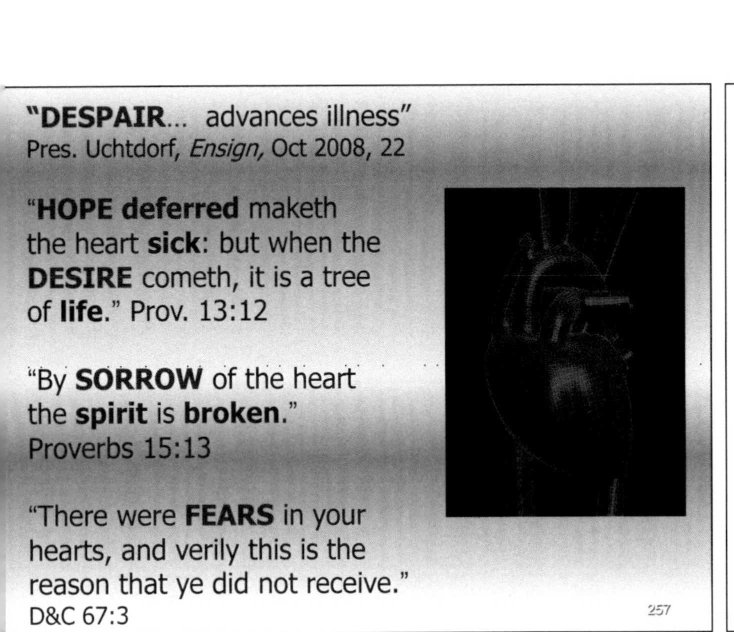

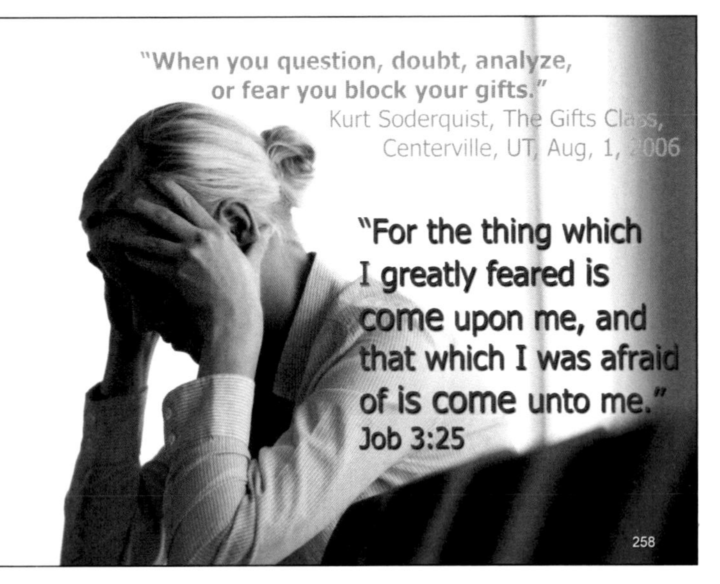

"**Doubt** and **faith** do not exist in the same person at the same time"
Joseph Smith, *Lectures on Faith* 6:12

"'Let not your heart be troubled, neither let it be afraid.' (John14:27) I submit to you, that may be one of the Savior's commandments that is ... almost universally disobeyed.
Jeffrey R. Holland, "Come Unto Me," April1998 *Ensign*

259

"How often have we sealed blessings of health and life upon our children and companions in the name of Jesus Christ and by the authority of the Holy Priesthood of the Son of God, and yet our **faith and prayers** did not succeed in accomplishing the desires of our hearts. **Why is this?** In many instances our **anxiety is so great** that we do not pause to know the spirit of revelation. . . . **We have anxiety instead of faith.**"
Brigham Young in *Journal of Discourses* 12:125

260

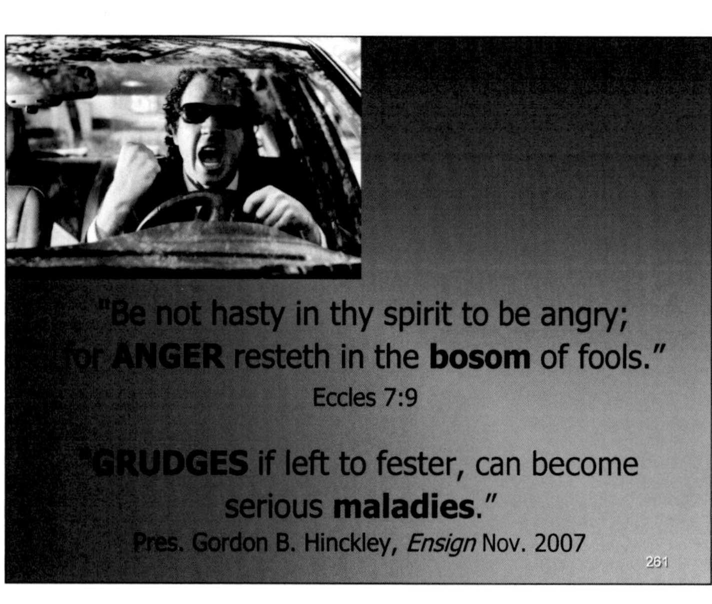

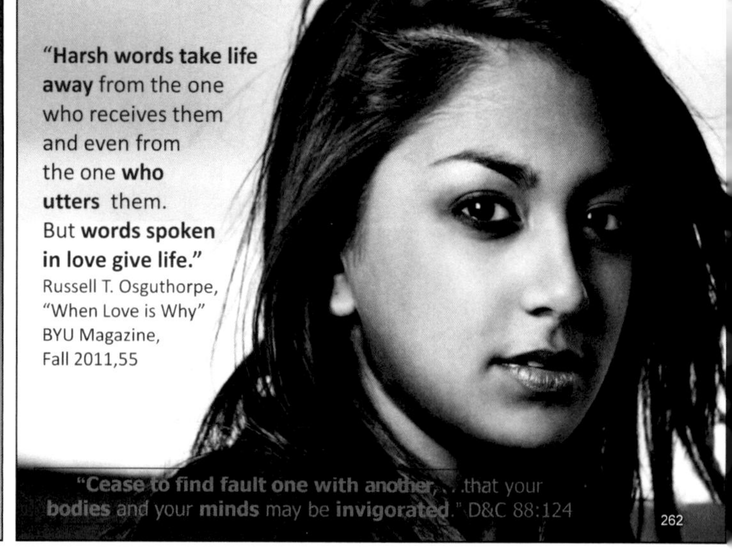

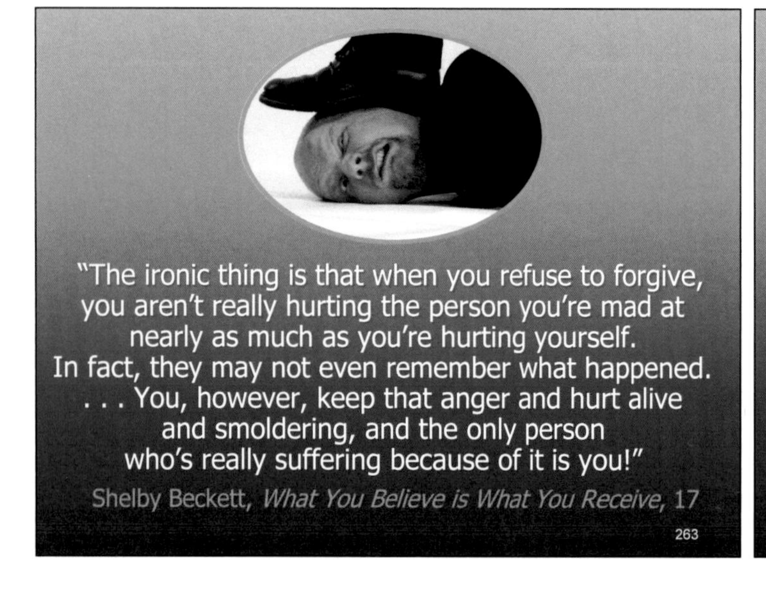

"Forgiveness is not approving or judging.
It is allowing the offender the free agency to be less than perfect and letting the Lord be his judge.
Forgiveness **releases us** from the hurt, anger or pain that is associated with the offense we feel."

Dr. Jan Graf, booklet "Graf Stress Management", 23

264

"Dr. Sidney Simon . . . [said] '**Forgiveness** is freeing up and putting to better use the energy once consumed by holding grudges, harboring resentments, and nursing unhealed wounds.' . . . Some recent studies show that people who are taught to forgive become 'less angry, more hopeful, less depressed, less anxious and less stressed,' which **leads to greater physical well being**. . . . **Only as we rid ourselves** of hatred and bitterness **can the Lord put comfort** into our hearts. . . . With all my heart and soul, I believe in the **healing power** that can come to us as we follow the counsel of the Savior "to forgive all men."

Pres. James E. Faust,
"The Healing Power of Forgiveness," *Ensign*, May 2007

265

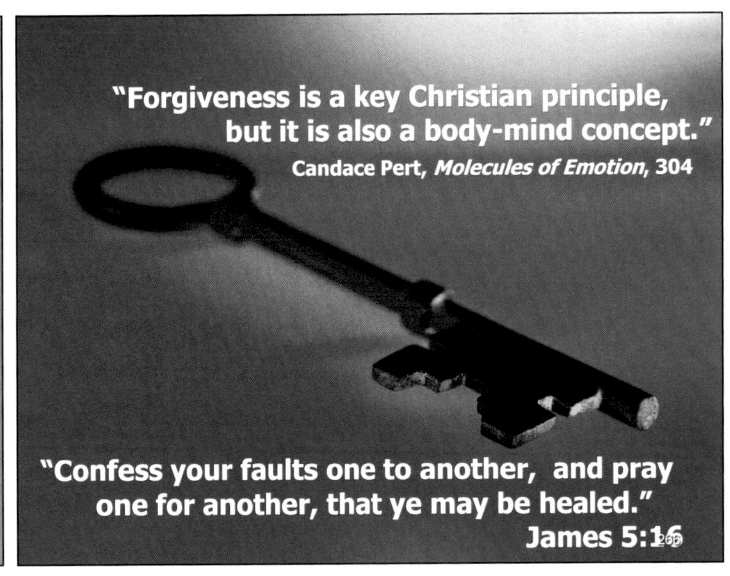

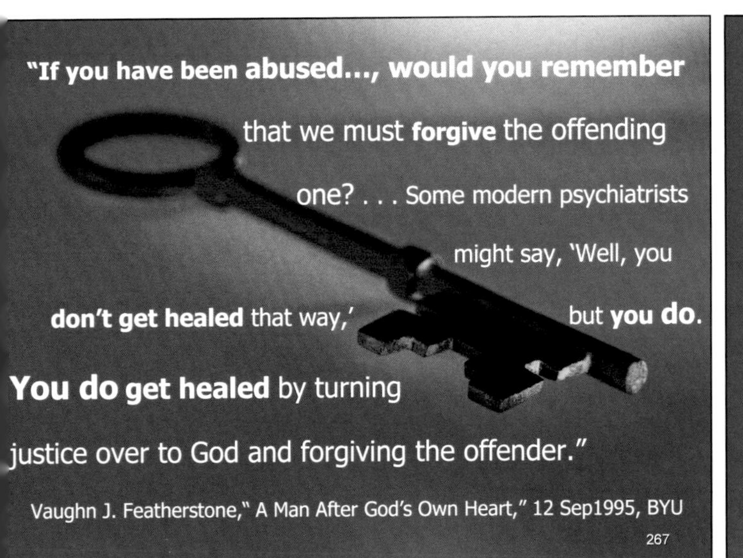

"There are 4 steps to forgiveness.

1. Forgive out loud [to yourself] to be more affective.
2. Be specific as to who you are forgiving and what you are forgiving them for.
3. Use present tense, 'I forgive' rather than 'I *can*, I *will*, I'd *like* to, I *should* or I *need* to forgive.'
4. Be sincere and live the '70 Times 7 Principle.'"

Dr. Jan Graf; Homework handout & notes; Centerville, UT; Dec. 3, 2011

268

70 Times 7 Principle

"Peter asked Jesus, 'Lord, how oft shall my brother sin against me and I forgive him? Till seven times?'
. . . Jesus saith unto him, 'I say not unto thee, until 7 times but until 70 times 7.'

Realize, this is not 490 offenses, but rather one offense **thought about** 490 times.
I believe Christ was telling Peter and us, if we could forgive and forget we could do it in one time, but he knows we have fantastic memories and we wouldn't forget. . . .

Each time we think of the hurt or guilt, we must forgive again."

Jan Graf, "Graf Stress Management" booklet, 25

269

"No matter how justified we may seem to be in our hatred of someone who has harmed us or a loved one, **it is the nature of the energy that passes through *us* that determines the pace of our healing.** We were not responsible for the original assault, but we nevertheless experience the consequences of continuing to process the event in negative ways. . . . **Any victim, though innocent of the initial violence, does violence to herself as she visits and revisits the experience, hurting herself with blame, resentment, self-hatred, and hatred for others."**

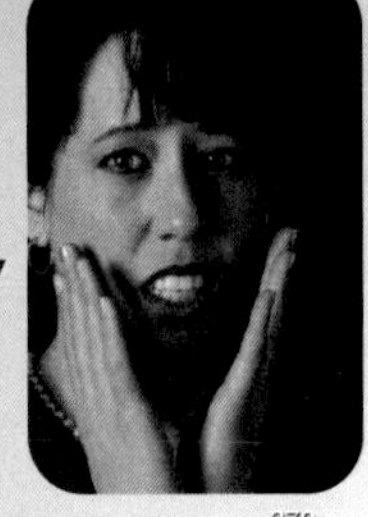

M. Catherine Thomas, *Light in the Wilderness*, 191

270

"Our own science has demonstrated that your **DNA** is directly tied to your ability to **forgive**, **allow** and **love**. . . . Scientific research has shown that as we change the way we **feel** about what's happened to us in our **past**, we change the chemistry of our **bodies** in the **present**."

Gregg Braden,
Walking Between the Worlds,
161, 164

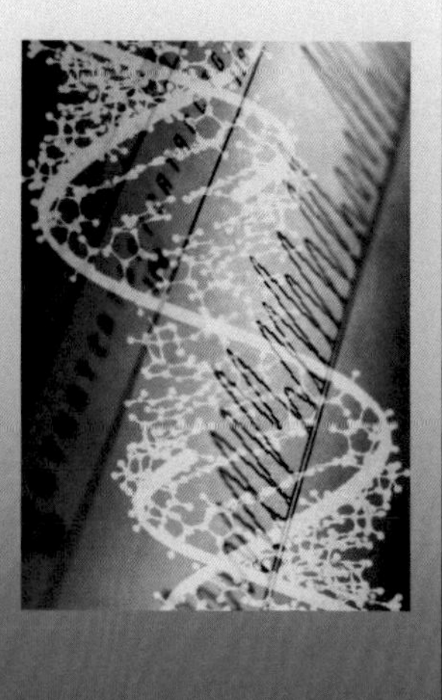

271

"The Savior's atonement is portrayed as the **healing power** not only for sin, but also for **carelessness, inadequacy,** and **all mortal bitterness.** The Atonement is not just for sinners. . . . We may view the Atonement too narrowly in our own lives."
Elder Bruce C. Hafen, "Beauty for Ashes," *Ensign*, Apr 1990, 7

272

"Commune with the Lord. . . . He is your best friend! He knows your pain because He has felt it for you already. He is ready to carry that burden. Trust him enough to place it at His feet and allow Him to carry it for you. Then you can have your anguish replaced with His peace in the very depths of your soul." Dallin H. Oaks, "He Heals the Heavy Laden" *Ensign* Nov 2006, 8

Sermon on the Mount by Carl Bloch

"**Praise be to Jesus** for bearing the **sins** and **pains** of all the family of Adam." Neal A. Maxwell, "Take Especial Care of Your Family," *Ensign,* May 1994

273

by John Bridges wikimedia commons

"And he shall go forth, suffering pains and afflictions and temptations of every kind; and this that the word might be fulfilled which saith he will take upon him the pains **and the sicknesses** of his people." Alma 7:11

"He is my salvation from sorrow and sin"
James Nicholson in *Hymns*, #89

274

"I was attacked with inflammatory rheumatism,... and suffered the most excruciating pain. . . . I could suffer no clothes upon me except a very light blanket. . . . The Prophet Joseph Smith came to see me. I told him I was **almost discouraged**, being **afraid** that my joints would be drawn out. He told me **I should never get discouraged, whatever difficulties might surround me**. If I were sunk into the lowest pit of Nova Scotia and all the Rocky Mountains piled on top of me, I ought **not** be discouraged, but **hang on**, **exercise faith**, and **keep up good courage**, and I should come out on **top** of the heap."

George A. Smith, "Memoirs," BYU Library, 49, quoted in Jack S. Bailey, *Let Not Your Heart Be Troubled*, 38-39

"I am impressed with Commander William Robert Anderson, the man who took the submarine Nautilus under the North Pole from . . . the Pacific to . . . the Atlantic. In his wallet he carried a tattered card with these words: **'I believe I am always divinely guided. I believe I will always take the right road. I believe that God will always make a way, even when there appears to be no way.'** I share his convictions."
Pres. Gordon B. Hinckley, *Standing for Something*, 111

276

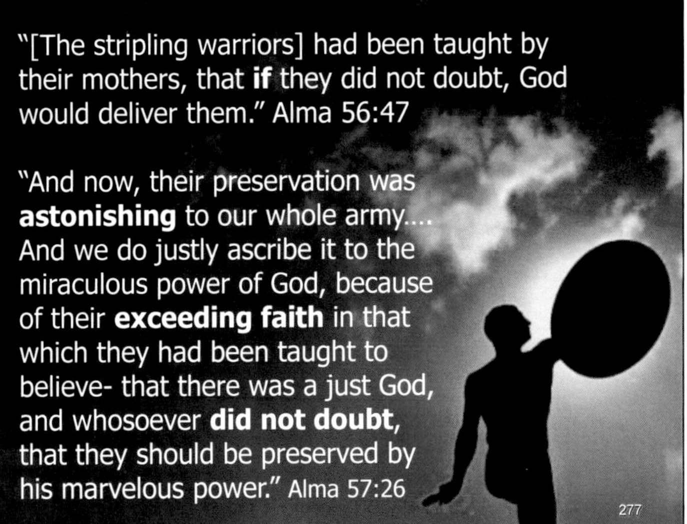

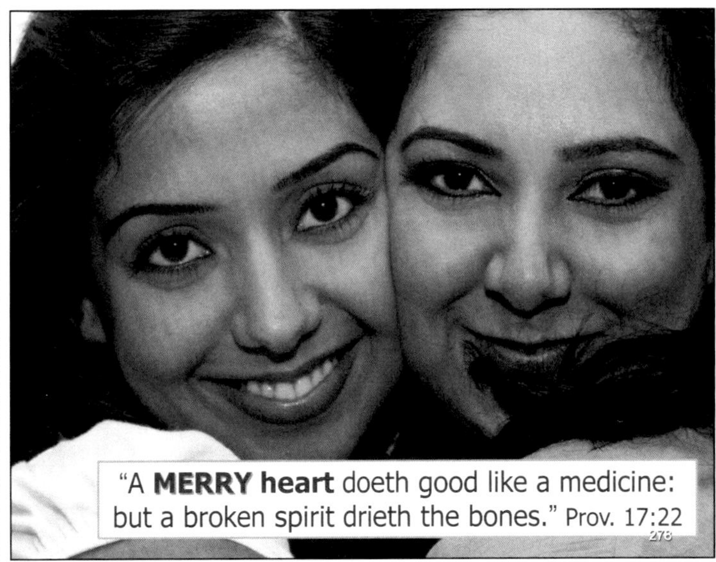

"Faith, then, is the first great governing principle which has power, dominion and authority over all things; by it they exist, by it they are upheld, **by it they are changed**, or by it they remain, agreeable to the will of God. . . . It is the first great governing principle which has power, dominion and authority over all things.' Joseph Smith *Lectures on Faith*, 1:8

"**Faith** is an intelligent **force.** Of what kind, I do not know . . . But it is superior to and overrides all other **forces** of which we know." J. Reuben Clark, Conf. Report 1960, 2

279

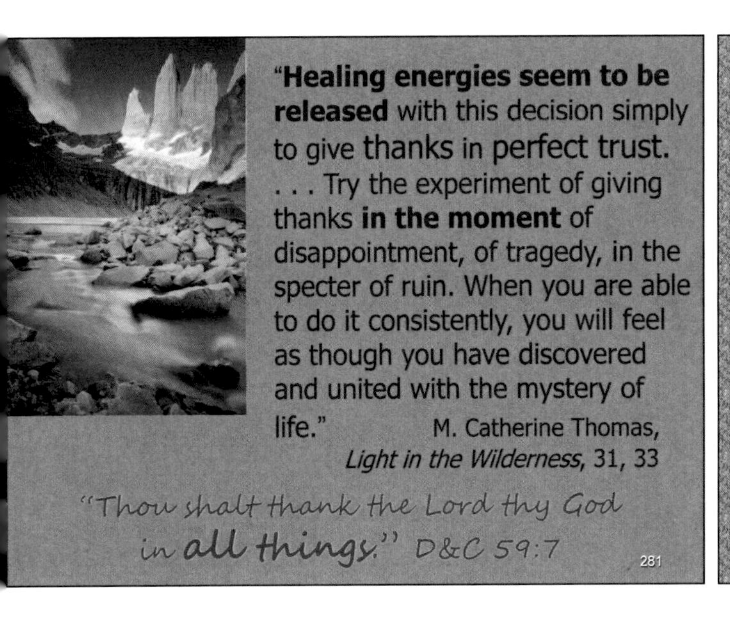

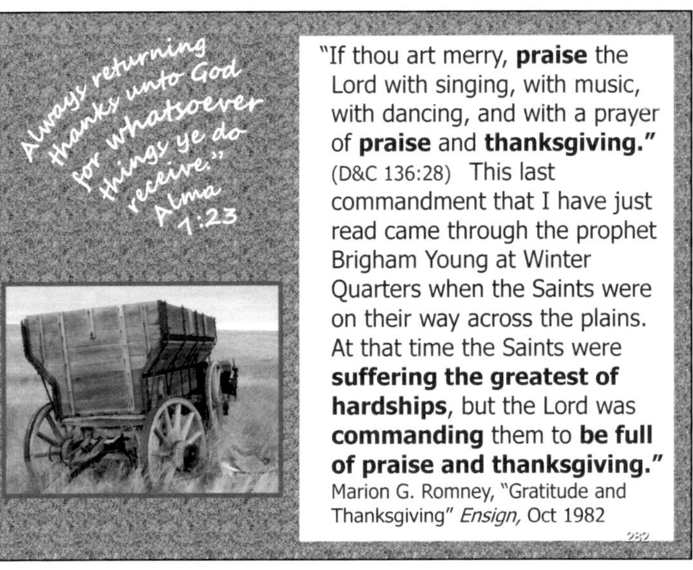

"We were about to be swallowed up in the depths of the sea. . . . My brethren . . . loosed the bands, which were upon my wrists and behold, they had swollen exceedingly; and also my ankles were much swollen, and great was the soreness thereof. Nevertheless, I [Nephi] did look unto my God and I did **praise** him all the day long; and I did not murmur against the Lord because of mine afflictions. . . . . I took the compass and it did work." 1 Nephi 18:15-16,21

283

GOD's ADVICE IN TRIALS

"Enoch saw that Noah built an ark . . . and the floods came and swallowed them up. And as Enoch saw this he had bitterness of soul , and wept over his brethren and said unto the heavens : **I will refuse to be comforted**; but the Lord said unto Enoch: **Lift up your heart,** and **be glad** and **look.** . . . And he beheld all the families of the earth. . . . And he cried unto the Lord. . . . And behold, Enoch saw the day of the coming of the Son of Man even in the flesh and his soul **rejoiced**.' Moses 7:43-47

284

"When we bless the people or things that have hurt us, we're temporarily suspending the cycle of pain."
Gregg Braden, *The Divine Matrix*, 176

"The faith of the saints can become exceedingly strong, abounding in righteousness unto the praise and glory of God." *Lectures on Faith*, 4:18

"**Love, praise and gratitude** are three of the most powerful healing frequencies of the body. . . . **Praising God** for any problem brings it into a frequency of healing."
Cliff Dunston, D.L. *Meridian Health*, 4,9

285

"The very act of praise **releases the power of God into** a set of circumstances and **enables** God to change them if this is His design. Very often it is our attitudes that hinder the solution of a problem. . . . The **prayer of praise** is the **highest** form of communion with God, and one that always releases a great deal of **power** into our lives." Merlin Carothers, *Prison to Praise*, 91-92

"Israel, Israel canst thou linger still in error's gloomy ways? . . . . Zion's walls shall ring with praise."
Richard Smyth in *Hymns #7*

286

"For my strength is made perfect in weakness. Most gladly therefore, will I **glory** in my **infirmities, that** the **POWER OF CHRIST may rest upon me.** Therefore, I take **pleasures** in infirmities, in reproaches, in necessities, in persecutions, in distresses for Christ's sake: for when I am **weak, then am I strong.**"

2 Cor. 12:9-10

287

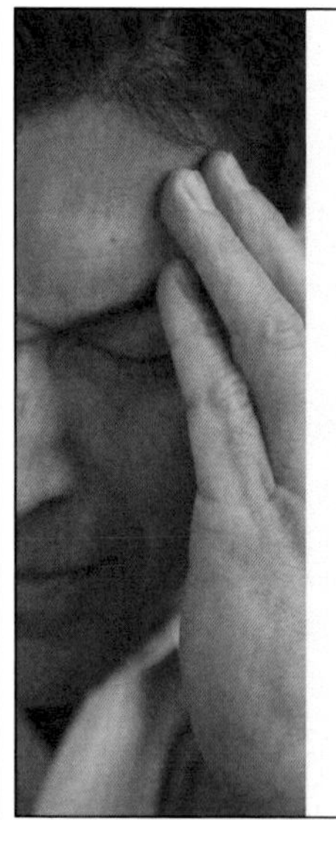

"**For many years I had suffered with painful headaches. . . . I just thanked God that I wasn't as bad off as some people. One day He said:** 'Why don't you try praising Me *for* the headache?' 'For it?' 'Yes, for it.' I began to lift up my thoughts in thanksgiving that God was giving me this headache as an opportunity to increase the power of Christ in my life. The headache got worse. I continued to thank God. . . . I realized that Satan and the power of Christ were at war . . . I held on to thoughts of praise and thanks. Suddenly I was being flooded with joy. Joy seemed to pour over every cell of my body . . . The headache was completely gone!"

Merlin Carothers, *Prison to Praise*, 79

288

"**When** I finally **let go** of needing my tumor to disappear, when I finally **accepted** its presence and **gave it permission** to be with me to the end of my days, when I **recognized** it as my friend, guide and teacher, when I felt **gratitude** for the motivation it had given me to **change** my **life** and my **thinking**, when I had **forgiven** all the people I had grudges with, my [brain] tumor no longer had a purpose and it melted away! Perhaps my most important step was **forgiving** my **body** and forgiving my **life** for taking me on a journey I hadn't planned or expected." Arielle Essex, D.O. "Arielle's Healing Story," 5-6

289

"Process for Staying in the Light

1. Release judgement of what is going on currently.
2. See it as perfect for your learning.
3. Praise God for the event just as it is.
4. Turn this burden over to the Savior with gratitude for the learning." © Cliff and Judy Dunston; "Principles of Praise" class; Centerville, UT; 9/10/11

"For I am made strong in His praise."
Lost Books of the Bible, Ode 16

290

"No way is hard where there is a simple heart.
Nor is there any wound where the **thoughts** are **upright:**
Nor is there any storm
in the depth of the illuminated thought:
Where one is surrounded on every side by beauty, there is nothing that is divided.
The likeness of what is below is that which is above; for everything is above:
What is below is nothing but the imagination of those that are without knowledge.
Grace has been revealed for your salvation.
Believe and live and be saved. Hallelujah."
The Lost Books of the Bible, Ode 34

291

Many NDEs teach similar ideas. Elaine Durham, *I Stand All Amazed*, 83

"My angel guide helped me understand that in the scene before me I was at the point of getting ready to enter earth, and that I had already helped choose the lessons I would like to learn from my stay in mortality. To learn these particular lessons, **I had been shown specific circumstances I would encounter, and specific trials I would need to endure.** These, if I made correct choices and appropriate responses to them, would provide the soul-growth I desired. And that was how everything in that realm was looked at, in terms of soul or spiritual growth."

292

Pres. Joseph F. Smith:

"I believe that our Saviour is the ever-living example to all flesh in all these things. He no doubt possessed a foreknowledge of all the vicissitudes through which He would have to pass in the mortal tabernacle. . . . He knew the work he had to do. . . . He is our example. . . .
If Christ knew beforehand, so did we.
But in coming here we forgot all, that our agency might be free indeed, to choose good or evil, that we might merit the reward of our own choice and conduct." *Gospel Doctrine*, 13

293

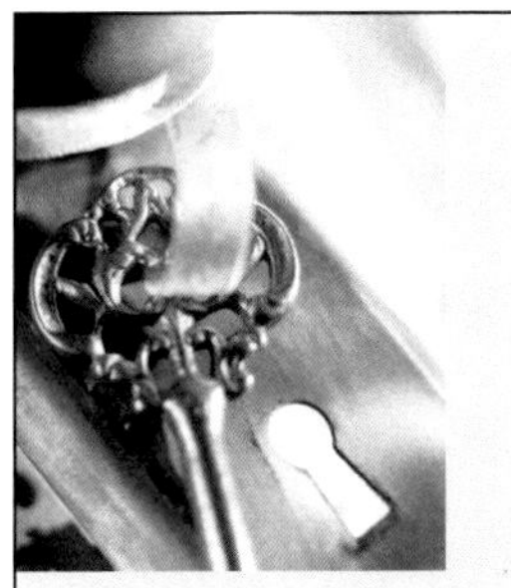

"Because illness can be such a powerful stimulus to change, perhaps the only thing that can force some people to resolve their deepest conflicts, successful patients often come to regard it as the greatest opportunity they have ever had for personal growth and development- truly a gift. Seeing illness as a misfortune, especially one that is undeserved may obstruct the healing system. Coming to see illness as a gift that allows you to grow may unlock it." Andrew Weil, M.D., *Spontaneous Healing*, 251"

294

"Illness is the result of imbalance. Imbalance is a result of forgetting who you are. Forgetting who you are creates thoughts and actions that lead to an unhealthy lifestyle and eventually to illness. The illness itself is a signal that you are unbalanced because you have forgotten who you are. Illness can thus be understood as a lesson you have given yourself to help you remember who you are."

Barbara Brennan, *Hands of Light,*

295

"Maybe to my spiritual higher self, none of [life's trials] felt bad. Maybe moving through this energy in the physical world and coming out of it was like taking a ride on Space Mountain at Disneyland: It was dark and bumpy; it jerked me around; I felt out of control most of the time, and I wasn't sure when it was going to end. When I am on the Space Mountain ride, I love it. I am yelling and waving my hands in the air. Maybe if in our deepest darkest moments we could grasp that our higher self is loving what we are going through, that it is like a wild ride, we would yell and wave our hands in the air. Our higher self really knows all is well and that the ride will come to an end."

Carol Tuttle, *Remembering Wholeness*, 37

296

"Consciousness underlies and organizes matter, and not the other way around. Changes in consciousness precipitate changes in matter."

Dawson Church,
The Genie in Your Genes, 357

297

"The greatest mystery a man ever learned, is to know how to control the human mind, and bring every faculty and power of the same in subjection to Jesus Christ; this is the greatest mystery we have to learn while in these tabernacles of clay."

Brigham Young in
Journal of Discourses 1:46

298

Chapter 6

Chase Darkness With Light

"Let us therefore cast off the works of darkness, and let us put on the armour of light."
Romans 13:12

299

??

George Ritchie, M.D., wrote in his near-death experience *Return From Tomorrow*, 59,61:

"All of the living people we were watching were surrounded by a faint **luminous glow**, almost like an **electrical field** over the surface of their bodies. . . . Was that **covering of light** some kind of **shield**, then? **Was it a protection** against . . . against disembodied beings like myself?"

300

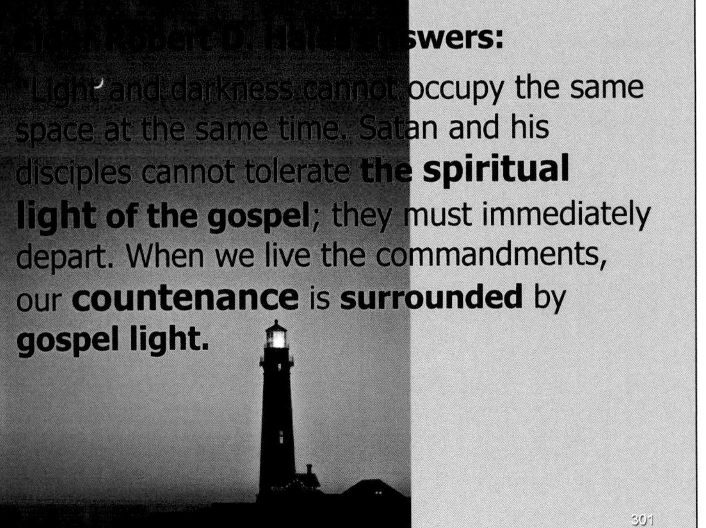

"If we **understand the reality of the Light of Christ** in everyone we see and . . . within ourselves, and we understand the great challenge that we have – the surroundings in which we live, the danger which sometimes besets us – we will have courage

and inspiration beyond that which we have known heretofore. And it *must* be so! And it *will* be so! **All of this is a dimension of gospel truth that too few understand.**"

Elder Boyd K. Packer, "The Light of Christ", *Ensign*, April 2005, 14

303

"There are myriads of disembodied evil spirits - those who have long ago laid down their bodies here and in the regions round about, among and around us; and they are trying to make us and our children sick." Brigham Young in *Journal of Discourses* 6:73-4

"It is an unhallowed principle to say that such and such have *transgressed* because they have been preyed upon by disease and death, for all flesh is subject to death; and the Savior has said, 'Judge not lest ye be judged." Joseph Smith in *HC* 4:11

304

"Satan gained the power to tempt individuals . . . , to possess their bodies, **to foster illness & disease** . . . It is Satan's business to **dwell in** and **with** all individuals who do not have the Holy Spirit with them, sometimes even gaining total possession of a person's body, so that he or she **loses agency** for a time. Partial possession may also occur, for whenever a human being becomes **angry**, he or she is at least partially possessed by Satan (James 1:20) . . . . **Satan can cause illness and death,** but only with permission from God."

Encyclopedia of Mormonism:
Macmillan, 1992,"Devils" by Chauncey C. Riddle, 380, 381

305

"A large percent of Jesus' healings involved the casting out of devils. . . .
When engaged in a healing mission, one must be ready to address **all aspects** of disease. Some sicknesses are of [evil] influence. . . . Psychiatrists tend to disbelieve . . . but **their paradigm is incomplete. Jesus dealt with devils as real personalities**, talking with them and ordering them out. . . . It is one of Satan's cleverest tricks to influence us not to believe in him nor his army." David Stewart, PhD,
Healing Oils of the Bible, 88-90

by James Tissot wikimedia commons

306

by Carl Bloch courtesy wikipedia

"**There are many spirits which are false spirits**, which have gone forth in the earth, deceiving the world. . . . Verily I say unto you, and **I say it that you may know the truth, that you may chase darkness** from among you." D&C 50:2,25

"We will not always be safe from the adversary's influence, even within our own homes. We need to protect our 'nestlings.' In order to do that, we must first acknowledge that Satan, the devil, lives; what his purposes are; what his **intentions** would be; and what **our defenses** should be. . . . Do we need any more evidence to understand that we are at war with the adversary? The revelations teach us **how to win this spiritual war**..." Boyd K. Packer, "Fledgling Finches and Family Life," 18 Aug 2009, Campus Educ. Week

307

"If thy whole body, therefore, be full of light, having **no part dark**, the whole shall be full of light." Luke 11:36

"...**darkened** neither in **body**, **limb**, nor **joint**" D&C 84:80

"Your **minds** in times past have been **darkened**." D&C 84:54

"He that saith he is in the light, and **hateth** his brother, is in **darkness** even until now."
1 John 2:9

308

"The **darkness** shall cover the earth, and **gross darkness the people**: but the Lord shall rise upon thee, and his glory shall be seen upon thee."
Isaiah 59:2

"All faces shall gather blackness" Joel 2:6, see also Nahum 2:10

"And the **mists of darkness are the temptations of the devil,** which blindeth the eyes, and hardeneth the hearts of the children of men, and leadeth them away into broad roads, that they perish and are lost."
1 Nephi 12:17

309

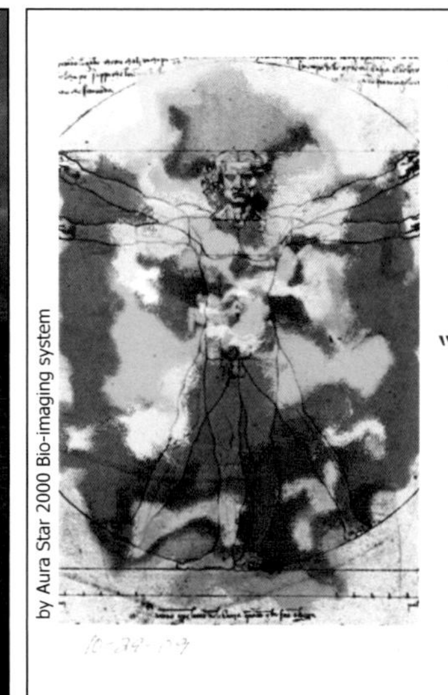

by Aura Star 2000 Bio-imaging system

Image of full body aura taken while recovering from a sore throat. Note **gray cloud** of **darkness** above head and **rusty brown** near neck.

"[Joseph Smith] decided that it was not lawful to teach the Church that **all disease** is of the devil, but if there is anyone who has this faith, let him have it **to himself**."
History of the Church 2:147

310

"The more wicked of these are the kind spoken of in scripture, as "foul spirits", "unclean spirits," spirits who afflict persons in the flesh, and *engender various diseases* in the human system. They will sometimes enter human bodies, and will distract them. . . . They will trouble them with dreams, nightmares, hysterics, fever, etc. . . . If permitted they will often cause death. Some . . . will cause a disagreeable smell about the person. Some cause deafness, others dumbness, etc. "
Parley P. Pratt, *Key to the Science of Theology*, 120-121

311

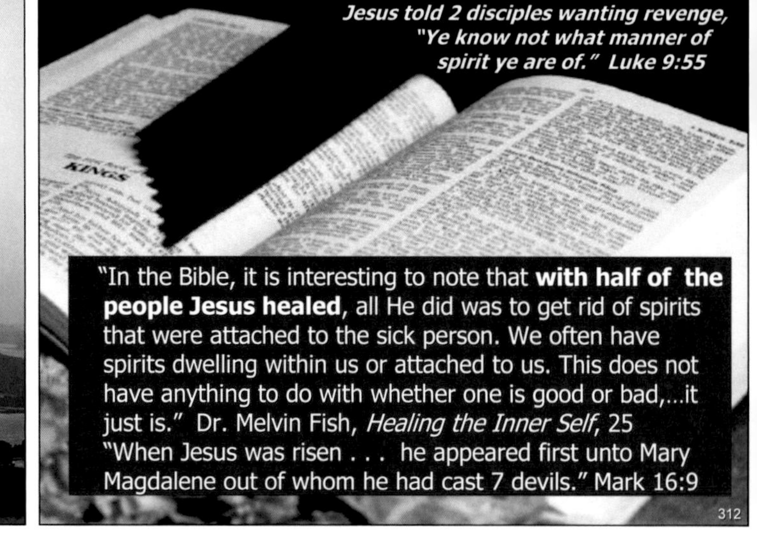

Brigham Young in JD 4:133

"You may now see people with legions of evil spirits in and around them; there are men who walk our streets that have more than a **hundred** devils in them and round about them, prompting them to all manner of evil, and some too that profess to be Latter-day Saints . . . . When [Pres. Jedediah Grant] was here the devils had power over his flesh, he warred with them and fought them, and said that they were around him by **millions**, and he fought them until he overcame them. **So it is with you and I.** I want you to understand these things; the spirits that afflict us and plant disease in our bodies, pain in the system, and finally death, have control over us so far as the flesh is concerned."

313

The adversary cannot make us do anything. He does lie at our door, as the scriptures say, and **he follows us** each day. Every time we go out, every decision we make, we are either choosing to move in his direction or in the direction of our Savior. **But the adversary must depart if we tell him to depart.** He cannot influence us unless we allow him to do so, and he knows that! The only time he can **affect our minds and bodies - our very spirits -** is when we **allow** him to do so." Elder Robert D. Hales, *Ensign*, May 2006, 6

314

Unable to cast Satan out of his presence 3 times, Moses succeeds by commanding in the Savior's name:

"And Moses received strength, and called upon God, saying: In the name of the Only Begotten, depart hence, Satan. And it came to pass that . . . Satan departed. . . . And now of this thing Moses bore record; but because of wickedness it is not had among the children of men."

Moses 1:21-23

This truth was lost to the world!

315

[Speaking of Moses 1] "Here we have the **key** that can dispel the powers of darkness and depression in our lives. We can command *in the name of Jesus* that Satan leave us, and Satan must go! As he leaves, our bodies, spirits, and emotions feel lighter. We experience a lifting sensation much like clouds lifting after a heavy storm, and we feel a sense of liberation and gratitude for our deliverance."

Garth Allred, *Unlocking the Powers of Faith*, 177

316

"As a servant of the Lord, I invoke His blessings upon you, you consummately precious young people, that you will be protected, that you will **learn how to hold the powers of the adversary in abeyance simply because you command it** (see James 4:7), and that he has no place with you. On the other hand, you learn to invite the Spirit of Revelation that will be constantly with you."

by Carl Bloch courtesy wikipedia

Boyd K. Packer, "The Instrument of Your Mind and the Foundation of Your Character" 2 Feb 2003, speeches.byu.edu

317

Heber C. Kimball related about Joseph Smith:

"One of his children was taken very sick; he laid his hands upon the child, [but] when it got better; as soon as he went out of doors, the child was taken sick again; he again laid his hands upon it, so that it again recovered. This occurred several times, when Joseph inquired of the Lord what it all meant; . . . he had an open vision, and saw the devil in person, who contended with Joseph, face to face for some time. He said it was his house, it belonged to him, and Joseph had no right there. Then **Joseph rebuked Satan in the name of the Lord,** and he departed and touched the child no more."

Woodruff, *Journal* 2:346-347 [Feb. 3, 1844] as quoted in Alexander L. Baugh, "Parting the Veil, BYU Studies 38, no 1 (1999), 42

318

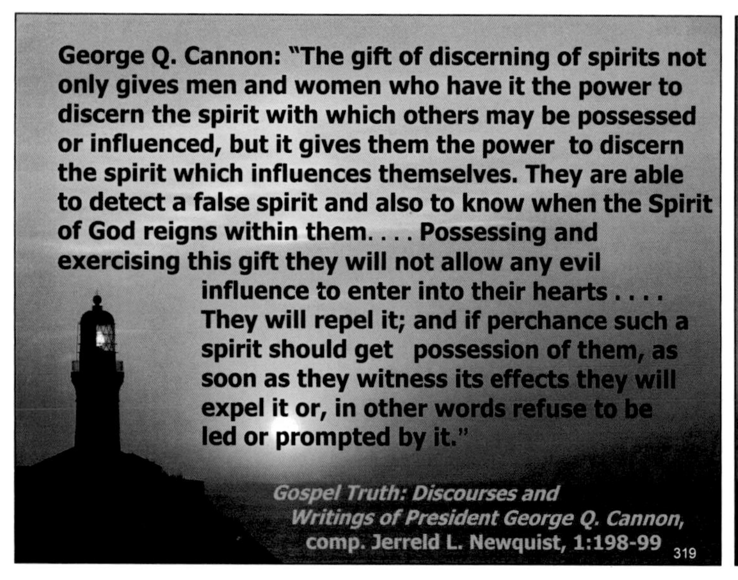

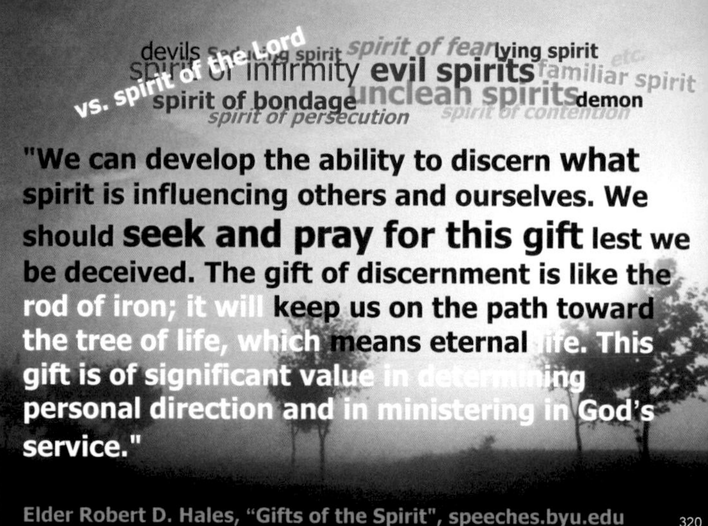

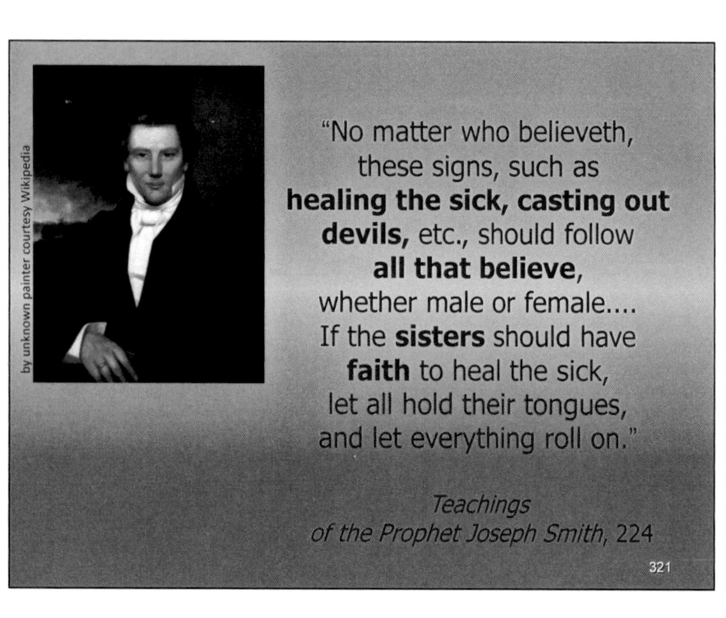

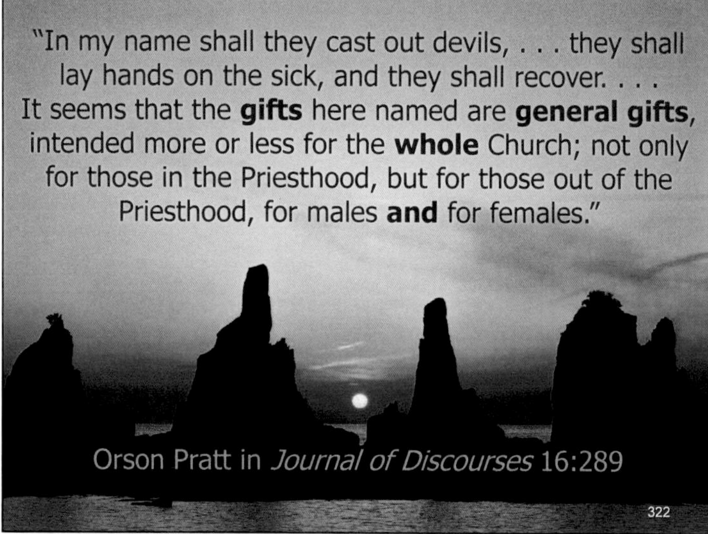

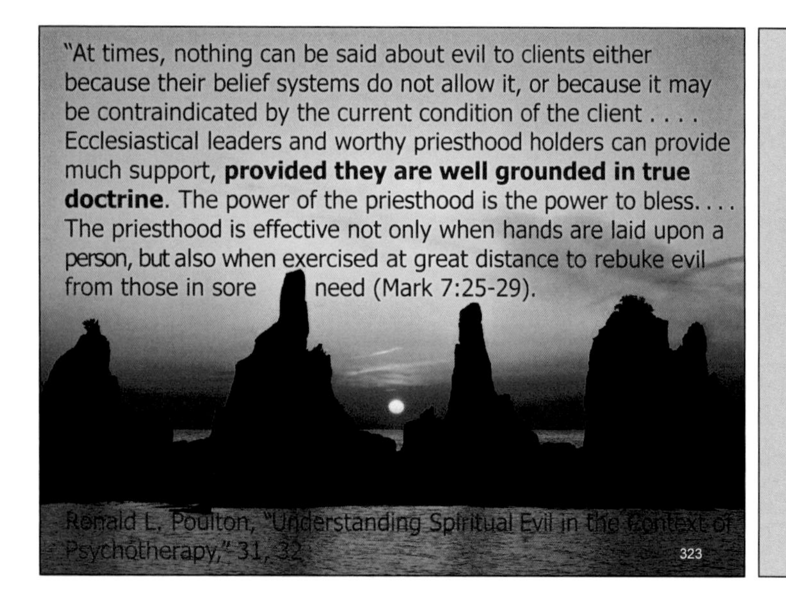

"If in cases of **healing** and **casting out devils, etc**., it happens that the receiver has **no command** of his own **mind**, as in cases of persons swooned, fainted, deranged or dead, then the **faith** of the administrator alone, or in connection with other friends and agents, **in his behalf**, is sufficient to do the work."

Parley P. Pratt, *Key to the Science of Theology*, 110 see Lectures on Faith 1:18,24

Orson Pratt: "Sometimes **sickness** can **deprive** an adult person of his **senses**, in that case his **friends may exercise faith for him.**"

Journal of Discourses, Vol 15. 289,290

324

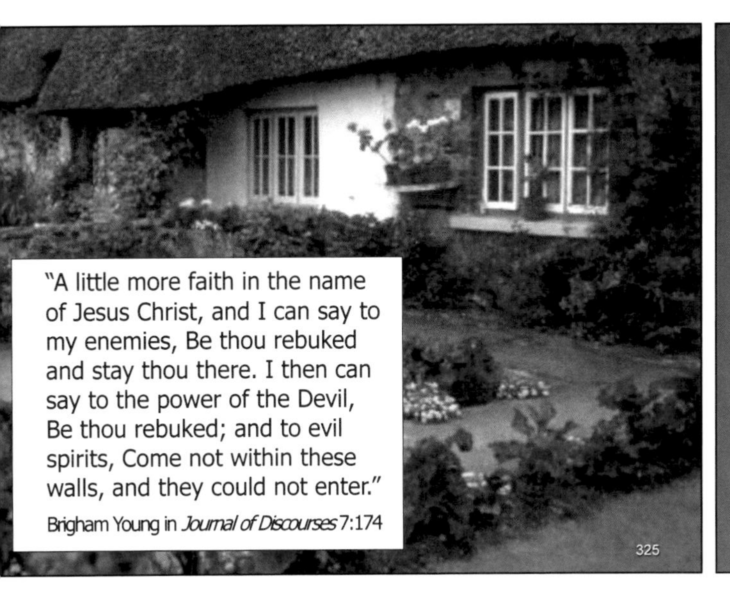

"A little more faith in the name of Jesus Christ, and I can say to my enemies, Be thou rebuked and stay thou there. I then can say to the power of the Devil, Be thou rebuked; and to evil spirits, Come not within these walls, and they could not enter."
Brigham Young in *Journal of Discourses* 7:174

325

"Darkness cannot exist in the presence of light. 'Let us therefore **cast off** the **works of darkness**, and **let us put on the armor of light**' (Romans 13:12), 'that **you may chase darkness** from among you' (D&C 50:25). What a thrilling revelation, to know that we can actually drive Satan away by **surrounding ourselves** with **a shield of light**."
Steven A. Cramer,
Putting on the Armor of God, 172

"Wherefore take unto you the whole armour of God, that ye may be able to withstand in the evil day, . . wherewith ye shall be able to quench all the fiery darts of the wicked."
Eph. 6:13, 16

326

"We are the container, the vessel, the receiver of light. If we are empty of light, darkness is in us. . . .
We cannot fill our vessels with light by concentrating on removing darkness, anymore than we can fill a container by concentrating on its emptiness. We only fill our vessels by bringing light into us to replace the darkness. Faith and repentance open up our souls and let the light of Christ pour in. They let us accept the atonement..."
B. Grant Bishop, *The LDS Gospel of Light*, 140

327

"Put on the **whole armor of God**, that ye may be able to stand against the wiles of the **devil**. For we wrestle not against flesh and blood, but against **principalities**, **powers**, against the **rulers of the darkness** of this world, against spiritual wickedness in high places."

Eph. 6:11-18

328

Elder F. Enzio Busche is an example of *POWER rather than FORCE:*

"I prayed with all the energy of my heart, 'Father, fill my soul with love.' I cried from the depths of my being . . . It was as if my skull was opened and a warm feeling poured down into my soul-down my head, my neck, my chest. As it was pouring down, it drove out all of the fear. . . . I told [the convulsing elder], with all the strength of my soul, "I love you my brother." In the very moment I did that, the evil

329

spirit left. . . . We are here to learn about the reality of the Living God and also to understand that the powers of darkness are real. . . . I treasure that experience more than anything because with all the prayers I was offering I was still not ready to control my *fear*, until I *opened* my *heart* to *fill it* with love. I learned that our purpose is to *fill our souls* with love."
Elder F. Enzio Busche, *Yearning For the Living God*, 270-272

"Wherefore, my beloved brethren, pray unto the Father with all the energy of heart, that ye may be filled with this love."
Moroni 7:48

330

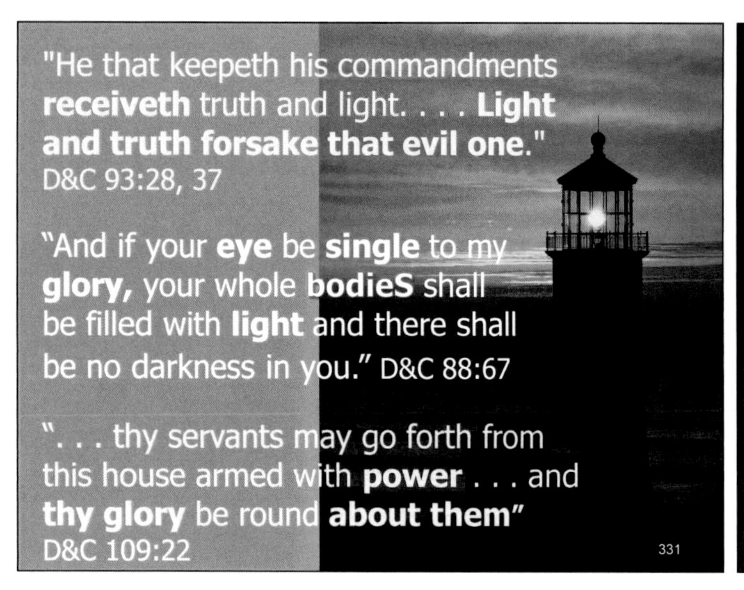

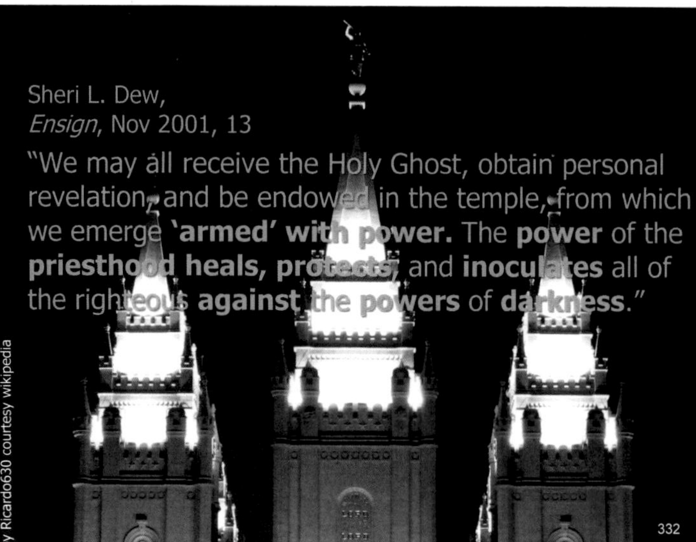

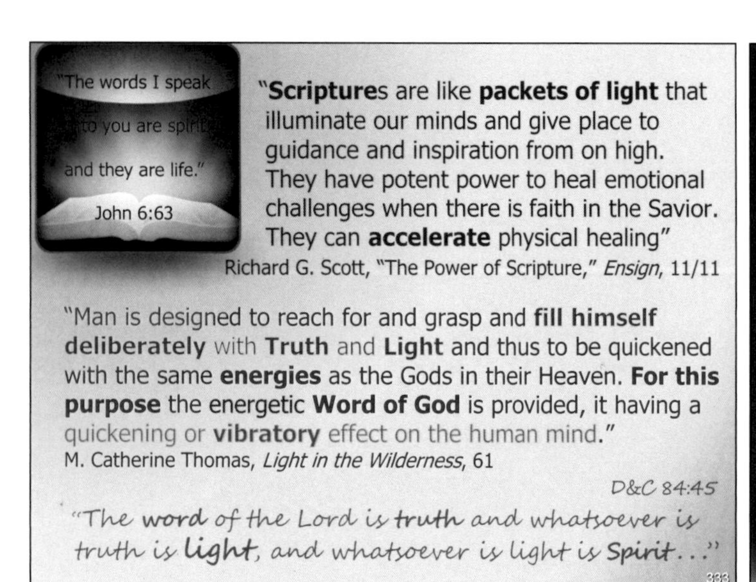

"**Pray always**, that you may come off conqueror; yea, that you may conquer Satan, and that you may escape the hands of the servants of Satan that do uphold his work." D&C 10:5

"**Prayer** is the pulsation of a yearning, loving heart in tune with the Infinite. It is a message of the soul sent directly to a loving Father. The language is not mere words but **spirit vibrations.**" David O. McKay, *Treasures of Life*, 308

"Why could not we cast him out? And Jesus said unto them, **Because of your unbelief**... nothing shall be impossible unto you. Howbeit ***this kind*** **goeth not out** but by **prayer and fasting.**" Matt. 17:19-21

334

"**Fasting brings light!** . . .
'And if thou draw out thy soul to the hungry, and satisfy the afflicted soul; then shall thy light rise in obscurity, and thy darkness be as the noonday.'" Isaiah 58:10
Brian Hales, *Light*, 126-127

"We can suggest no remedy for these multiplied evils, to which poor human nature is subject, except a good life, while we are in possession of our faculties; prayers and fastings of good and holy men; and the ministry of those who have power given them to rebuke evil spirits and cast out devils, in the name of Jesus Christ."
Parley P. Pratt, *Key to the Science of Theology*, 122

335

"**Inspiring music** may fill the soul with heavenly thoughts, move one to righteous action, or speak peace to the soul. When Saul was troubled with an evil spirit, David played for him with his **harp**; Saul was refreshed and **the evil spirit departed**. (See 1 Sam. 16:23)"

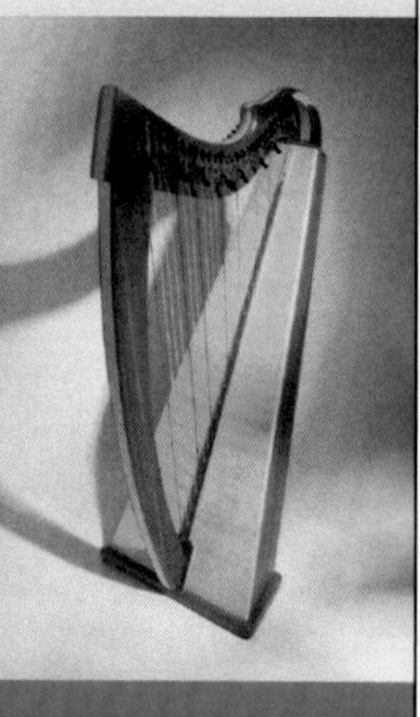

Pres. Ezra Taft Benson,
"Do Not Despair," *Ensign*, Oct 1986, 2

336

"[Evil] spirits don't like essential oils. They are repelled by them. Their **high vibrations**, put there by God, are too much and make them want to leave."
David Stewart, PhD,
Healing Oils of the Bible, 89

"There was no point upon which the Prophet Joseph dwelt more than the discerning of Spirits."
George A. Smith in Ehat & Cook, *Words of Joseph Smith*, 21

337

"I was beginning to learn that Praise was not just a form of worship or prayer, but also a way of waging spiritual warfare. . . . The enemy's arrows just can't penetrate the **joy** of someone who is praising the Lord. . . . While we praise Him, He sends our enemies scurrying."
Merlin Carothers,
Prison to Praise, 96,97

338

"Do you wish to prevail- to conquer the **powers of darkness** when they present themselves? If you do, **prepare yourselves** against the day when **these powers shall be made manifest with more energy** than is now exhibited. Then you can say, the evil powers that have been made manifest, the agents that came and tempted me, came with all their force, I met them face to face and **conquered by the word of my testimony**, by **patience**, by the **keys** which have been bestowed upon me, and which I held sacred before God, and **I have triumphed over the adversary and over all his associates.**"

Masterful Discourses of Orson Pratt, ed. Lundwall, 518-20

339

Helaman 13:37

"Behold, we are surrounded by **demons**, yea, we are encircled about by the angels of him who hath sought to destroy our souls. Behold our iniquities are great. O Lord, canst thou not turn away thine anger from us? **And this shall be your language in those days.**"

340

"Sometimes spirits do not make their transition to heaven after the death of their physical bodies . . . . These spirits remain on the earth plane and are called Earthbound spirits. At some point they may end up entering and residing in an unsuspecting human host,

whose energy field is weakened due to intense emotions such as depression, anger, fear, hate, grief, compassion; physical **illnesses**; **surgery**; or the use of **drugs and alcohol**. These unwanted houseguests, the spiritual hitchhikers, **bring their baggage** of physical, mental, emotional, and spiritual problems with them, which in turn **become** the patients' problems."

Shakuntala Modi, M.D., *Remarkable Healings*, 594

341

"Because [unclean spirits] still carry all of the accumulated Darkness from their mortal experience with them- they make anyone who they interact with partakers of that Darkness. When they are around or in us, they actually add their "baggage" to ours. Because of this, feelings of sickness, depression, confusion, fear, addictions and more, are often times not actually our feelings and conditions, but theirs. When they are removed, their baggage leaves as well . . . . For those who want to improve their life, THIS IS THE FIRST STEP.

Dr. Christopher E. Palmer,
Spirits and Spiritual Interactions, 48, back cover

342

"When nervous breakdowns occur, thought forms are out of order.
The images distort, superimpose, run riot. The ego loses control.
Thought forms of invading discarnate entities merge with the thought forms of the living mortal, serve to amplify them and give urges to the ego– which is often unable to resist or control them. . . . He seems to **remember past lives which belong instead to the invading discarnate."**

Harold Sherman, *How to Picture What You Want*, epilogue as quoted in Rex Wadham, "The Nature of Brain Chatter," 3

343

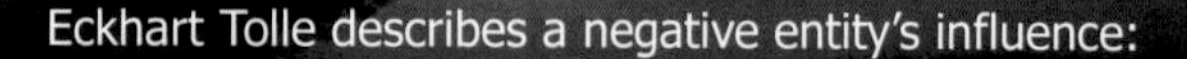

Eckhart Tolle describes a negative entity's influence:

"Some pain-bodies are obnoxious but relatively harmless, for example, like a child who won't stop whining. Others are vicious and destructive monsters, true **demons**. Some are physically violent; many more are **emotionally** violent. Some will attack people around you or close to you, while others may attack you, their host. **Thoughts** and **feelings** you have about your life then become **deeply** negative and self-destructive. **Illnesses** and accidents are often created in this way. Some pain-bodies **drive** their hosts to suicide."
Practicing the Power of Now, 78

344

Dr. Edith Fiore, *The Unquiet Dead*, 3, 67, 112
"More than 500 possessed patients ... my office suffering the gamut of psychological & psychosomatic symptoms problems . . . At least 70% of my patients were possessed and it was this condition that caused their *dis-ease*. Most of these people were relieved- through depossession techniques - of more than 1 entity. . . . **Highly sensitive people** are particularly prone to possession. . . . Excessive negative emotions like anger, depression & grief all lower the frequency of the aura . . . Fatigue, especially exhaustion, and illness also weaken the aura's protective capacity."

345

"What opens a person up? . . .
Soft, porous, & fuzzy boundaries or edges around auras . . . Patients report that different physical and emotional conditions, behaviors and situations can **open** their shields . . . **sickness, anesthesia, surgery, accidents, drugs, alcohol, video games, entities, occupations**. . . . Even **too much** compassion can open the shield."

Shakuntala Modi, M.D. *Remarkable Healings*, 215,218

346

"The year is 2020. . . . We understand that . . . **we are** actually vessels of **light** and **sound**. . . .
My grandchildren ask me in amazement why we used to medicate children or classify them as mentally ill because their **vibrational frequency** was higher than their parents' and because they were **spiritually advanced**. . . . I tell them we used to use terms like psychotic, hallucinogenic, schizophrenic, hyperactive, autistic, and attention deficit with people who were actually very **evolved** and **connected with their extrasensory perceptions and spiritual powers**. My grandchildren relate to words like **intuitive, empathic, precognitive**, and **visionary**, which we use more to describe an individual with highly developed **spiritual senses**." Carol Tuttle, *Remembering Wholeness*, 170-171

347

"There are a **great variety of spiritual gifts** given; but none of these gifts are given for the exclusive benefit of the individual possessing them. . . . [God] is not willing that the stewards over these rich treasures should hoard them up for their own exclusive use, when there are others equally worthy of enjoying the same. They are **commanded to give**, not a part, but the whole, to the pure in heart, that all may be equal in the enjoyment of these precious gifts. . . . So likewise the gifts of healing . . . , each to be exercised **for the benefit of all**, though ministered through **many channels."**

Masterful Discourses of Orson Pratt, ed. Lundwall, 644

348

"I ask, **is there a reason for men and women being exposed more constantly and more powerfully, to the power of the enemy, by having visions than by not having them?** There is and it is simply this - ***God never bestows upon his people, or upon an individual, superior blessings without a severe trial to prove them***, to prove that individual, or that people to see whether they will keep their covenants with him, and keep in remembrance what he has shown them. **Then *the greater the vision, the greater the display of the power of the enemy.*** *So when individuals are blessed with visions,* revelations or great manifestations, look out, then the Devil is nigh you and *you will be tempted **in proportion** to the visions, revelation, or manifestations you have received."* Brigham Young, *JD 3:205-206*

349

Chinese fable quoted by George A. Smith

"A man traveling through the country came to a large city, very rich and splendid; he looked at it and said to his guide, 'This must be a very **righteous** people, for I can only see but **1** little devil in this great city.' The guide replied, 'You do not understand, sir. This city is so perfectly given up to wickedness, corruption, degradation, and abomination of every kind, that it requires but **1** devil to keep them all in subjection.' Traveling on a little further, he came to a rugged path and saw an old man trying to get up the hillside, surrounded by **7** great, big, coarse-looking devils. 'Why,' says the traveler, 'this must be a tremendously **wicked** old man! Only see how **many** devils there are around him!' 'This,' replied the guide, 'is the only **righteous** man in the country; and there are **7** of the biggest devils trying to turn him out of his path, and they all cannot do it.'" *JD* 5:363-64

350

"We read that Satan shall be bound a thousand years. **How is this to be accomplished?** By our becoming so impregnated with the principles of the Gospel – with the Holy Ghost- that the enemy will have **no place in us** or in our families... The adversary is first to be driven from ourselves, then from our families, then from our neighbors, next from our territory, and eventually from the nations, until he shall find no place upon the face of the whole earth: then will he not be bound?... He will be **chained** to all intents and purposes when he can have no influence- no power- no tabernacles into which he can enter. . . If we will do this, and be united as to the heart of one man, we shall banish Satan from our presence, and eventually **from this earth**." Daniel H. Wells in *JD* 5:43 see

351

"That person who cannot obtain power in the name of Jesus to cast out devils **in this life** has great reason to fear lest the devil shall have power over him in the next. What assurance has anyone that he shall obtain a complete salvation from the power of the devil, when his spirit shall leave the body, if he cannot claim the promise of Jesus, and cast him out while in this world? One of the **purposes,** then, which Jesus had in view in bestowing this blessing, was that believers might learn to prevail against the devil **before** they should enter the invisible world of spirits. . . . As there is no Scripture to do away with this promise, not any reason to prove it unnecessary, it must be intended for believers **of all ages**, until the devil is bound."

Masterful Discourses of Orson Pratt, 603-604

352

"We talk about Satan being bound. Satan will be bound by the power of God; but he will be bound also by the determination of the people of God not to listen to him, not to be governed by him. The Lord will not bind him and take his power from the earth while there are men and women willing to be governed by him. That is contrary to the plan of salvation. To deprive men of their agency is contrary to the purposes of God."
George Q. Cannon, *Gospel Truth*, 186

"We are the generation which shall learn to bind Satan, for we will listen to him no more in our hearts."
Carolyn Ringger, *Faith Unpuzzled*, xiii See 1 Nephi 22:26-27

353

"Life itself depends upon the existence of opposites. Thus, if there are good gifts that come from God, there are also evil gifts that spring forth from Satan."
Bruce R. McConkie, *A New Witness for the Articles of Faith*, 376

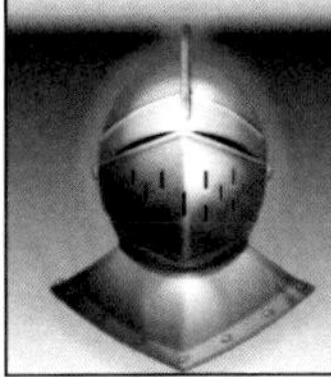

"If you fear the darkness, you feed it.
If you ignore the darkness, you feed it.
If you see the light in it, you conquer it."
Ranae Johnson, Ph.D.

354

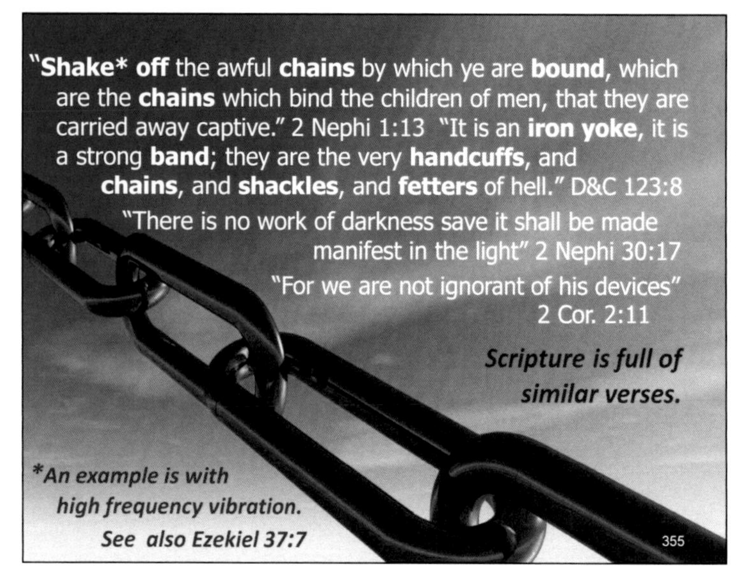

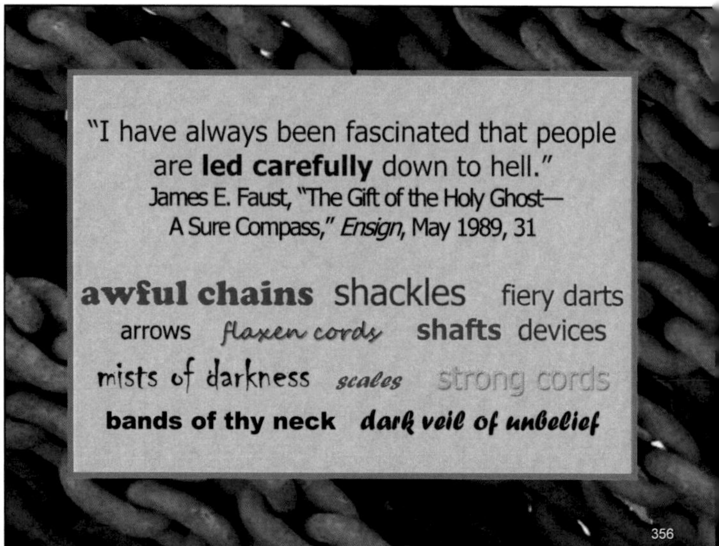

Jack Angelo,
Your Healing Power, 200

"Energetic material being stored in the etheric body sets up energy blocks which act on the physical. . . . Healers with well-developed high sense perception are able to look into the etheric body and see the forms taken by negative energies which are being stored there, or can sense them in other ways. . . . Etheric material which needs to be removed can be . . . a liquid, as lumps, as a mass . . ., as threads, as spines . . . They all give the same impression, which can sometimes be quite unpleasant, that they should not be there."

"We could not help beholding the exertions of Satan to blind the eyes of the people, so as to hide the true light that lights every man that comes into the world." **Joseph Smith in *HC 1: 206***

357

"Under hypnosis, [my] patients often report finding different types of devices in their bodies and in their surroundings. According to the patients, Satan and his demons can build these. . . .They are actually spiritual devices, but they have a physical effect on the patient. . . . When these devices are removed, the patients' symptoms sometimes disappear almost immediately. . . . My research clearly shows that earthbound and demon entities are the most common cause for depression . . . and psychiatric problems in general." Shakuntala Modi, M.D., *Remarkable Healings,* 344-345, 361

"I beheld multitudes of people who were sick, and who were afflicted with all manner of diseases, and with devils and unclean spirits . . . And they were healed by the power of the Lamb of God; and the devils and the unclean spirits were cast out." 1 Nephi 11:31

358

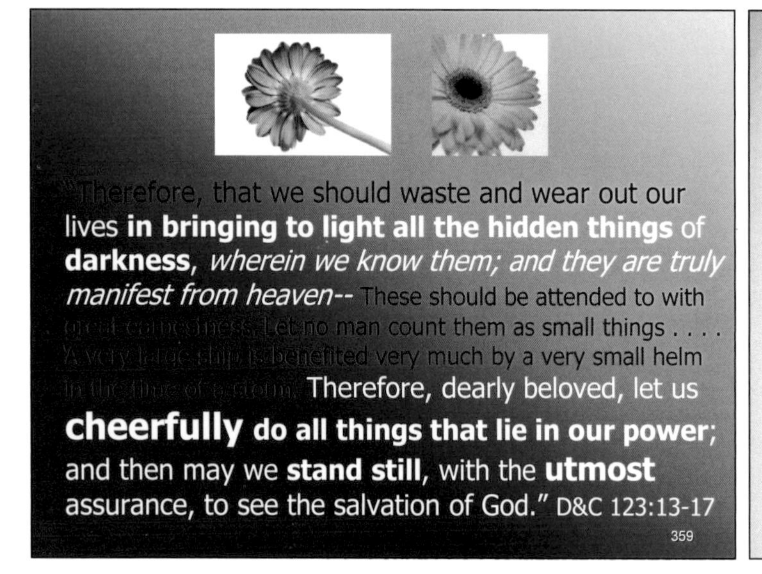

Brigham Young:

"When a man is **full** of the **light of eternity,** then the eye is not the only medium through which **he sees,** his ear is not the only medium by which **he hears,** nor the brain the only means by which **he understands."**

***Journal of Discourses* 1:70**

360

"Where there is **true faith** there are miracles, visions, dreams, **healings and all the gifts of God** that he gives to his saints."
Bible Dictionary, Faith, 67

"[Angels'] business is to comfort and instruct individual members . . . to heal them by the laying on of hands in the name of Jesus Christ or tell them what means to use in order to get well, to teach them good things, to sing them a song, to warn them of approaching danger, or to deliver them from prison or from death." Parley P. Pratt, *Key to the Science of Theology, 116-17*

361

WARNINGS

"Be ready always to give an answer to every man that asketh you a reason of the hope that is in you with meekness and fear: Having a good conscience; that whereby they speak evil of you, as of evil doers they may be ashamed that falsely accuse your good conversation in Christ. For it is better that ye suffer for well-doing than for evil doing."
1 Peter 3:15-17

362

"There are **many** that keep their **gifts** to themselves. The **persecution** some of these people have . . . [had] is incredible. **Incredible** from the standpoint that it comes from family, friends, fellow church members and from **people that profess to believe in gifts, revelation and healing**. . . . 'Wo unto him that shall deny the Christ and his works! Yea, wo unto him that shall deny the revelations of the Lord, and that shall say that the Lord **no longer** worketh by revelation or by prophecy, or by **gifts**, or by tongues or by **healings**, or **by the power** of the Holy Ghost!'(3 Nephi 29: 5-6)"
Doug Mendenhall, *Possibilities*, 69

363

"Require not miracles, except I shall command you, except casting out devils, healing the sick, and against poisonous serpents, and against deadly poisons; and ***these things ye shall not do, except it be required of you by them who desire it.***"
D&C 24:13-14

364

"In this regard, you and I are much like the long, thin strands of glass used to create the fiber-optic cables through which **light signals** are transmitted over very long distances. Just as the glass in these cables must be pure to **conduct** the light efficiently and effectively, so we should become and remain worthy **conduits** through whom the Spirit of the Lord can operate. But brothers and sisters, we must be careful to **remember** in our **service** that **we are conduits** and **channels**; **we are not the light.**" Elder David A. Bednar, "Seek Learning by Faith" see also 2 Nephi 26:29

365

"Spirit helpers work at all levels and will help the patient at these levels if required to do so. But this will depend on the quality of your energy field. . . . It should be appreciated by healers, who are aware of what their spirit helpers are saying and doing, that to convey any of this to the patient may not be either helpful or appropriate. Further, it is against the Code of Conduct (mentioned earlier) to give this kind of information to a patient."
Jack Angelo, *Your Healing Power*, 199 see also 169

366

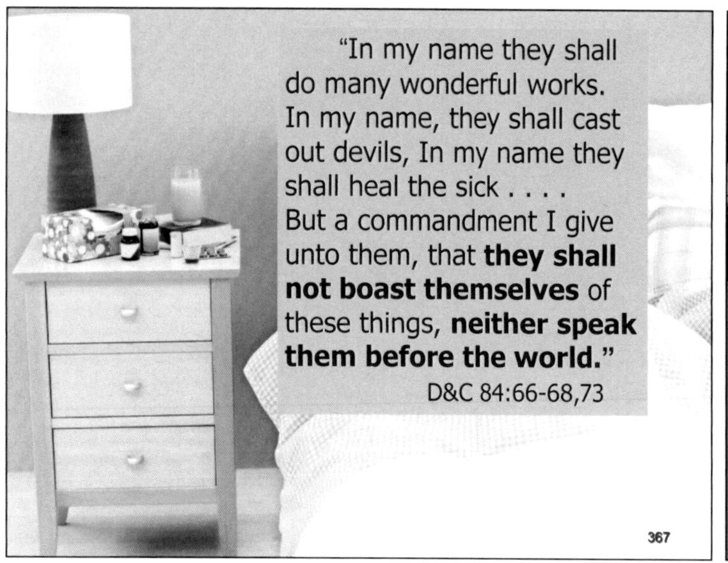

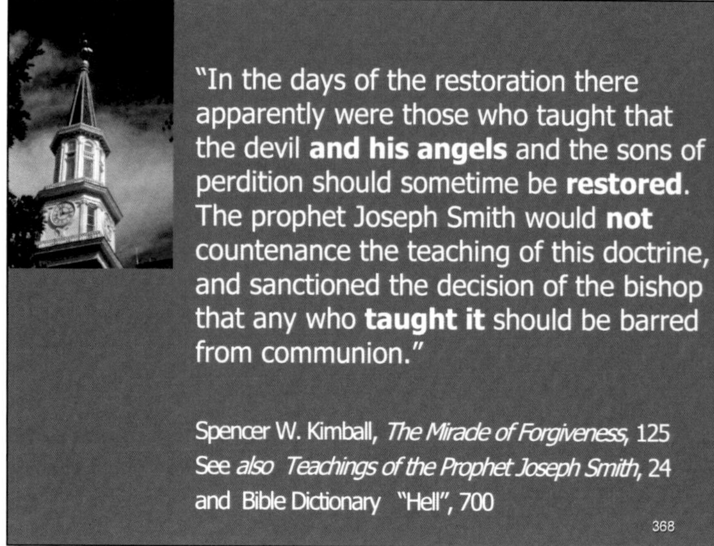

"There is **no fundamental principle** belonging to a human system that **ever goes into another** in this world or in the world to come: I care not what the theories of men are. We have the testimony that God will raise us up, and he has the power to do it. **If any one supposes that any part of our bodies**, that is, the fundamental parts thereof, **ever goes into another body, he is mistaken.**"

President Joseph Smith in
History of the Church, Vol. 5:339

369

"If, on the one hand we admit the principle of communication between the spirit world and our own, and yield ourselves to the **unreserved or indiscriminate guidance** of every spiritual manifestation, we are **liable to be led about by every wind of doctrine** and by **every kind of spirit** which constitute the varieties of being and of thought in the spirit world. Demons, foul or unclean spirits, adulterous or murderous spirits, those who love or make a lie, **can communicate** with beings in the flesh, as well as those who are more true and virtuous."
Parley P. Pratt in *Journal of Discourses* Vol.2, Discourse12

370

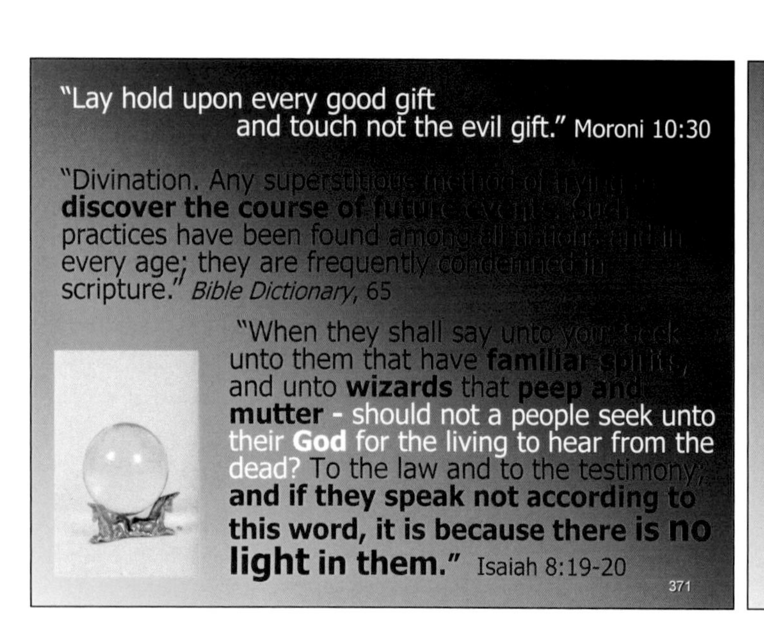

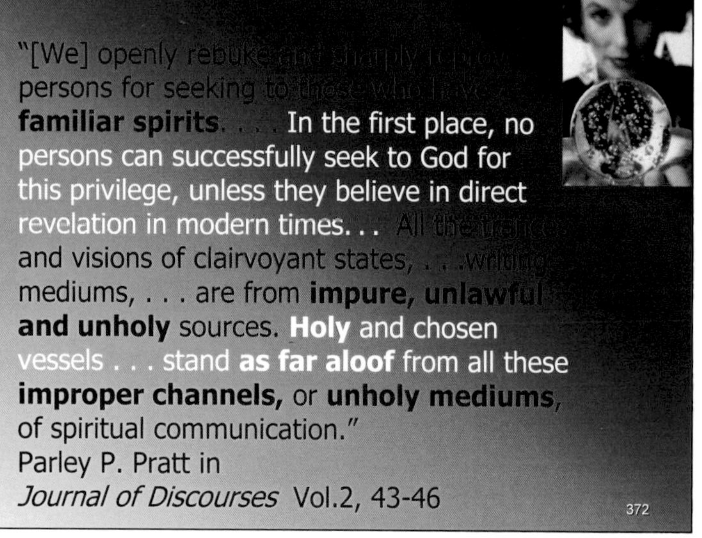

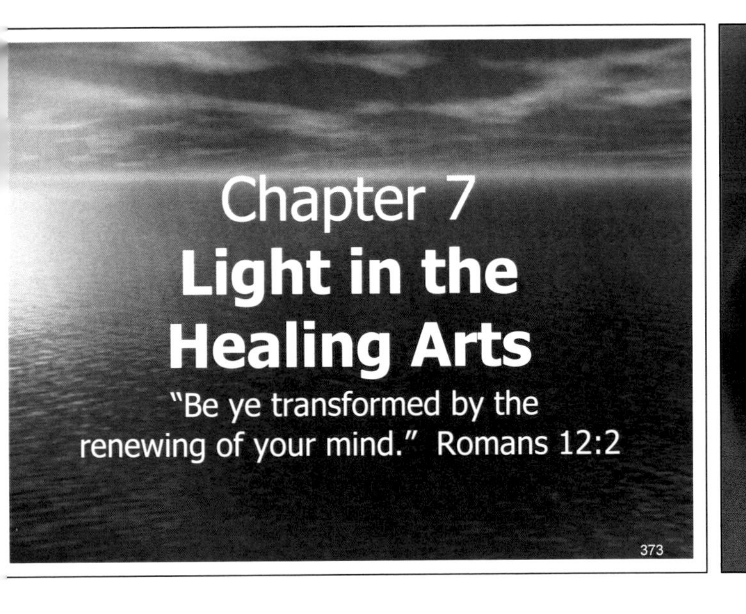

"There is an energy in the Universe (and in the human body) that is not identical with electromagnetic energy. . . . That energy plays the role of "software" for human processes on all levels, physiological, psychological and mental. Traditional Chinese Medicine says that Chi (the software) can be altered not only with the help of needles, but with herbs, essential oils, food and special exercises, called Tai Chi and Qi-gong."

Boyd Martin, "What Subtle Energy Is and Its Value to Health"

374

"Dr. Dossey provides the scientific and medical proof that the spiritual dimension works in healing. Citing the work of scientists . . . , he conclusively demonstrates that spiritual tools . . . have measurable, powerful, & profound effects on how we heal. His argument forces us to go beyond the practices of **conventional medicine**, which he calls **Era I**, and **mind/body medicine**, which he calls **Era II,** leading us to a new dimension, the **spiritual "nonlocal"** dimension of **Era III**. What was viewed in the past as random or episodic events in healing are shown . . . to be related & connected to a higher force at work. . . the **nonlocal mind.** This vision of the coming era in medicine ['**Eternity Medicine'**] . . . will surely change the face of medicine forever." *Reinventing Medicine,* book jacket

375

"Chemical medicine is what we've had in the past. . . . The simple metaphor is – if you put bacteria in a glass of water and throw some silver colloidal particles in there, it'll kill the bacteria. People thought that was due to the **contact** and that led to **chemical medicine**. But, if you, in fact, have the same experimental setup except you put the silver in *as an electrode* in a fluorescent tube and focus **light** on the jar, then you *still* kill the bacteria. That leads to **energy medicine**. Furthermore, we have found that, if in the same room you have the jar with the bacteria in the water and you plug in an *intention-imprinted electrical device* – then, in short order, you can kill the bacteria. That's really *information* that's been exchanged. And that leads to ***information medicine.***"

William A. Tiller, PhD
themetamorphoses.com/p2a_scientists.html retrieved 12/2/11

376

"We can define Energy Medicine. It's the diagnostic & therapeutic use of energy. These are **ordinary energies**. **There's nothing mythical here**: heat, light, sound, gravity, pressure, vibration, electricity, magnetism, chemical energy, electromagnetism- the basic **forces** that **surround** & **interpenetrate** us. So Energy Medicine includes a whole range of hands- on, hands- off **methods**, energy **techniques** and **devices.** The **hands on** methods range from acupuncture to zero balancing, chiropractic, cranial- sacral, osteopathy, and so on. Energy Medicine involves **energy** of particular **frequencies** and intensities and wave shapes and other characteristics that stimulate the repair and regeneration of one or more tissues. That's my definition."

"Dr. James Oschman on Energy Medicine," youtube

377

"Matter, wherever found and in whatever form, always possesses energy... **Energy** appears in **many forms,** such as heat, **light**, electricity, magnetism, gravitation, and, according to the gospel**,** the **many spiritual forces."**

John A. Widtsoe, *Rational Theology,* 12

378

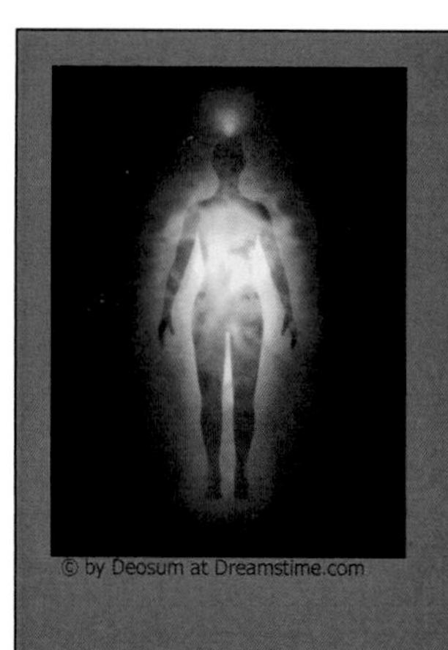
© by Deosum at Dreamstime.com

"Healing involves a strengthening of the underlying integrity of an individual's human energies and their repatterning in a healthier way. . . . One individual, acting as a healer, can help another by assisting in the repatterning of their energy and in the reestablishment of its rhythmic flow." Susan Wagner, M.D., *A Doctor's Guide to Therapeutic Touch*, 29

379

"Disease is, in a sense, scrambled **information**. We can access the appropriate information – and **that's what a number of those new energy modalities are doing**- they are basically **correcting** that **information** scrambling."

Lynne McTaggart on DVD
"The Living Matrix–
The New Science of Healing"

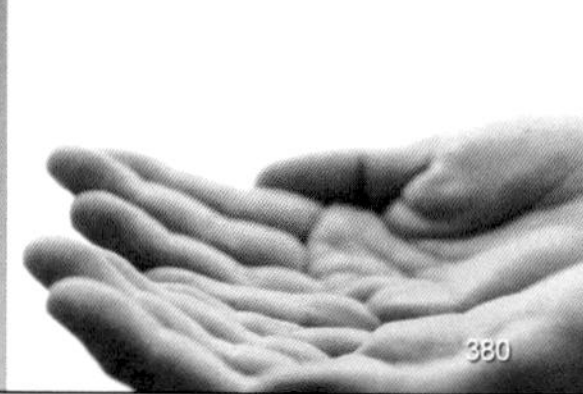

380

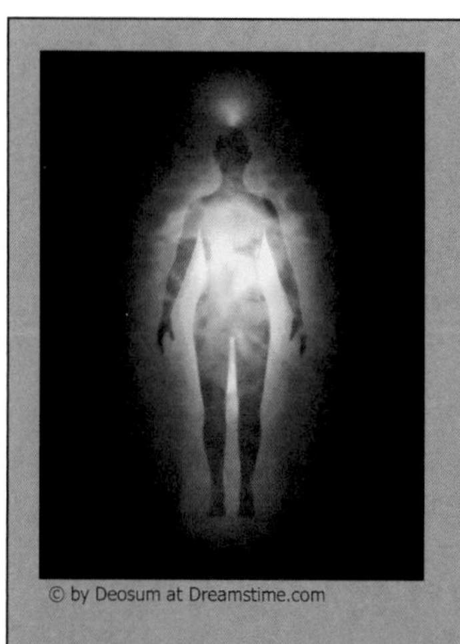
© by Deosum at Dreamstime.com

"Interestingly, we now know that the body heals through frequency, vibration and resonance and it's communicated through light."

William Tiller, PhD
see williamtiller.org

381

"In modern neuroscience, it is now known that your brain has a number of circuits that explain short-term memory, but there's **no circuitry for long-term memory**. This is where your **biophoton field** comes in . . . In highly simplistic terms, your mental body can be viewed as a highly sophisticated computer that processes, stores and retrieves **information**, which is then used to **regulate** your physical body. . . . [Dr. Fritz-Albert Popp] proved that **biophotons** originate from your **DNA** and that they are laser-like in nature. . . . The **DNA** inside each cell **vibrates** at a **frequency** of several billion hertz . . . . The vibration is created through the coil-like contraction and extension of your DNA -- which occurs several billion times per second -- and every time it contracts, it squeezes out one single **biophoton; a light particle**. That **photon** contains all the information on everything going on in your DNA at that moment.

382

... All the photons that are emitted from your body communicate with each other in this highly structured **light field** that surrounds your body, and which is the actual **carrier** of your long-term memory. . . . Your **DNA** sends **information** out on a photon, and on the same photon the information of all the biophotons from your body is broadcast back to your **cells**. . . . . A fascinating alternative practice that Dr. Klinghardt has started using, based on this **science**, is to use **tools that work with light** to **influence** your **biophoton field** in beneficial ways. For example, transmitting the **information** of nutrients in the form of **light** into your biophoton field can affect your body in the same way as eating the nutrient! It's really fascinating stuff."

Dr. Joseph Mercola; "5 Principles that Can Heal Almost Any Illness" part 2; post June 3, 2008; articles.mercola.com

383

Photons from laser by US Air Force

"Recent scientific thinking on the fundamental **properties of light** is indeed stunning. Today scientists even describe light as a **'carrier'** (See 2 Nephi 33:1...) or **'messenger'** (See D&C 45:9) or **'mediator'** (See 2 Nephi 2:27–28). How profound are the doctrines of the Lord!" Robert R. Steuer, "The Power of Light and Truth." Ensign, May 2008, 99-101

384

"[Joseph Smith] declared that a refined medium... fills all space, whereby **intelligence** is **conveyed** from **place to place.** In the terms of Joseph Smith, the forces of nature, such as heat, light and electricity, are simply various manifestations of the **intelligence** of the Holy Spirit; in the terms of science, of the **energy** of the universal ether. **The parallelism is complete**. The Holy Spirit, in "Mormon" theology corresponds with the ether of science."

John A. Widtsoe, *Joseph Smith as Scientist*, 141-142

385

"Energy is **in-FORM-ation** which creates a **vibration** that manifests into a **pattern** which emits a **signal** that can be found somewhere along an **electromagnetic spectrum.**"

Dr. Sari Suttka,
Layers of Light Leadership Retreat,
Park City, UT, March 2006

386

"[Fritz Albert] Popp came to realize that **light** in the body might even hold the **key** to health and illness.... He went on to use **biophoton emission** as a tool for measuring the **quality** of **food**.... Health was a state of perfect **subatomic communication**, and ill health was a state where **communication** breaks down. **We are ill when our waves are out of synch**.... **If we could take in** the **photons** of other **living** things, we also might be able to use the **information** from them to **correct** our own **light** if it went awry."

Lynne McTaggart, *The Field*, 52

387

"Then shall thy **light** break forth as the morning and thine **health** shall spring forth speedily." Isaiah 58:8

"Therapists practicing Qigong and **other forms of energy healing** have been found to **emanate large electromagnetic fields** from their **hands**." Dawson Church, *The Genie In Your Genes*, 121

"Your hands hold powerful medicine-'energy medicine'" Christiane Northrup, MD foreword in Donna Eden, *Energy Medicine for Women*, xv

388

"Could it be that the abilities that are so often characterized as paranormal ... including increased **electromagnetic fields** are indeed the **scientifically measurable** results of the **real influence** of the **light of Christ** on the soul of man? Once again... science and religion are not enemies but companions in a marriage which unites all truth."

Brent & Wendy Topp, *Glimpses Beyond Death's Door*, 254

389

"The **light** of the **body** is the **eye**." Matt. 6:22

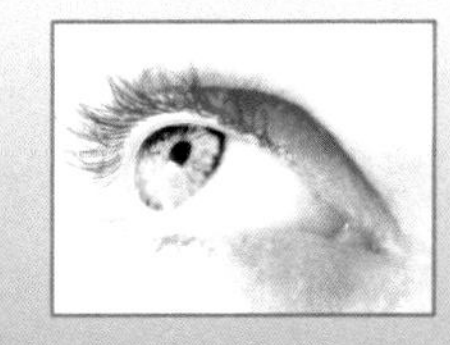

Dr. Eric Pearl teaches that healing actually occurs through the eyes. This has been my experience with generational issues... see Robert Ross, "Reconnective Healing with Dr. Eric Pearl" awarenessmag.com

"Much of the trapped energy comes out through the eyes I believe that the eyes are truly the windows to our souls." Ranae Johnson, PhD, *Reclaim Your Light Through the Miracle of Rapid Eye Technology*, 44

390

"It is given **to abide in you, the record of heaven**... the **truth** of all things; **that which quickeneth all things, which maketh alive all things**; that which **knoweth** all things and hath **all power** according to wisdom."
Moses 6:61

391

"The energy of the electromagnetic spectrum apparently is but a small part of the spectrum of God's light. The light of God and Christ -- life, intelligence... laws, truth, spirit, words, conscience, knowledge, understanding, the everlasting gospel, mercy, **virtue, compassion... may, indeed, just be different lengths of the same energy** scientists have named gamma rays, x-rays, ultraviolet light, visual light, infrared light ... All the medical knowledge which helps heal the sick is but a simple form of the **atoning power of Christ that heals not only bodies but our souls.**"

B. Grant Bishop, M.D., *The LDS Gospel of Light*, 15

392

"Whether **activated** by an exercise regimen like T'ai Chi, an electromechanical stimulation method like acupuncture, a biofeedback or EDS machine, Energy Psychology, or your belief system, the point of therapy is to **restore full function and balance** to the **body's electromagnetic energy system."**

Dawson Church,
The Genie in Your Genes, 142

393

"Energy medicine functions at the high level of general wellness. It is nonspecific tuning up every cell, organ, and system of organs. As such, it is the place to start treatment, not a place to go once the remedies offered by allopathic medicine have been exhausted, as so many patients do."

Dawson Church, PhD,
The Genie in Your Genes, 344

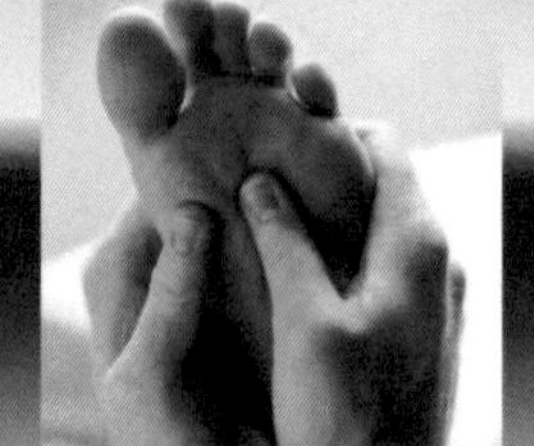

Example: Foot Zoning

385

"I have come to the view that we are **always radiating and receiving** from each other on many, many bands, and the only band that our present science knows about is the **electromagnetic one**. The higher dimensional bands are not yet quantitatively available to us because the instruments we have are designed primarily on the electric atom molecule level of reality, and therefore **confined** to radiations that go slower or equal to the velocity of electromagnetic light. . . . Many of these [energies], I feel, travel faster than the velocity of light and therefore **cannot be accessed** by the conventional instruments."

William A. Tiller, PhD "Professional Comments and Research" themetamorphoses.com/p2a_scientists.html

395

"Every man has an **atmosphere** which is affecting every other. Man cannot escape for one moment from this **radiation** of his character. This constantly weakening or strengthening of others. . . . By these qualities he will constantly affect the **world**. This **radiation** to which I refer comes from what a person really is, not from what he pretends to be. Every man by his mere living is **radiating** sympathy, sorrow, or morbidness, cynicism, or happiness or hope, or any other hundred **qualities.** Life is a state of radiation and absorption. **To exist is to radiate. To exist is to be the recipient of radiation."** Pres. David O. McKay, "The Mission of B.Y.U." 27 Apr 1948

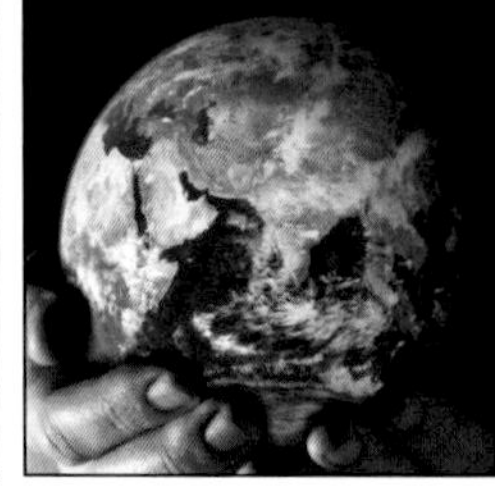

396

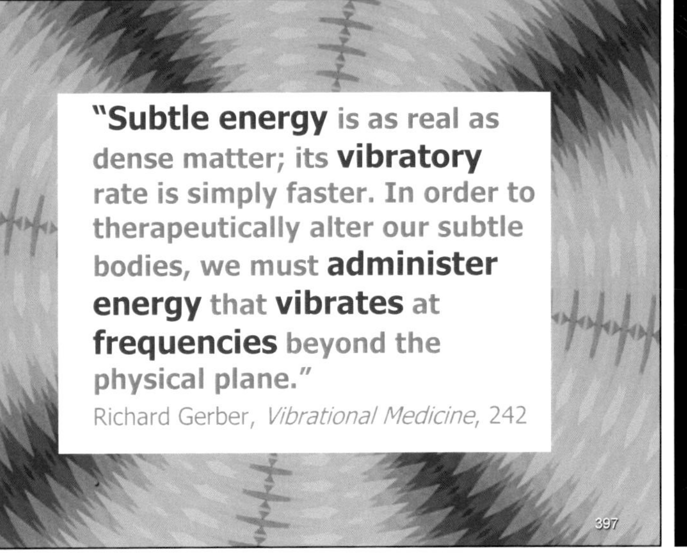

"The leading theory that explains how energy healing works involves the concept of **resonance** . . . . the foundation of all **energetic communication."**

Gary E. Schwartz, PhD,
The Energy Healing Experiment-Science Reveals Our Natural Power to Heal, 224

"Perhaps one day, healers will be known as resonant physicians."

Richard Gordon, *Quantum Touch*, 18

398

"A common example of **resonance** is illustrated with two stringed instruments, placed on opposite sides of the same room. As the lowest string of one instrument is plucked the same string on the second instrument will **vibrate.** No one touched the string; it is **responding** to the **waves of energy** that traveled across the room and **found resonance** with the second string."

Gregg Braden,
Walking Between the Worlds, 210

"Healers often have the effect of synchronizing client's energies. During healing sessions, the **brain waves** of the healer and of the recipient often enter a state of **coherence** and synchrony, becoming unified in a **single energy field**. This **unity** has been shown to raise the level of hemoglobin in the recipient's blood, reduce the severity of pain, lower anxiety and heal wounds more rapidly."

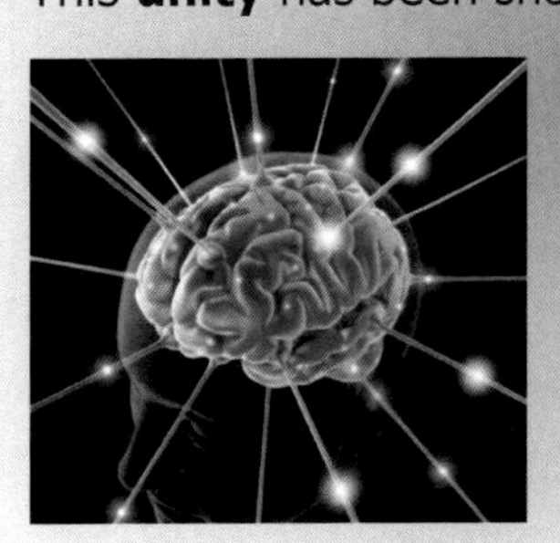

Donna Eden,
Energy Medicine, 61

400

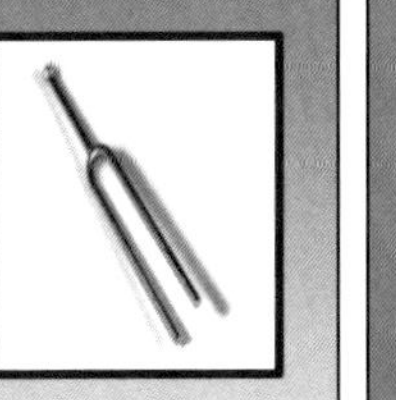

"When truth shall touch the cords of your heart they will **vibrate;** the **intelligence** shall illuminate your mind, and shed [its] **lustre** in your **soul,** and you shall begin to understand the things you once knew, but which had gone from you."

John Taylor, *The Life and Teachings of Jesus and His Apostles*, 331

401

"Every thought, feeling, emotion and material object is composed of energy. Everything, including the thoughts, feelings, and emotions, has its own unique frequency of vibration. Thoughts and emotions are energy. Things of a negative or destructive nature have a very low frequency of vibration and things that are positive have a very high frequency of vibration."

Melvin Fish, PhD, *From Darkness Into Light*, 17

402

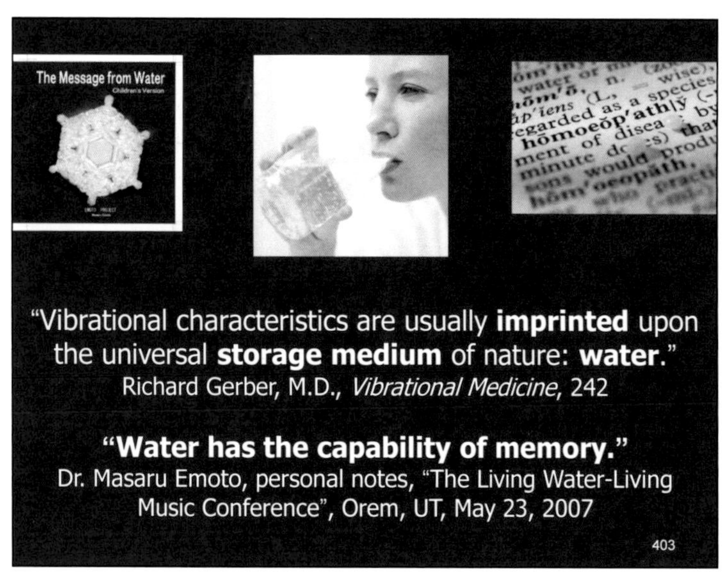

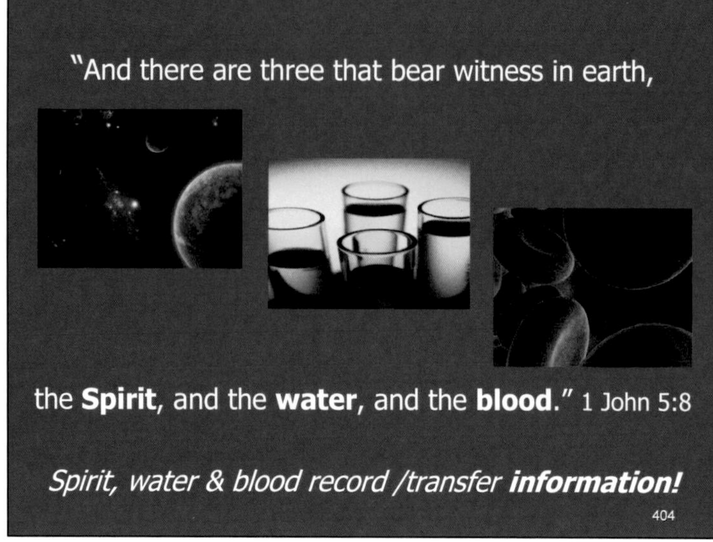

"The **voice** of thy brother's blood **crieth** unto me from the ground." Genesis 4:10

"Innocent blood, which **crieth** from the ground against them." D&C 136:36

"The **cry** of the blood of the saints shall ascend up to God" 2 Nephi 26:3

"His blood would **cry** from the ground to the Lord his God" Alma 20:18

A few of several examples

405

Rustum Roy,
"The Latest Science on Water," Jan 14, 2007, rustumroy.com

"We all assume that while water may differ in purity or degree of contamination, all reasonable pure waters are "just water."... **Nothing could be more wrong or more limiting a mistake**. In the last several years a small group of scientists, chemists, physicists, and most relevantly, material scientists, on the basis of long, detailed studies have concluded the very opposite is true. . . . The leading physicist notes that there are 64 changes of water from one form to another. There are certainly many, many different "waters," with **different structures** and, therefore, different properties. . . .
It's not "just water" anymore."

406

"**It is structure** (not composition) that (largely) controls **properties**. . . . Water can indeed have its properties and hence its structure changed rather easily in non-linear ways without any change of composition. . . . The data . . . require a major re-thinking on the structure(s) of water. . . . **Structures change properties vastly more easily and dramatically than chemistry changes them** . . . Such an enormous structural pliability also provides a plausible framework for the claims of the most reliable workers in the field of "subtle energies" to be able to change the structure and properties of water."

R. Roy, W. A. Tiller, I. Bell, & M.R. Hoover; "The Structure of Liquid Water..." 578, 599, 605; rustumroy.com

407

CYMATICS

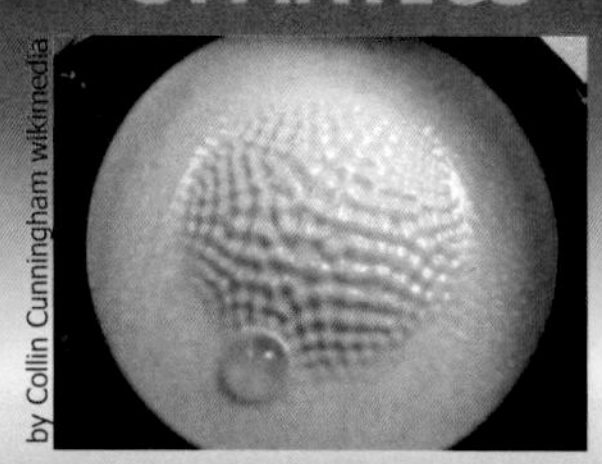

by Collin Cunningham wikimedia

Sound vibrating patterns in a cornstarch and water solution. Sound aligns matter!

"The amazing power of **sound** to **change** and **shape matter** is fundamental to all life and many spiritual technologies. In the beginning was the word - or in Sanskrit, 'Nada Brahma, the world is sound. . . . CYMATICS is the study of wave phenomena pioneered by the late Swiss scientist Dr. Hans Jenny. . . who succeeded in making visible the subtle power through which **sound** ***structures*** **matter**."

Jeff Volk, "Sound Insights," Kindred Spirit, cymaticsource.com

408

Courtesy EmotoProject.org

Dr. Masaru Emoto is internationally renowned for showing there is a **vibrational** pattern in all matter and that **words influence those vibrations**. His experiments photographing frozen water crystals show that **water** is **affected by words** and **connected** to our **consciousness.** Water exposed to loving words (spoken or written) formed complex patterns while negative words didn't crystallize or formed incomplete patterns.

409

Brigham Young: "These are the **mysteries** of the kingdom of God upon the earth, to **know how to purify** and **sanctify** our **affections,** the **earth** upon which we stand**,** the **water we drink,** the **houses** in which we dwell…, that when strangers come into our country they may feel a hallowed influence and acknowledge a **power** to which they are strangers."

Journal of Discourses 10:176

Energy Medicine teaches all of the above.

410

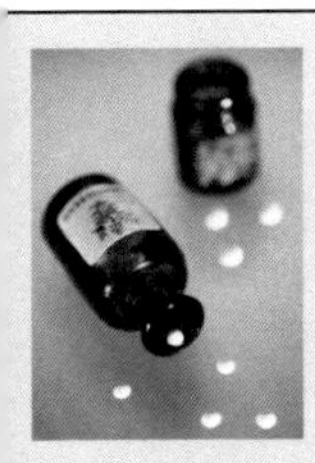

"The **homeopathic** approach utilizes minute quantities of medicinal substances to create therapeutic physiological changes through subtle-energy field interactions. . . . It is the **vibrational signature** of the substance and **not** its **molecular** properties which are utilized for healing benefits. . . . The sensitivity of homeopathic dilutions to energies such as heat, magnetic fields, and even ultrasound suggests that homeopathic remedies are indeed **energetic medicines** with **mechanisms different** from those of conventional drugs. . . . Homeopathy is gradually making a comeback on the American medical scene, not because doctors' attitudes are changing, but because the health-care market is now being driven by **educated** and **enlightened** medical consumers."

Richard Gerber, M.D., *Vibrational Medicine*, 89, 506, 509

411

"Energy can be defined most simply as '*information* that vibrates.' "

Cyndi Dale, *The Subtle Body*, 3

"We're changing the *information flow* in the body by very consciously and deliberately changing the energy patterns - the pattern of energetic movement."

Stuart Grace Greene, "Science of **ASYRA**," www.Asyra.com/VideoDemos.html

412

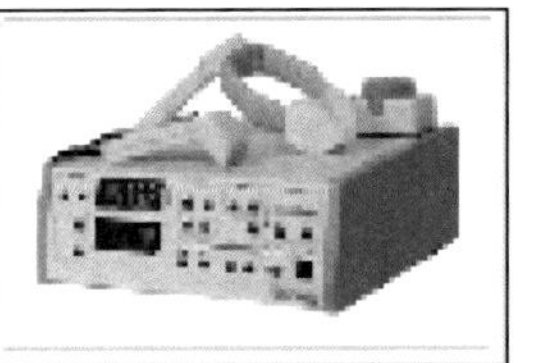

"Very **weak electromagnetic fields** at the appropriate **frequencies** can be as effective, or even better, than other approaches for reducing inflammation, counteracting diseases, and enhancing longevity.
The mechanism involves **resonance,** the process by which **a field** of a particular **frequency** or wavelength can transfer **vibrational energy** to an object. Clinical application of electromagnetic resonance have the advantage that they **can act at a distance** using tiny fields that excite or energize natural processes taking place **deep within** the body."

James Oschman, PhD

as quoted in Wolf-Dieter Kessler, MD, PhD, Ondamed, 2

413

"**Trapped emotions** can create depression, anxiety, and other unwanted feelings that you can't seem to shake. They can **interfere** with proper **function** of your body's **organs** and **tissues,** wreaking havoc with your physical health, causing **pain, fatigue** and **illness.** Yet, no matter how great your suffering may be, the **invisible energy** of trapped emotions will remain **undiagnosed** by conventional medicine, even though they **may** be a **major causative factor** in your **physical** and **emotional** difficulties."

Dr. Bradley Nelson, *The Emotion Code*, 11

414

"What is this **'energy'** referred to by so many alternative healers, who associate it with the release of emotion and the restoration of health? . . . . Many ancient and alternative healing methods refer to a mysterious **force** . . . It's my belief that this mysterious **energy** is actually the free flow of **information** **carried by** the biochemicals of **emotion**... Almost every other culture but ours recognizes the role played by some kind of **emotional energy release**, or catharsis, in healing."

Candace Pert, *Molecules of Emotion*, 276 415

"The **Light of Christ** is as **universal** as sunlight itself. Wherever there is human life, there is the Spirit of Christ. Every living soul is possessed of it. This Light of Christ, which **gives life**, is within you. The **evil one** will attempt to **obscure it**. **It can be so clouded with confusion** so far as to convince you that it does not even exist."

Boyd K. Packer, "The Light of Christ", *Ensign*, Apr. 2005, 8 416

"I think EFT will dramatically change your world.... By simply tapping near the end points of your energy meridians you can experience some profound changes in your emotional and physical health.... The cause of *all* negative emotions is a disruption in the body's energy system. This includes fears, phobias, anger, grief, anxiety, depression, traumatic memories, PTSD, worry, guilt and all limiting emotions."

Emotional Freedom Technique

Gary Craig, *The EFT Manual*, 1, 43-44, 49 or see eft.mercola.com 417

Emotional Freedom Technique

Image courtesy Joseph Bennette

Energy psychology is standard protocol for the *Green Cross* who responds to psychological needs after disasters.

"It seems preposterous to those with an investment In today's medical system that energy tapping could have such powerful results. Yet clinical practice is providing a base of evidence for the efficacy of this simple intervention."

Dawson Church, *The Genie in Your Genes, 311* 418

"After more than three decades as a clinical psychologist carefully monitoring the field's developments, I find that the energy approach... is the innovation that has made the **most profound difference** in helping my clients. **Energy psychology** can shift problematic beliefs, behaviors and emotions so rapidly because it allows the therapist to alter the client's brain chemistry with a precision, yet gentleness, that is **unprecedented** in psychotherapy. And while energy methods can be extraordinary tools in the hands of a skilled clinician, perhaps their most important application is how **empowering** they can be **in your own hands."**

David Feinstein, Donna Eden & Gary Craig, *The Promise of Energy Psychology*, 1-2 419

"**Another reason for skepticism is that EFT looks weird**. These techniques will have you talking to yourself, rolling your eyes around in your head, and humming a song while tapping on various parts of your body. **They don't even remotely resemble the practice of psychology** as most people know it, and may be way outside your belief system. Once you **understand the logic behind them**, however, these techniques become obvious. And you may wonder why they weren't discovered earlier."

Gary Craig, *The EFT Manual*, 32 420

"My theory: I am suggesting that meridians and Qi (or Spirit energy) are part of our Spirit bodies, or at least how our spirit bodies communicate with our physical bodies. I am also suggesting that acupuncture points can have direct impact on that Spirit energy, thus improving the relationship of the spirit and the body.... These points - when stimulated through needling, **pressure** or vibration - can help the Qi flow normally."

Joe Holcomb, N.D.; "Acupuncture: An LDS Perspective;" LDS Holistic Living Conf.; June 25, 2011; South Jordan, UT, personal notes

421

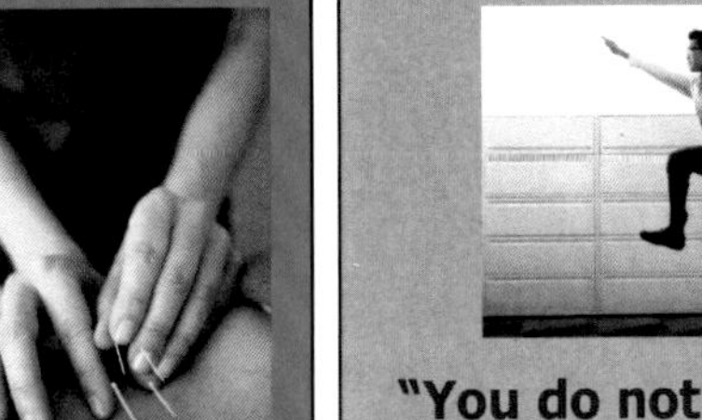

"Belief is the strongest pill in the universe."
Rustum Roy, rustumroy.com

"You do not have to believe in these techniques for them to work. Some people mistakenly conclude that EFT gets results simply because people believe in it. The fact is that people rarely believe in these techniques at first. They are almost always skeptical, at least to a degree. Despite the usual lack of belief by newcomers, the results obtained by EFT occur undiminished. People make improvements in spite of their skepticism."

Gary Craig, *The EFT Manual*, 32

422

RET is a natural, safe way to release stress and trauma. RET simulates REM sleep, your body's own natural release process. This powerful quick release happens *without reliving* the trauma.

Accessing the whole mind/body system while in an awake state allows you to be in control of your own journey. RET releases negative **patterns**, negative **thought forms** and **emotions**.

www.RapidEyeTechnology.com

423

"Rapid Eye is a spiritual technology affecting the physical, emotional and mental levels . . . using blinking, breathing and eye movement Techniques. . . . The other half of RET is education (Life Skills) based upon 7 universal principles to successfully manage & understand life: Thought, Perception , Choice & Accountability, Cause & Effect, Abundance & Gratitude, Health & Healing, Rhythm & Harmony."

Dr. Ranae Johnson, *Reclaim Your Light Through the Miracle of Rapid Eye Technology*, 1, 27-28

424

BODY CHART

showing where trapped emotion is often stored. Rapid Eye Technicians use a much more detailed chart. Other charts are by Louise Hay, Karol Truman, Donna Eden, Dr. Bradley Nelson, Dr. Ryke Geerd Hamer (German New Medicine), HADO in Japan, . . .

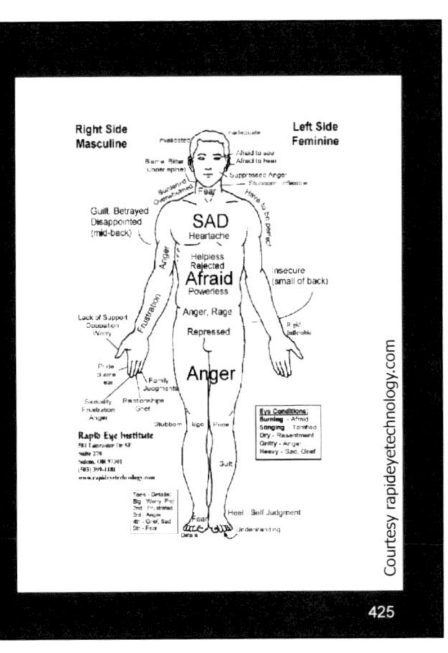

425

"All things whatsoever God in his infinite wisdom has seen fit and proper to **reveal to us,** while we are dwelling in mortality, in regard to our **mortal bodies**, **are revealed to us** in the abstract, **and independent of affinity of this mortal tabernacle**, but are **revealed to our spirits** precisely as though we had no bodies at all; and those **revelations** which will save our **spirits** will save our **bodies."**

Moses & Serpent Photo by Mike Young

Teachings of the Prophet Joseph Smith, 355

426

Some doctors in the U.S. write prescriptions for Reiki, which is taught in medical schools in Europe.
see Barnett & Chambers, *Reiki Energy Medicine,* 86, 2

MEDICAL CENTER

NAME ______ AGE ______
ADDRESS ______ DATE ______

℞ Reiki = Spiritually guided life force energy

"Reiki (pronounced **ray**-key) is a precise method for connecting universal energy with the body's innate powers of healing."

☐ LABEL SIGNATURE
REFILL 0 1 2 3 4 5 PRN NR

"Matter may act upon the ether and the ether upon matter; but **ether acts most effectively upon ether**, and matter upon matter." John A. Widtsoe, *Joseph Smith As Scientist*, 111

427

"Can anyone refuse to believe that man, highly organized as he is, can **"tune"** himself to be in harmony with the forces of the universe? ....Heat, light, magnetism, electricity, and the **other forces,** become, then, simply **various** forms of **God's speech,** any of which may be **understood,** if the proper **means of interpretation** is at hand."
John A. Widtsoe, *Joseph Smith As Scientist*, 125

428

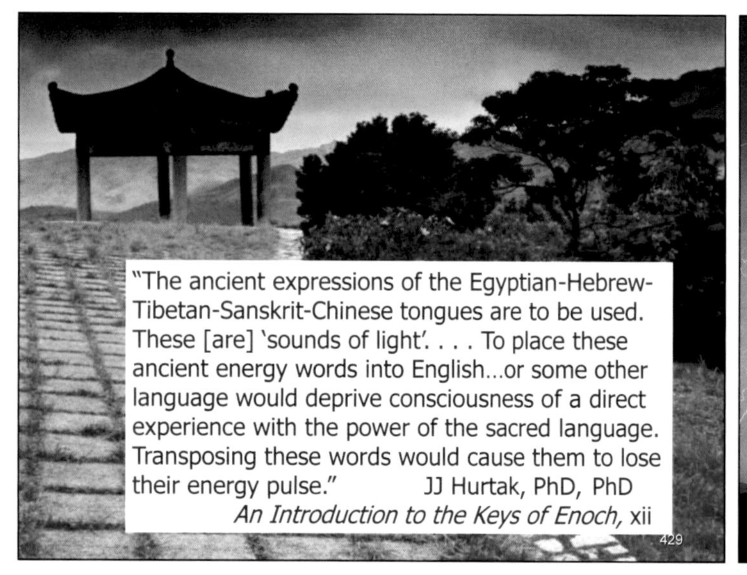

"Vast, unnumbered forces lie about us. The possible power of man, as he grows in knowledge, is quite beyond our understanding. All that is required of man is that he **place himself in harmony with the interacting forces,** operating in all directions. If the forces are not fully understood, he must **search them out,** and as best he can, must place himself so that they are **with him** rather than **against** him."

John A. Widtsoe, *Rational Theology*, 158

430

"There has never been a step taken from that day to this, in **discovery** or invention, where the Spirit of the Lord (that is, the spirit of which Joel spoke, the **Light of Christ**, not the Holy Ghost!) was not the prevailing force, resting upon the individual, which caused him to make the discovery or the invention. The world does not understand that but it is perfectly clear to me; **nor did the Lord always use those who have faith, nor does he always do so today**. He uses such **minds as are pliable** and can be turned in certain directions to accomplish his work, **whether they believe in him or not."**

Joseph Fielding Smith,
Doctrines of Salvation, 1:178

432

"God has been using not merely his covenant people, but other peoples of the world as well, to carry out a work that is too demanding for the limited numbers of Latter-day Saints to accomplish. Good and great men and women . . . who have thought profoundly . . . have been inspired by God under many circumstances to deliver dimensions of light and truth . . . [including] Zarathustra, Bautama Buddha, Lao Tzu, Muhammed, and Guru Nanak."

Orson F. Whitney,
91st Annual Conference, SLC, 1921,32-33

433

"I teach them correct principles and they govern themselves." Joseph Smith
Quoted by John Taylor in *JD* 10:57-58

". . . If there is anything **virtuous**, lovely or of good report or praiseworthy, we seek after these things." Article of Faith #13

"Every thing which inviteth to do good, and to persuade to believe in Christ, is sent forth by the power and gift of Christ; wherefore ye may know with a perfect knowledge it is of God." Moroni 7:16

434

"Energy Medicine is a *field* of medicine that uses non-toxic methods to balance biological energy flow. Energy Medicine includes **techniques** called **'modalities'** and **tools** which demonstrate the ability to **clear** and **re-pattern** the unseen **subtle energy system.** Energy healing addresses the energetic foundation of life - light - **which regulates all other systems.** The energy system responds to vibration, frequency and input from the five senses. It might be used in conjunction with conventional medical care." Tamara Laing, MRET

435

"Joseph Smith recognized the existence of **media which render the unknown known. . . . By the use of proper instruments, the world outside of the five senses may be brought within man's consciousness. . .** .As the prophet placed himself in tune with the unknown, he became less dependent on external aids. . . . .Joseph Smith recognized the **various means** whereby **man's senses** may be **enabled** to **seize upon and comprehend the natural forces** which to man's unaided senses must remain unknown forever."
John A. Widtsoe, *Joseph Smith As Scientist*, 121, 124, 125

436

"Crystals have the most orderly structure in nature. . . . Amethyst has the ability to change the molecular structure of things. . . . Like the quartz crystals, other gems have their own unique healing properties."
Richard Gerber, M.D.,
***Vibrational Medicine*, 338-39,359,368**

437

"The forming of a **crystal** . . . is, somehow, connected with an **intelligent purpose** and will. . . . **Rocks** and **trees** and **beasts,** are for the use of man, to be used by him in moderation and with wisdom. . . . **Whoever** teaches that **any part of the universe is not** for the benefit of man, **is in error.** The Church possessing the truth, always **fosters, encourages** and **respects** all honest investigation of **nature.**"
John A. Widtsoe,
Rational Theology, 155,156,158

438

"When we compare our **knowledge** and our **intellectual powers** with the glimmerings of light that we see manifested in the **brute creation**, we may exclaim that man is something, that he is advanced far beyond... He is, indeed, something compared with the small glimmerings of light that exist in the brute creation, in the beasts of the field, in the fowls of the air, and in the fishes of the sea; all these have some degree of knowledge & understanding; and **some of them have some degree of information and knowledge that man is not in possession of.**"

Masterful Discourses of Orson Pratt, 522

439

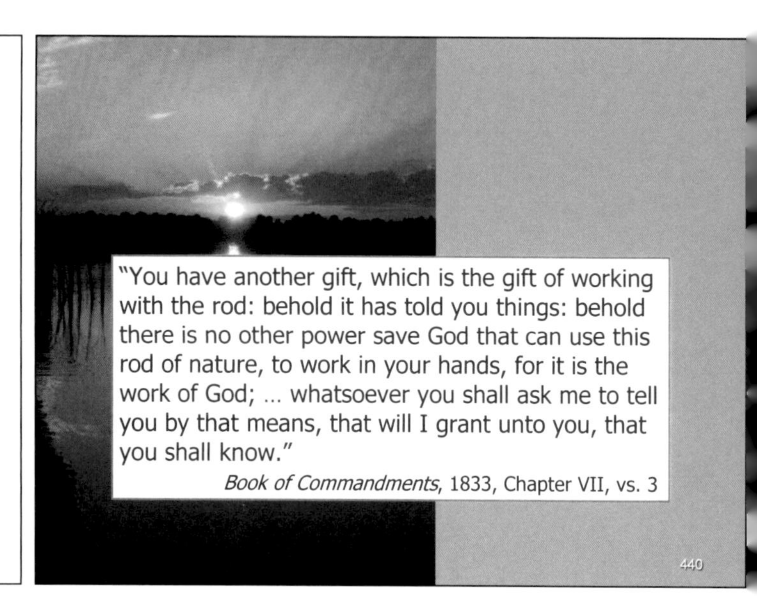

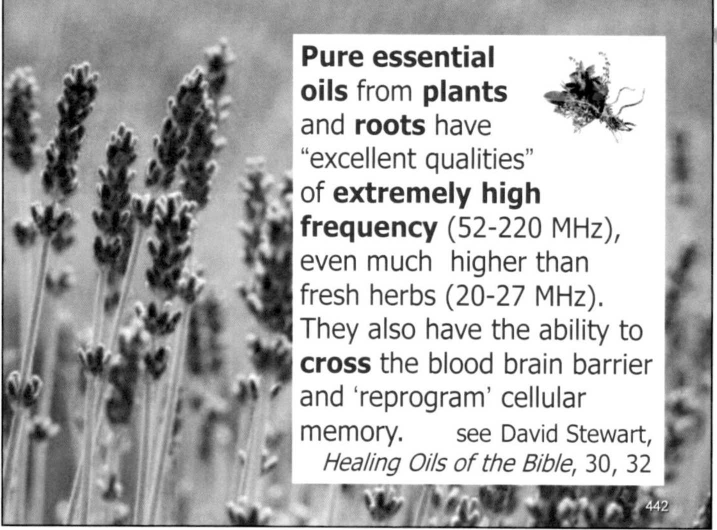

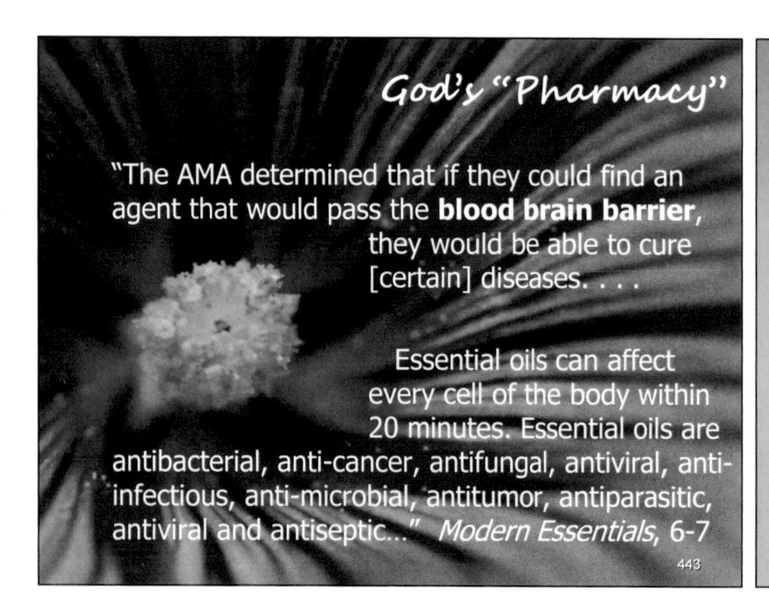

*~ There are **grounding** oils & **mood-affecting** oils, oils of **joy**, **calming** oils, **invigorating** oils . . .~*

Oils: Frankincense & Myrrh

"**God** hath anointed thee with **the oil of gladness . . .** all thy garments smell of **myrrh** & aloes & **cassia . . .** whereby they have **made thee glad.**" Psalms 45:7

". . .The amygdala plays a **major** role in the **storing** and **releasing** of **emotional trauma**. The only way to stimulate this gland is with fragrance or the sense of smell. Therefore, essential oils can be a **powerful key** to help **unlock** and **release** emotional trauma." *Modern Essentials*, 7

444

Flower Essences

"In this work you are working strictly with the ethereal **vibration** of the plant, the **intelligence** of it."

Richard Gerber, M.D., *Vibrational Medicine*, 250

445

"This [Voyager/Galaxy Light & Sound] machine synchronizes the right and left hemisphere of the brain. . . . It gives a full light spectrum & tones."
Ranae Johnson, PhD rapideyetechnology.com

"The idea of shining a specific color on a diseased part of the body for treatment will sound preposterous to most, but think about it: UV and infrared, both invisible parts of the electromagnetic spectrum, are already recognized as useful in medicine, so why should anyone be surprised that the rest of the spectrum, ie., visible light, is also useful?"
William Campbell Douglass, M.D., *Into the Light*,

446

"While [artificially generated electro magnetic] fields do not lead to appreciable harm in most people, **sensitive** individuals can be **devastated**." Donna Eden, *Energy Medicine*,297

"Devices that have their own electromagnetic fields... **interfere** w/ the electromagnetic **system** in & around **the body**." qtd. Dr. Klinghardt in Stephanie Marohn, *The Natural Medicine Guide to Bipolar Disorder*, 62

"**The body acts like an antenna** for ambient electric fields in the home and builds up electric tension against the ground- which interferes with **numerous biological & physiological functions.** Body voltage increases towards the center of the body. . . . The 2-step EMF Solution for the **autistic** child. . . results: instant improvement of sleep and mood. Other neurological biomedical improvements. Increased responses to neurosensory treatment modalities may take a few months but are dramatic." Dietrich Klinghardt, M.D. "Energy Medicine and Autism" powerpoint, klinghardtacademy.com [see also "earthing"]

447

"A **high energy interrupter** on the skin is determined by location. The **most** disorganization occurs on the head, front center and back-center of the body as well as feet and hands. **Body piercings** on the tongue, navel and face are also included as **major energy interrupters**."

Power Zone Health, "Quantum Life Support for the 21st Century, retrieved from www.2lolii.com, 2007

448

Pres. Gordon B. Hinckley:

"The Church discourages **tattoos**. It also discourages the **piercing of the body** for other than medical purposes, although it takes no position on the minimal piercing of the ears by women for one pair of earrings."
"Your Greatest Challenge, Mother," *Ensign*, Nov 2000, 99

This is similar to Joseph Smith teaching the Word of Wisdom before scientific explanations were available.

449

More self-help techniques:

RET's **I**mmediate **R**elease **T**echnique (IRT) acupressure *with* eye work

Rapid **E**ye **T**echnology's **Energy Circles**: create goals 1st energetically and *act as if* already gratefully received

Donna Eden's 5 minute **Daily Energy Routine** can improve performance, reduce anxiety... (see *Energy Medicine)*

Vocalize gratitude for life's conditions *just as they are*, "I am grateful for the opportunity to experience ________ because of all the learning it gives me."

450

Look yourself in the eyes in a mirror daily
and say honestly out loud several times:

I deeply love and accept myself,
just the way I am.

"Give thanks in ALL things... be grateful for the challenges & the pain! It gets your attention to let you know you're out of balance." David Fairbourn, "Keys to Unlock Generations," class manual, 21

451

Use the Hawaiian Ho'oponopono technique often, particularly when triggered. Say out loud:

"I love you. I'm sorry. Please forgive me. Thank you."
Joe Vitale & Ihaleakala Hew Len, Ph.D., *Zero Limits*, 32

Forgive EVERYTHING. Be grateful for all things.
Aspire to praise *in all things.*

452

"Many **health problems** reveal a **lack of forgiveness**. There is someone or something you are holding a grudge against (sometimes your own personal guilt, or sometimes blaming God). Often these grudges began long long ago, before you had the ability to understand or view things from a better perspective. They can even be **passed down** the **ancestral tree**."

Arielle Essex, NLP Master, "Arielle's Healing Story," 6, www.practicalmiracles.com

453

"RNA and DNA carry the frequencies that we are given by our ancestors. They establish not only the color of our skin, hair and eyes, but also our thinking patterns and behavior. . . .
It seems that errors in beliefs or thinking are passed down for 4 generations if our ancestors did not repent of their thoughts or deeds. It is suggested that when we discover addictive behavior . . . we may turn these burdens over to Christ and clear the energy of these imprints from our RNA and DNA. . . . Our healing is not complete until we forgive these ancestors for their woundedness."

Cliff Dunston, DL, *Meridian Health*, 28, 29

454

"DNA IS NOT DESTINY
The new science of **epigenetics** rewrites the rules of disease, heredity, and identity"
Ethan Watters, *Discover*, Nov. 2006

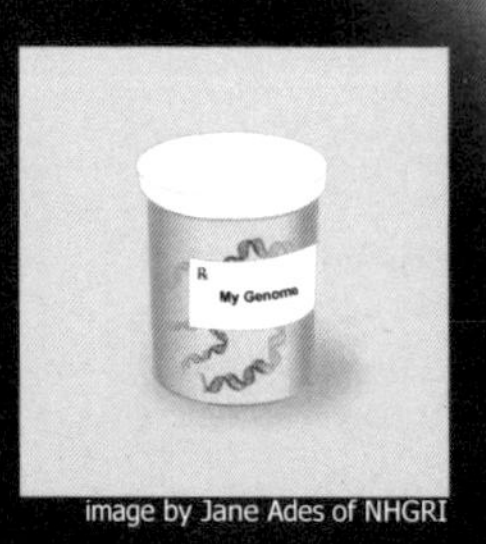

image by Jane Ades of NHGRI

"Our DNA is not a fixed code but a flexible code."
Margaret Ruby, *The DNA of Healing*, 6-7

"We are *not* limited by the Laws of physics and biology as we know them today, we can change and 'upgrade' by choice."
Gregg Braden, "The Science of Miracles", Hay House DVD

455

"The new science of **Epigenetics**, which literally means "control above the genes," has completely upended our conventional understanding of genetic control. Epigenetics is the science of how environmental signals select, modify, and regulate gene activity. This new awareness reveals that **our genes are constantly being remodeled** in response to life experiences. Which again emphasizes that **our perceptions of life shape** our **biology."**

Bruce H. Lipton,
The Biology of Belief, xv

by Jane Ades courtesy NHGRI

456

"For 400 years... mainstream medicine and science believed that brain anatomy was fixed.... Brilliant scientists, at the frontiers of brain science,... showed that **the brain changed** its structure [and] called this fundamental brain property 'neuroplasticity.'

by Jane Ades NHGRI

... **Thinking, learning and acting** can **turn our genes on or off,** thus shaping our brain anatomy and our behavior - surely one of the most extraordinary discoveries of the 20th century.. . . In the course of my travels,... I saw people **rewire their brains with their thoughts**. . .
Like all revolutions, this one will have profound effects."

Norman Doidge, M.D., *The Brain that Changes Itself, xvii-xix*

457

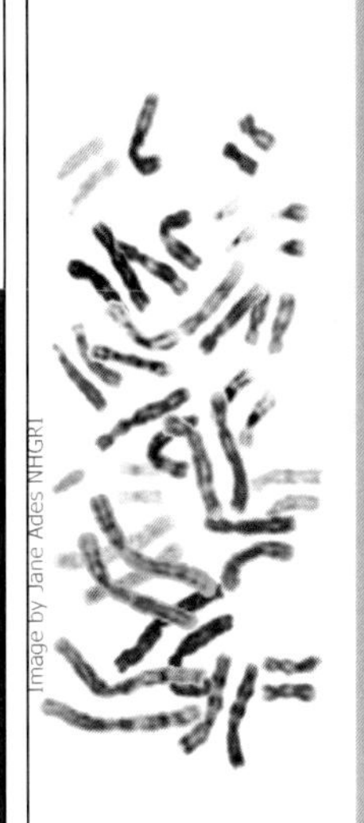

Image by Jane Ades NHGRI

"**The Fundamental Law of Heredity**

Living beings shall propagate- after their kind... to inherit the **physical**, ***mental*** and ***spiritual*** **traits**, ***tendencies*** and ***powers*** that characterize... parents."

James E. Talmage, *Jesus the Christ*, 81

We inherit generational tendencies!

458

"It is not necessary for us to be consciously aware of the **message** that our cells are receiving. Each DNA, and consequently, each cell is impacted. . . . This message is then imprinted in the **memory** of each cell and creates an identity and an **energ**y all its own. This cell **memory** is **automatically** and unconsciously referred back to when the need arises. . . [governing] our beliefs and attitudes from that time on."
Karol Truman, *Feelings Buried Alive Never Die*, 29-30

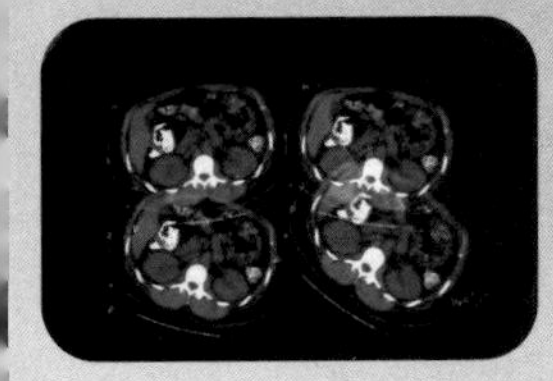

"**Far more likely**, in my judgment, is that our cells and organs function to **receive** and **transmit thought."**
Larry Dossey, MD*, Reinventing Medicine,* 179

459

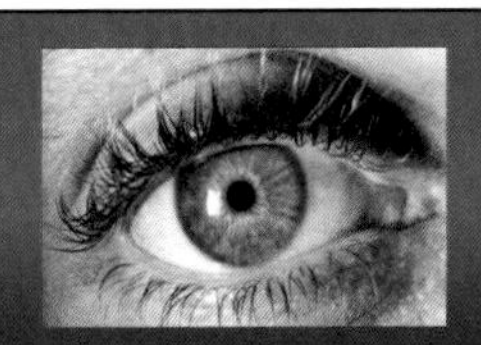

"A particular **pattern** will continue to run in a **family** until the pattern is broken or resolved. Unfinished business from an **ancestor** can affect our lives and actually show up in the DNA and the **eyes.** As we release **unprocessed emotions**, we are not only healing our lives but also healing the pain of untold **generations**." Dr. Ranae Johnson, *Reclaim Your Light Through the Miracle of Rapid Eye Technology*, 63

"And that wicked one cometh and taketh away **light** and **truth**, through disobedience, from the children of men, **and because** of the **tradition of their fathers."** D&C 93:39

460

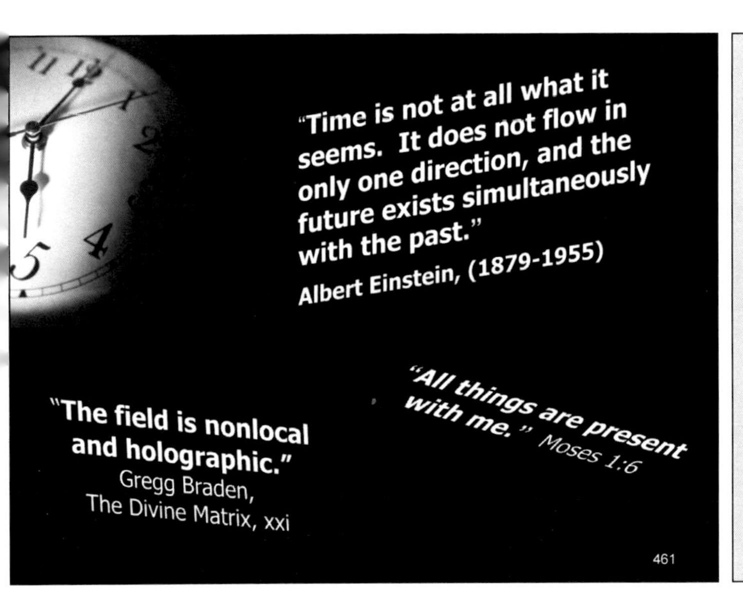

"Time is not at all what it seems. It does not flow in only one direction, and the future exists simultaneously with the past."
Albert Einstein, (1879-1955)

"All things are present with me." *Moses 1:6*

"The field is nonlocal and holographic."
Gregg Braden,
The Divine Matrix, xxi

461

Barbara Ann Brennan,
Light Emerging, 6

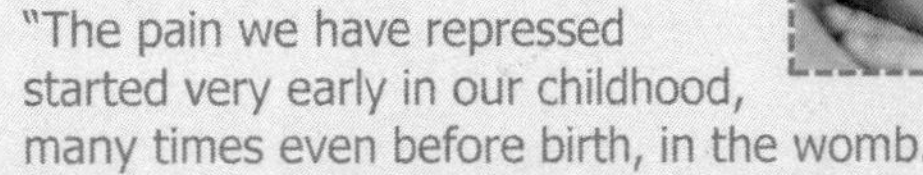

"The pain we have repressed started very early in our childhood, many times even before birth, in the womb."

"Ah! How few mothers realize the **effect** of their own mental condition upon the minds of their offspring. Long before many are aware does the **little one partake of the feelings and sensations** of the mother. . . . When swayed by the stronger and more tempestuous **emotions** of anger, hate or fear do **these tender ones partake, to a very great extent, of the same sensation."**
Dr. Ellis Shipp qtd. in Susan Evans McCloud, *Not in Vain,* 151

462

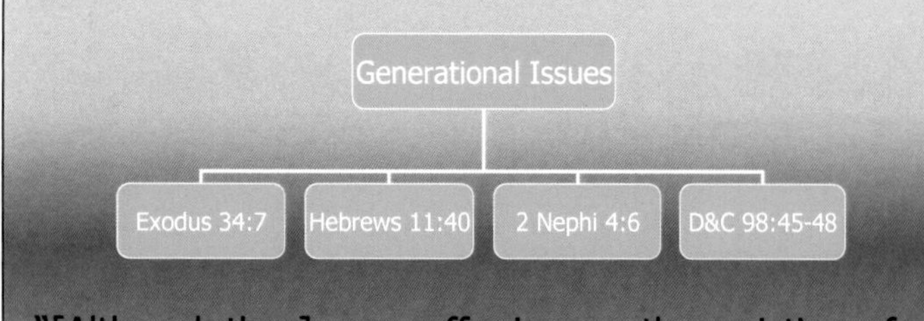

"[Although they] may suffer innocently as victims of violence, neglect, and exploitation, through the grace of God some find the strength to "metabolize" the poison within themselves, refusing to pass it on to future generations. **Before them were generations of destructive pain; after them the line flows clear and pure.**"

Carlfred Broderick, "Saviors on Mount Zion", *Ensign*, Aug. 1986, 38

463

Exodus 20:5 "...I the Lord am [possessing sensitive and deep feelings], visiting the iniquity of the fathers upon the children unto the third and fourth generation" Deut. 5:9 "...visiting the [**effects of sin**] of the fathers upon the children unto the third and fourth generation" *[additions from footnotes]*

464

"On average, 90% of **Indigo children**-those labeled ADD/ADHD /Autism Spectrum/Bipolar/mental disorders, OCD, addictions-have problems & health challenges caused by **generational** issues." Rebecca Rocque, Indigo Children Workshop, Logan, UT, 2007

"Bipolar disorder, chronic anxiety, or depression, schizophrenia, addiction, hyperactivity in children, aggressive behavior, and autism can all lead back to **systemic family issues**. In fact, Dr. Klinghardt estimates that 'about 70% of **mental disorders** across the board go back to systemic family issues that need to be treated. People try to treat them **psychologically**, on the 3rd level and it cannot work. This is not the right level. Similarly, focusing on the **biochemistry** is not going to fix the problem when the source is at the 4th level.'" Stephanie Marohn, *The Natural Medicine Guide to Bipolar Disorder*, 70

465

"**Unresolved trauma** does not appear to go away with death, but plays out in a variety of ways in **later generations**. Often, unresolved trauma from previous generations becomes the source, and the **causative event** of illness in later generations.... Most people overlook this and can never help their patients. I use this work for all **autistic children** that come to my practice.... When we resolve issues in the **family history** there is often magical improvement in these children. By **healing the trauma** of the past these children are healed in the present."

Dietrich Klinghardt, M.D., "The 5 Levels of Healing , www.mercola.com, Levels 4 & 5, personal notes

466

Dr. Dietrich Klinghart is internationally acclaimed for his **<u>Five Levels of Healing</u>:**
1. Physical 2. Electromagnetic
3. Mental 4. Intuitive 5. Spiritual
that comprehend chronic illness.

"Health and illness are a reflection of the state of these 5 levels. . . .Any health problem can originate on any of the 5 levels. . . . An imbalance on one level, if untreated, spreads upward or downward to the other levels. . . . Unless upper-level imbalances are addressed, restoring balance at the lower levels will not produce long-lasting effects. . . . Therapeutic intervention at the lower levels has a very slow, and little penetrating effect upwards. . . . But if you do an intervention on the 3rd or 4th level, it can correct the [block] on the 2nd level immediately, within seconds or minutes, [Dr. Klinghardt] notes." Stephanie Marohn, *Bipolar Disorder*, 59-60, 72

467

"Rather than a **genetic inheritance** of a **physical** weakness, it is an **energetic legacy** of an **injustice** with which the family never dealt ... It usually involves a family member who was excluded in a previous generation. When the other family members don't go through the deep process of grieving the excluded one, whether the exclusion results from separation, death, alienation, or ostracism, the [energetic] interference of that exclusion is passed on. . . . [Dr. Klinghardt says,] 'We call it **surrogate** healing.' " Stephanie Marohn, *The Natural Medicine Guide to Bipolar Disorder*, 65,66,68

468

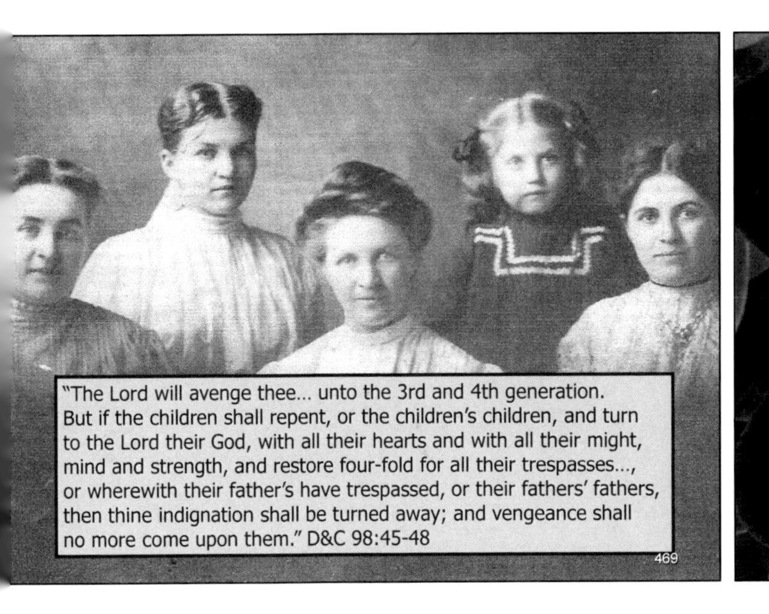

"The Lord will avenge thee... unto the 3rd and 4th generation. But if the children shall repent, or the children's children, and turn to the Lord their God, with all their hearts and with all their might, mind and strength, and restore four-fold for all their trespasses..., or wherewith their father's have trespassed, or their fathers' fathers, then thine indignation shall be turned away; and vengeance shall no more come upon them." D&C 98:45-48

469

"**Clean** 'from the blood of this generation'... meant persons by [the gospel & ordinances] ... would be cleansed; that whatever they had **inherited, of the human, of the sinful, of the weak, down through the centuries** would be overcome until it would be proper to say that the **impurities of the past** had been redeemed in the present personality."

Truman Madsen, *Joseph Smith the Prophet*, 83

470

"Our **faith** becometh **unshaken**, insomuch that we truly can **command** in the name of Jesus and the very trees obey us, or the mountains, or the waves of the sea." Jacob 4:6

"Properly **gifted** persons **control the elements**, move mountains,... quench the violence of fire, are carried by the power of the Spirit from one congregation to another..."
Bruce R. McConkie, *A New Witness for the Articles of Faith*, 373

"The man who progresses through his increase in **knowledge** and **power**, becomes a **co-laborer** with God, and can be said to be a help to God." John A. Widtsoe, *Rational Theology*, 26

471

"Everything good and useful, and glorious, and calculated for the benefit of man, is for you. Whether **wisdom** or **knowledge** or revelation, or prophecy, or **visions**, or heavenly **dreams**, or **beholding of angels** or the spirits of the just, whether . . . **healings** or **miracles**, all are for you through **the mighty principle of faith**. Seek, then for the rich treasures of faith; seek it with your whole hearts, seek it more diligently than all things else of an earthly nature. **Seek for faith and power** over your fallen **natures**, to faith and power over **pestilence**s, . . . seek for power over death. . . Seek for faith that you may control the **laws** and **elements** of nature, that they may be subservient to your happiness."
Masterful Discourses of Orson Pratt, 473-74

472

"If a man has power to part the veil and converse with **angels** and with the **ministering spirits** who dwell in the realms of **light**, surely **this is a gift of the Spirit**
Bruce R. McConkie, *A New Witness for the Articles of Faith*, 374

"**Man is not alone;** he walks in the midst of such heavenly company, from whom he may expect help **if he seek it strongly**." John A. Widtsoe, *Rational Theology*, 64

"We have the spirits of the ancients, also, administering to the Saints: Who have you now in your midst? Have you Abraham and Isaac and the Apostles Peter, James and John? Yes, you have them right in your midst- they are talking to you all the time." *Life of Heber C. Kimball*, 460-61 as quoted in Oscar W. McConkie Jr., *Angels*, 101

473

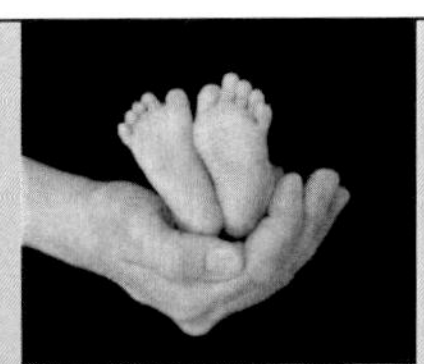

"Healing is real. **Everyone** can do it.
...Your **love** has impact and value.
The ability to work as a healer is simply a gift.
It is a gift that we need only **discover**.
This ability is ours at birth.
It comes as standard equipment on **all** humans - **hardwired** into the system."

Richard Gordon, *Quantum-Touch*, 7

474

"Elder John Groberg offered a marvelous insight into the 'essences of eternity,' which he said are light, life and love. This being so, he said, each of us must become a conduit of love, must each be a receptacle for these essences. (Regional Conference, Provo, Utah, January 27, 2002)"

Quoted in: Catherine Thomas, *Light in the Wilderness,* 170

475

"As I have researched healers and healing, I have been primarily impressed by the commonality of loving intent amongst healers. They work in a position of heart-centered **unconditional love** when they work with another living being's energy field. It appears that **love** may be a **real energetic force**, not merely a catalyst for action, transformation and healing."

Richard Gerber, M.D., *Vibrational Medicine*, 527

476

"The heart generates the largest electromagnetic field in the body. . . . The magnetic component of the heart's field is around 5000 times stronger than that produced by the brain . . . and can be measured several feet away from the body with Superconducting Quantum Interference Device (SQUID) - based magnetometers." Rollin McCraty, Ph.D., chapter summary of *Clinical Applications of Bioelectromagnetic Medicine*, heartmath.org

"Although the **heart field is not the body's aura** or the prana described in ancient Sanskrit traditions, it may well be an expression of the energy that begins in this area."
Gregg Braden, *The Divine Matrix*, 50

National Institutes of Health

477

"Hearts knit together in unity and in love"
Mosiah 18:21

by HeartMath Institute

"[Our] research elucidates the intriguing finding that the electromagnetic **signals** generated by the **heart** have the capacity to **affect others** around us. Our data indicate that one person's heart signal can affect another's **brainwaves**, and that **heart-brain** synchronization can occur between two people when they interact." R. McCraty, M. Atkinson & D. Tomasino."Science of the Heart," HeartMath Research Center, 21

478

"I would be my brother's keeper,
I would learn the healer's art.
To the wounded and the weary,
I would show a gentle heart."

Susan Evans McCloud, "Lord, I Would Follow Thee," Hymns, #220

479

"When we are in the **presence** of individuals whose lives are filled with the fruit of the spirit, who possess the **peace** that the Savior promised (John 14:27) **we feel it**. . . . This '**sympathetic affinity**' or feeling of peace in the presence of righteous people, was **one of the gifts** given to the Prophet Joseph Smith by the Lord to discern between those who had the Spirit and those who did not." Jeffrey Marsh, *The Light Within*, 80,82

"Everyone in distress, everyone beset with illness or other adversity, whoever came within the presence of this son of God, **drew virtue and strength from him. To be in his presence was to be healed,** if not physically, then indeed spiritually...." *Teachings of Presidents of the Church - George Albert Smith,* xxxviii, quoted by Elder Matthew Cowley

480

“I believe that **love** is the **connective tissue** of the **universe. It holds it together.** Love can heal anything. Healers not only work from a place of love, they teach patients to love themselves.”

Barbara Ann Brennan, *Light Emerging,* 61

“God is love.” 1 John 4:8

“Our Savior’s love shines like the sun with perfect light.”

Edward L. Hart, *Hymns* #113

483

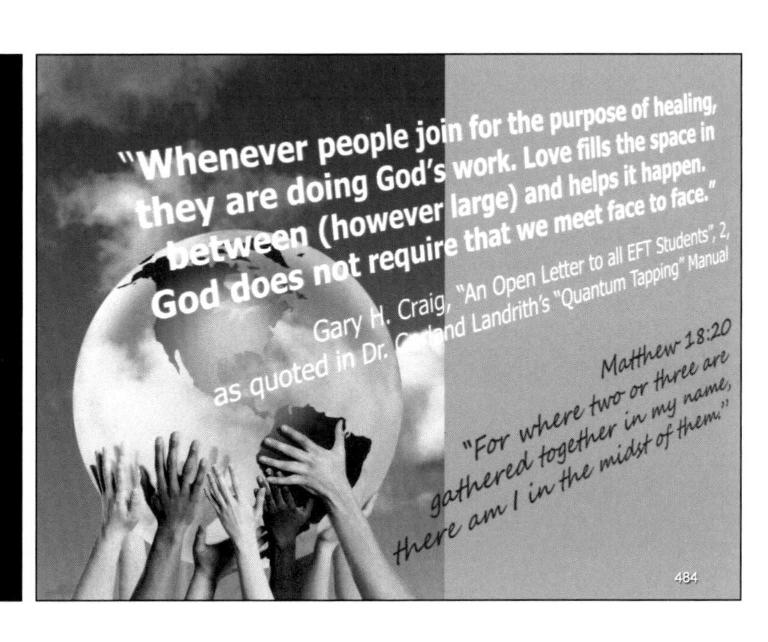

“Mormons have had difficulty explaining the **dual nature** of a God with physical parts on one hand and universal presence in the cosmos on the other. Interestingly, **our theology coincides with what scientists now know about the nature of light,** especially since the scriptures repeatedly inform us that **our God is light**. Is the grand secret of the nature of God that he is both infinite and finite- the ultimate expression of matter, energy and light? Is he both wave and particle, energy and matter, spirit and body, everywhere and somewhere, universal yet personal...?”

B. Grant Bishop , *The LDS Gospel of Light,* 30

485

“Biological life depends on the use of energy of photons from the sun. This energy is then converted into electron energy and as a result, a series of transformations in complex chains of albuminous molecules are converted into our body energy. It can be said that biological life is based on light energy, and organic compounds serve as the working material for the conversion of this energy. The basic ingredients for all conversions are water and air. Consequently, we are all **children of the Sun** living on the **light of the world. And we ourselves emit light.”**

Konstantin Korotkov, korotkov.org/scientific-basis/

486

"It would really appear, . . . that simple physical force, **may be converted** by the animal body into other and more complex forces, or modes of motion, such as the **so-called life force**. . . . The answer must be that the **ultimate particles** of the matter composing the living thing are so **arranged or organized** that the great **natural forces may be converted into life force**....
It is generally assumed, that the human body is so **organized** that the forces of heat, **light** and undoubtedly others, **may be converted into higher forms,** peculiar to living things."

John A. Widtsoe, *Joseph Smith as Scientist*, 60

487

"Scripture and science describe a similar universal energy, perhaps even the same essence, while using their own unique terminology. Quantum physicists refer to the Zero point field while prophets teach that intelligence in the Light of Christ is the subtle governing energy which fills all space and also manifests as consciousness."

Tamara Laing, M.Ed.

488

"In the fundamental laws that underlie all nature, there is a perfect harmony between science and 'Mormonism.' Few religions can say as much."

John A. Widtsoe, *Joseph Smith as Scientist, 141*

489

"Thou hast a gift... Remember it is sacred and cometh from above."

D&C 6:10 see 8:8

490

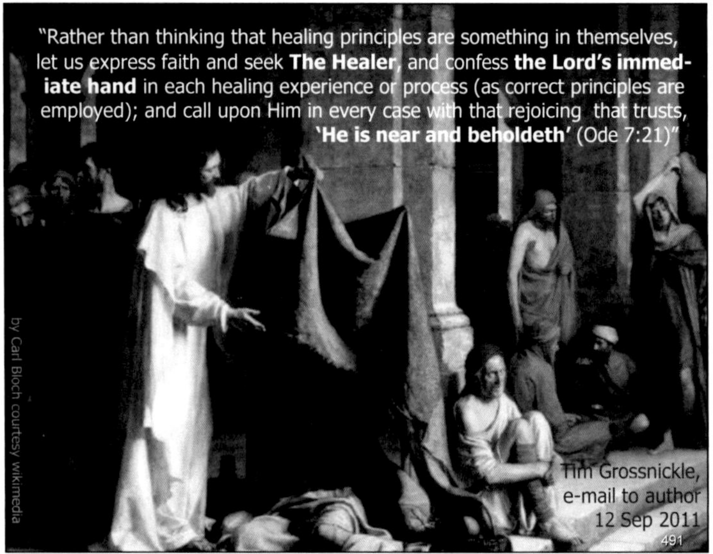

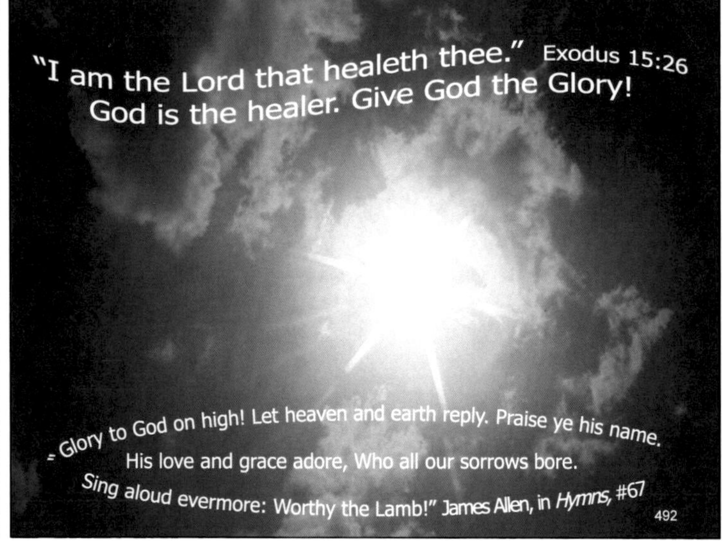

Works Cited

Allred, Garth. *Unlocking the Powers of Faith.* American Fork, UT: Covenant, 1993.

Anderson, Farley M. *Nature's Answer.* Bear River, UT: Replenishing, n.d.

Angelo, Jack. *Your Healing Power*. London: Piatkus, 1994.

"Attack the Problem Not the Child," *Family Home Evening- Love Makes Our House a Home*, n.p.: The First Presidency of The Church of Jesus Christ of Latter-day Saints.

Bailey, Jack S. *Let Not Your Heart Be Troubled.* Bountiful, UT: Horizon, 1978.

Ballard, Melvin J. "Three Degrees of Glory" 22 Sep 1922, Ogden Tabernacle, Mount Ogden Stake.

Barnett, Libby and Chambers, Maggie. *Reiki Energy Medicine.* Rochester: Healing Arts, 1996.

Barrow, Eleanor. Cartoon. *Quantum-Touch* by Richard Gordon. 19.

Baugh, Alexander L.. "Parting the Veil: The Visions of Joseph Smith" BYU Studies 38, no 1 (1999) https://ojs.lib.byu.edu/spc/index.php/BYUStudies/article/.../6541

Beckett, Shelley. *What You Believe is What You Receive.* Tulsa: Options Unlimited. 2006.

Bednar, David A. "Seek Learning by Faith" Address to CES Religious Educators. 3 Feb 2006. Jordan Institute of Religion. http://www.lds.org/library/display/0,4945,5344-1-2783-5,00.html

"BIOFIELD THERAPEUTICS The Sub-Section from Alternative Medicine: Expanding Medical Horizons" A Report to the NIH on Alternative Medical Systems and Practices in the United States. Prepared by members of the Ad Hoc Advisory Committee to the Office of Alternative Medicine, NIH., n.d.,n.p. retrieved 25 Feb 2012 from www.shentherapy.info/images/ biofield %20therapeutics.pdf

Bischoff, Marco. "Biophotons- The Light in Our Cells." Zweitausendeins, Frankfurt, 1998. extracted from: transpersonal.de/mbischof/englisch/webbookeng.htm . 31 Jan 2011.

Bishop, B. Grant. M.D. *The LDS Gospel of Light. n.p. 1998.*

A Book of Commandments for the Government of the Church of Christ. pub. by W.W. Phelps, 1833. retrieved 27 Feb 2012 http://en.fairmormon.org/Oliver_Cowdery_and_the_%22rod_of_nature%22

The Book of Mormon, The Doctrine and Covenants and The Pearl of Great Price; Salt Lake City: The Church of Jesus Christ of Latter-day Saints, 1981.

Boswinkel, Johan. "The Science of Biophotons Healing with Light." 16 Aug 2011. http://compmed.com/people-helping-people/science-of-biophotons-light-that-heals/ retrieved 15 May 2012.

Braden, Gregg. *The Divine Matrix.* Carlsbad: Hay House, 2007.

---. *Secrets of the Lost Mode of Prayer.* Carlsbad: Hay House, 2006.

---. *Walking Between the Worlds.* Bellevue: Radio Bookstore, 1997.

Brennan, Barbara. *Light Emerging.* New York: Bantam Books, 1993.

Bruce, Robert. *Energy Work.* Charlottesville: Hampton Roads, 2007.

Busche, F. Enzio. *Yearning For the Living God.* Salt Lake City: Deseret Book, 2004.

Cannon, George Q. *Gospel Truth.* compiled by Jerreld L. Newquist. Salt Lake City: Deseret, 1974.

Carothers, Merlin. *Prison to Praise. 1970.* Escondido: 2005.

Chopra, Deepak. *Quantum Healing.* New York: Bantam, 1990.

---. *The Seven Spiritual Laws of Success;* San Rafael,CA: Amber-Allen, 1994

Church, Dawson, PhD. *The Genie in Your Genes: Epigenetic Medicine and the New Biology of Intention,*Santa Rosa: Energy Psychology Press, 2009.

Cox, James. *Becoming Spiritually Centered.* Santa Clara, UT: National Marketing, n.d.

Smith, Henry A. *Matthew Cowley Man of Faith.* Salt Lake City: Bookcraft, 1954.

Craig, Gary *The EFT Manual.* Santa Rosa: Energy Psychology, 2008.

Cramer, Steven A. *Putting on the Armor of God.* Springville, UT: Cedar Fort, 1992.

Daughters in My Kingdom- the History and Work of Relief Society, Salt Lake City: The Church of Jesus Christof Latter-day Saints, 2011

Devenyns, Roger with Eden, Donna. "Living a Better & Fuller Life with Energy Medicine." The LifeConnection [Vista, CA] Sep. 2010, Vol. 26, No. 9, 8-9+

Diamond, John, M.D. *Your Body Doesn't Lie. New York:* Warner Books, 1979.

Doidge, Norman, M.D. *The Brain That Changes Itself.* New York: Penguin, 2007.

Dossey, Larry, M.D. *Reinventing Medicine.* New York: Harper San Francisco, 1999.

Dunston, Cliff, D.L. *Meridian Health.* n.p.: n.d. [47 E. Amber Rd, Saratoga Springs, UT 84045]

Dunston, Judy CHT, CAS and Dunston, Cliff, D.L.. "Principles of Praise" class. Centerville, UT. 11 Sep. 2011.[meridianhealth1.com]

Durham, Elaine. *I Stand All Amazed.* Orem, UT: Granite, 1998.

Eadie, Betty J. *Embraced by the Light.* Placerville, CA: Gold Leaf, 1992.

Eden, Donna. *Energy Medicine.* New York: Tarcher Putnam, 1999. 1st Tradeback Edition.

Eden, Donna and Feinstein, David, PhD. "Principles of Energy Medicine" The Energy Medicine Handout Bank. 28 July 2009. energymed.org/hbank/handouts/principles_ener_med.htm

Ehat, Andrew F and Lyndon Cook, eds. *Words of Joseph Smith*, Salt Lake City: Bookcraft, 1980

Emoto, Dr. Masaru. "The Living Water-Living Music Conference" Orem, UT. 23 May 2007

Encyclopedia of Mormonism. MacMillan, 1992. http://lib.byu.edu/digital/Macmillan/

The Ensign of The Church of Jesus Christ of Latter-day Saints. Salt Lake City, UT. (Citations in text)

Essex, Arielle, D.O., NLP Master. "Arielle's Healing Story" 5-6. retrieved 2011. www.practicalmiracles.com

Eyring, Henry B. "Gifts of the Spirit for Hard Times" CES Fireside, 10 Sep 2006, lds.org

Fairbourn, David, PT, CNP. *"Keys to Unlock Generations"* class manual. n.p., n.d., [www.davidfairbourn.com]

Featherstone, Vaughn J.. "A Man After God's Own Heart" 20 Feb 1999. http://advance.byu.edu/devo/featherstone95.html

Feinstein, David; Eden, Donna; and Craig, Gary. The Promise of Energy Psychology. retrieved from http://books.google.com/books?id=KcOgygktLGoC&printsec=frontcover#v=onepage &q&f=false

Feynman, Richard P.. *QED The Strange Theory of Light and Matter.* Princeton: Princeton University Press, 1985.

Fiore, Edith, PhD. *The Unquiet Dead.* New York: Ballantine Books, 1987.

Fish, Melvin, PhD. *Healing the Inner Self-From Darkness Into Light;* n.p.,1999.

Fontaine, Karen L. with Kaszubski, William. *Absolute Beginner's Guide to Alternative Medicine.* Indianapolis: QUE, Sam's Publishing, 2004.

Gardner, Stan M., M.D. CNS. "Thinking Yourself to Better Health" Meridian Magazine. www.meridianmagazine.com

Gerber, Richard, M.D. *Vibrational Medicine.* Rochester: Bear and Co., 2001.

Gibson, Arvin S. *They Saw Beyond Death.* Springville, UT: Horizon, 2006.

Goldberg, Burton. *Alternative Medicine-The Definitive Guide*. Compiled by the Burton Goldberg Group.Tiburon, CA: Future Medicine, 1993, 1997

Gordon, Richard. *Quantum-Touch The Power to Heal.* Berkeley: North Atlantic Books, 2002.

Graf, Jan, M. *"Graf Stress Management"* St. George, UT: 1998. [grafstressmanagement.com]

Green, Stuart Grace. "Science of ASYRA" www.Asyra.com/VideoDemos.html

Gregor, M. Darren. "Exploring the Next Level of Healing for Humanity" Wisdom. retrieved 3 May 2012. wisdom-magazine.com/Article.aspx/1163/

Grossnickle, Tim. "Re: Odes" e-mail to the compiler. 12 Dec 2011.

Hales, Brian. *Light*. Springville, UT: Cedar Fort, 2004.

Hales, Robert D.. "That Ye May Be the Children of Light" 3 Nov. 1996. www.byub.org/talks/transcripts/devo/1993/8/devo199381-202.pdf

---. "Gifts of the Spirit," 1 Aug 1993. _http://.speeches.byu.edu/reader/reader.php?id=7094

Hay, Louise. *Heal Your Body.* Carlsbad: Hay House, 1982.

Hawkins, David, M.D. PhD. *Power Vs. Force.* Carlsbad: Hay House, 2002.

Hinckley, Gordon B. *Standing for Something*, New York: Times, 2000, 1st Edition

The Holy Bible. Salt Lake City: The Church of Jesus Christ of Latter-day Saints, 1986.

The Holy Bible New Revised Standard Version. New York: Oxford University Press, 1989.

Horne, Dennis. *Faith to Heal and to Be Healed.* Springville, UT: Cedar Fort, 2009.

Horner, Dr. Christine. *Waking the Warrior Goddess.* North Bergen: Basic Health, 2005.

Hunt, Valerie. *Infinite Mind.* 1989. Malibu: Malibu Publishing, 1996.

Hurtak, J.J. *An Introduction to the Keys of Enoch.* 1975. Los Gatos: The Academy for Future Science, 2001.

Hymns of The Church of Jesus Christ of Latter-day Saints. Salt Lake City: The Church of Jesus Christ of Latter-day Saints, 1985.

Isackson, Darla. "The Transformative Power of the Mind-Body Connection" Meridian Magazine. http://www.ldsmag.com/component/zine/article/9334

Johnson, Ranae, PhD. *Reclaim Your Light Through the Miracle of Rapid Eye Technology.* n.p. 1996.

---. Skills For Life Teacher's Manual. n.p. 1987. 9/05

Journal of Discourses, (1855-86). (Vols. 1-26) London. www.scriptures.byu.edu

Katie, Byron. *Loving What Is.* New York: Harmony Books, 2002.

Kimball, Spencer W. *The Miracle of Forgiveness.* 1969. Salt Lake City: Bookcraft, 1978

---. *Teachings of Spencer W. Kimball*, ed. Edward L. Kimball. Salt Lake City: Bookcraft,1982.

Klinghardt, Dietrich MD, PhD. "Energy Medicine and Autism" 11 Sep 2010. Kirkland, WA. PowerPoint. http://www.klinghardtacademy.com

---. "The Five Levels of Healing" Explore! Volume 14, Number 4, 2005. pdf retrieved from www.klinghardtacademy.com

Korotkov, Konstantin. "Report of the experimental results of the educational sessions of the International Academy for Scientific Mental Healing (Drossinakis IAWG) under the direction of Prof. Dr. Konstantin Korotkov." Appendix 16. 20-22 Feb 2012. St. Petersburg. retrieved from http://heilerschule-drossinakis.de . 3 May 2012.

Laing, Tamara, MRET. *What Else Is There?* manuscript

Landrith, Garland, PhD. "Dr. Garland Landrith's Quantum Tapping Technique" class manual; n.p.: n.d.; [garland@theuniversewithin.com]

LDS Holistic Living Conference. 25 June 2011. South Jordan, UT. [www.ldsholisticliving.com]

Lectures on Faith. compiled by N.B. Lundwall. Salt Lake City: Bookcraft, n.d.

The Life and Teachings of Jesus and His Apostles. Salt Lake City: The Church of Jesus Christ of Latter-day Saints, 1978.

Lipton, Bruce H. PhD. *The Biology of Belief.* Carlsbad:Hay House, 2008.

The Living Matrix–The New Science of Healing, DVD, (Hillsboro, OR: Beyond Words, 2009)

Madsen, Truman G. *Joseph Smith the Prophet.* Salt Lake City: Bookcraft, 1989.

Marohn, Stephanie. *The Natural Medicine Guide to Bipolar Disorder.* Charlottesville: Hamptom Roads, 2003.

Marsh, Jeffrey. *The Light Within.* Salt Lake City: Deseret Book, 2000

Martin, Boyd. "What Subtle Energy Is and Its Value to Health." Subtle Energy Solutions Vibrant Living Newsletter. n.d. 9 Mar 2012. Vibrantliving.sublteenergysolutions.com/ newsletter-role-background.html

McConkie, Bruce R. *Mormon Doctrine.* Salt Lake City, Bookcraft, 1966.

---. *A New Witness for the Articles of Faith.* Salt Lake City: Deseret Book, 1985.

McKay, David O. *"The Mission of Brigham Young University"* 27 Apr 1948. 29 Dec. 2008. http://education.byu.edu/mckay/48apr27.html

---. *Treasures of Life;* comMp. by Clare M. Middlemiss, Salt Lake City: Deseret Book, 1962

McCloud, Susan Evans. *Not in Vain.* Salt Lake City: Bookcraft, 1984.

McCraty, Rollin PhD. "Chapter Summary" from *Clinical Applications of Bioelectromagnetic Medicine*. Ed. by P. J. Rosch and M. S. Markov. New York: Marcel Dekker, 2004: 541-562. retrieved from http://www.heartmath.org

R. McCraty, M. Atkinson & D. Tomasino. "Science of the Heart," HeartMath Research Center

McTaggart, Lynne. *The Field.* New York: HarperCollins, 2008.

Mendenhall, Doug. *Possibilities.* n.p. n.d., 2002.

Mercola, Joseph, M.D., Interview with Klinghardt, Deitrich, M.D., "5 Principles that Can Heal Almost Any Illness" part 2. 3 June 2008. retrieved 2010.http://articles.mercola.com/videos. aspx personal notes.

---. Interview with Dr. David Holt "German New Medicine- How You Control Your Own Healing" post 28 Feb 2008. 17 Feb 2012. http://articles.mercola.com/videos.aspx

---. "Your Body Literally Glows with Light" 15 Aug. 2009. articles.mercola.com

Modern Essentials. Spanish Fork,UT: Abundant Health, 2011.

Modi, Shakuntala, M.D. *Remarkable Healings.* Charlottesville: Hampton Roads, 1997.

Moody, Raymond, Jr. M.D. *Life After Life.* Harrisburg, PA: Stackpole Books, 1976.

Moyers, Bill. *Healing and the Mind.* New York: Doubleday, 1993.

Myss, Caroline. *Anatomy of the Spirit.* New York: Three Rivers, 1996.

---. *Why People Don't Heal and How They Can.* New York: Three Rivers, 1997

Nelson, Bradley, D.C. *The Emotion Code.* Mesquite, NV: Wellness Unmasked, 2007.

Nibley, Hugh. "What is 'The Book of Breathings?'" BYU Studies 11, no. 2 (1971): 153-87. byustudies.byu.edu

Northrup, Christiane , M.D. *Women's Bodies Women's Wisdom. New York: Bantam, 2010.*

---, Foreword. *Energy Medicine for Women.* By Donna Eden. New York: Penguin, 2008. 18 Sep 2012. http://www.innersource.net/em/read-foreward-by-christiane-northrup-md.html

Oschmann, James PhD. "Dr. James Oschman on Energy Medicine" retrieved 2011, personal notes, www.youtube.com/watch?v=VFN32U69LBk

Osguthorpe, Russell T. "When Love is Why" BYU Magazine, Fall 2011,55

Osteen, Joel. *Become a Better You.* New York: Free Press, 2007

Old Testament Student Manual -- 1 KINGS-MALACHI. Salt Lake City: The Church of Jesus Christ of Latter-day Saints, 2003.

Packer, Boyd K., , *A Dedication - To Faith*, BYU Speeches of the Year, Provo, 29 Apr. 1969, 6

---. "Fledgling Finches and Family Life," web. Devotional Address ,18 August 2009, BYU, Campus Education Week, 11 Feb 2012. www.speeches.byu.edu

---. "The Instrument of Your Mind and the Foundation of Your Character," Fireside address BYU, 2 February 2003. retrieved 11 Feb 2012 speeches.byu.edu

Palmer, Keller, Choi, Toronto. *Religions of the World.* Provo: Brigham Young University, 1997.

Palmer, Christopher E., D.C. *Spirits and Spiritual Interactions.* n.p. creatspace.com, 2010.

Pearl, Dr. Eric. *The Reconnection.* Carlsbad: Hay House, 2001.

Pert, Candace; *Molecules of Emotion*; New York: Scribner, 1997.

Pierce, Virginia, *A Heart Like His,* Salt Lake City: Deseret Book, 2006.

Poulton, Ronald L.; "The Nature of Spiritual Evil in the Context of Psychotherapy" unpublished manuscript. retrieved from tamarasbook.blogspot.com

Pratt, John P.; "Science and the Light of Christ," 22 Mar 2006. MeridianMagazine. 4 Feb 2010. www.johnpratt.com/items/docs/lds/meridian/2006/zpe.html

Pratt, Parley P. *Key to the Science of Theology.* Heber City, UT: Archive Publishers, 2000.

Pratt, Orson. *Masterful Discourses of Orson Pratt*. comp. N.B. Lundwall. Salt Lake City: Bookcraft, 1962.

"Quantum Life Support for the 21st Century," Power Zone Health. retrieved 2007. www.2lolii.com

Ritchie, George, M.D. *Return From Tomorrow.* 1978. Grand Rapids: Fleming H. Revell, 2003.

Ringger, Carolyn. *Faith Unpuzzled.* Pleasant Grove, UT: 2003.

Roberts, B.H. *A Comprehensive History of the Church, Vol. 2.* Provo: Brigham Young University, 1976.

Rocque, Rebecca. "Indigo Children Workshop" Utah State University. Logan, UT, 2007. personal notes. [www.healingheartsandhomes.com 755 W. 240 S. Lehi, UT 84043]

Ross, Robert. "Reconnective Healing with Dr. Eric Pearl" Awareness Magazine. Nov/Dec 2005. Anaheim, CA. 4 Feb 2012. www.awarenessmag.com/novdec5/nd5_reconnective_healing.htm

Roy, Rustom. "The Latest Science on Water" 14 Jan 2007. www.rustomroy.com

Roy, R; Tiller, W.A.; Bell, I & Hoover, M.R. . "The Structure of Liquid Water..." www.rustumroy.com

---. Whole Person Health Summit. Chair speaker. 15 April 2005. Holiday Inn Select. Bethesda, MD. personal notes.

Ruby, Margaret; *The DNA of Healing,* Charlottesville, Hampton Roads, 2006

Schwartz, Gary E., PhD. *The Energy Healing Experiment-Science Reveals our Natural Power to Heal.* New York: Atria, 2007 .

The Science of Miracles – The Quantum Language of Healing, Peace, Feeling and Belief," DVD, An Illustrated Interview with Gregg Braden, Hay House, 2009

Scriptural Teachings of the Prophet Joseph Smith, comp. Joseph Fielding Smith/Church Historians Office, 1938, retrieved from scriptures.byu.edu

Seaward, Brian Luke. *Managing Stress*. Retrieved 26 Feb 2012. Sudbury, MA: Jones and Bartlett, 2009. amazon.com/Managing-Stress-Principles-Strategies-Well-Being/dp/0763735329

Smith, Henry A. *Matthew Cowley-Man of Faith*. Salt Lake City: Bookcraft, 1954.

Smith, Joseph F. *Gospel Doctrine.* 1919. Salt Lake City: Deseret Book, 1939. 7th Edition.

Smith, Joseph Fielding. *Answers to Gospel Questions. 5 Vol.* Salt Lake City: Deseret Book, 1957-1966.

---. *Doctrines of Salvation.* ed. Bruce R. McConkie, 3 vols. Vol. _ Salt Lake City: Bookcraft, 1954-56.

Soderquist, Kurt. MSW, LMFT,TFT, CMI "The Gifts Class" Centerville, UT, 1 Aug 2006.

Stewart, David, PhD. *Healing Oils of the Bible.* Marble Hill, MO: Care Publications, 2003.

Suttka, Sari. D.C. "Zero to Zone in 2.5 Seconds" Keynote presentation, Layers of Light International Leadership Retreat. Park City, UT. 9-11 March 2007.

Talmage, James E. *Jesus the Christ.* Salt Lake City: Deseret Book, 1973.

Teachings of Presidents of the Church- George Albert Smith, SLC: The Church of Jesus Christ of Latter-day Saints, 2011

Teachings of the Prophet Joseph Smith. (1938) comp. by Joseph Fielding Smith. SLC: Deseret Book, 1977.

"The Odes of Solomon" in *The Lost Books of the Bible and The Forgotten Books of Eden,* Collins-World Publishers. retrieved 3 Dec 2011. goodnewsinc.net/othbooks/odesolmn.html

The Teachings of Harold B. Lee. ed. Clyde J. Williams. SLC: Bookcraft, 1996.

The Teachings of Spencer W. Kimball. ed. Edward L. Kimball. Salt Lake City: Bookcraft, 1991. 1982

Thomas, M. Catherine. *Light in the Wilderness.* Provo: Amalphi, 2008.

W. Tiller,PhD, W. Dibble Jr., PhD and M.J. Kohane,PhD; *Conscious Acts of Creation: The Emergence of a New Physics*; Walnut Creek, CA: Pavior, 2001

William Tiller, PhD as quoted on sjlreconnectivehealingar.com/science.php retrieved 3 May 2012.

Tiller, William A. PhD. "Professional Comments and Research." qtd. on themetamorphoses.com/p2a_scientists.html retrieved 2 Dec 11.

Tolle, Eckhart. *Practicing the Power of Now*. Novato, CA: New World Library, 1999.

Topp, Brent and Wendy Topp. *Glimpses Beyond Death's Door.* Orem, UT: Granite, 2005.

Trudeau, Kevin. *Natural Cures They Don't Want You to Know About.* Elk Grove Village, IL: Alliance, 2004.

True to the Faith. Salt Lake City: The Church of Jesus Christ of Latter-day Saints, 2004.

Truman, Karol. *Feelings Buried Alive Never Die.*1995 Las Vegas: Olympus Distributing, 1991.

Tuttle, Carol. *Remembering Wholeness.* Seattle: Elton Wolf, 2002.

Vastenburg, Dietrich. "Morphology of Isolated Rat Cortical Neurons and Information Transferred via a Biophoton Device" retrieved from luxpura.nl 30 May 2012

Verdon-Roe, Vivienne, PhD. "The Miracle of QiGong" The Life Connection [Vista, CA] Sep. 2010,Vol. 26, No. 9,10-11.

Vitale, Joe and Ihaleakala Hew Len, PhD. *Zero Limits.* Hoboken: John Wiley & Sons, 2007.

Volk, Jeff. "Sound Insights" Kindred Spirit Magazine. UK. Issue 60. Autumn 2002. retrieved fromwww.cymaticsource.com

Wadham, Rex A.. Assoc. Prof. "The Nature of Brain Chatter" No. 1 in a series. "A Collection of Quotes Relating to the Nature of Brain Chatter or What is More Commonly Known as Inner Speech" Dept. of Elementary Education. BYU. n.d. [obtained from Smith, Cindy. E-mail to compiler. 18 Aug 2010.]

---."Spiritual Radiation" No. 3 in a series "A Collection of Quotes on the Principle of Spiritual Radiation" Dept. of Elementary Education. BYU. n.d. [obtained from Smith, Cindy. "Re: Spiritual Radiation" E-mail to the compiler. 18 Aug 2010.]

Wagner, Susan M.D. *A Doctor's Guide to Therapeutic Touch.* New York: Berkley Publishing Group, 1996.

Watters, Ethan. "DNA is Not Destiny" Discover Magazine. 22 Nov. 2006. retrieved from discovermagazine.com/2006/nov/cover

Weil, Andrew, M.D.. *Spontaneous Healing.* New York: Fawcett Columbine, 1995.

Whole Person Health Summit. Bethesda, MD. Apr 14-17, 2005. Campaign for Better Health & Friends of Health. [wholepersonhealing.com]

Widtsoe, John A.. *Joseph Smith as Scientist.* 1908; Layto,UT: Eborn Books, 1990.

---. *Rational Theology.* 1915. Salt Lake City: Signature Books, 1997.

Wilde, Bradley R.. *I Made Me Sick.* manuscript. [100 Ta Bi Drive, Worland, WY, 82401]

---. *The Safe Box of Health.* Worland, WY: Wilde Natural Health Publishing, 2011.

Woodruff, Wilford. *Leaves From My Journal.* in *Three Mormon Classics.* comp. Preston Nibley, Salt Lake City: Bookcraft, 1988

Young, Brigham, *Discourses of Brigham Young.* compiled by John A. Widtsoe. 1954. Salt Lake City: Deseret Book, 1978

Young, Sharlene. *Clearing Your Twelve Chakras*. n.p.: n.d. [455 Wormwood Ave. SE, Salem, OR 97306. www. rapideyetechnology.com]